MATHEMATICS
IN
ARISTOTLE

MATHEMATICS

IN

ARISTOTLE

By

SIR THOMAS HEATH

OXFORD

AT THE CLARENDON PRESS

Oxford University Press, Ely House, London W. 1

GLASGOW NEW YORK TORONTO MELBOURNE WELLINGTON
CAPE TOWN SALISBURY IBADAN NAIROBI DAR ES SALAAM LUSAKA ADDIS ABABA
BOMBAY CALCUTTA MADRAS KARACHI LAHORE DACCA
KUALA LUMPUR SINGAPORE HONG KONG TOKYO

FIRST PUBLISHED 1949
REPRINTED LITHOGRAPHICALLY IN GREAT BRITAIN
AT THE UNIVERSITY PRESS, OXFORD
BY VIVIAN RIDLER
PRINTER TO THE UNIVERSITY
1970

PREFACE

MATHEMATICS IN ARISTOTLE is the result of work done during the last years of my husband's life, which he devoted to reading all that had been written on the subject and to making his own translations from the Greek.

His eagerness to return to this work too soon after a serious illness in 1939 was probably instrumental in hastening his end.

After his death in 1940 I found the manuscript (which I took to be unfinished) and consulted Sir David Ross as to the possibility of getting it completed. He most kindly read it through and, to my immense satisfaction, reported that the rough copy was, in fact, complete and advised that the fair copy, much of which was already done, should be finished in typescript.

This I undertook to do myself, and it proved not only a welcome distraction from the more disturbing elements of 'total war', but, in addition, an unexpectedly enjoyable introduction to the fascinating world of Aristotle, which I had hitherto regarded as far above the head of one not a classical scholar. I had, however, not failed to remark the concomitance of Aristotelian learning with a love of music. During a short visit to Corpus Christi College during the presidency of Thomas Case, I had the unforgettable experience, having returned somewhat early from a Balliol Sunday concert, of discovering the President and my husband playing, by candle-light on the Broadwood grand piano, with unrestrained fortissimo, the four-hand arrangements of Haydn Symphonies. The conventional fiction obtained that my being a professional pianist precluded such indulgence within my hearing!

My very grateful thanks are due to Sir David Ross for his invaluable help and encouragement. For the reading of the proofs I am indebted to him and to Mr. Ivor Thomas, M.P., whose knowledge of Greek mathematics has been of the greatest assistance. Having no Greek myself, I have to thank Mr. Kerry Downes and Mr. P. R. W. Holmes for their assistance in transcribing the Greek quotations, and also my son Geoffrey T. Heath who, since his demobilization, has helped me in reading proofs and revising Greek quotations, mathematical figures, and formulae.

I regret the absence of a bibliography, as my husband left no note of authorities consulted, though some indications are given in footnotes as well as in the text.

1948   ADA MARY HEATH

SUMMARY OF CONTENTS

I

INTRODUCTION

ARISTOTLE'S VIEW OF MATHEMATICS IN RELATION TO THE SCIENCES

(a) General

MATHEMATICS is, according to Aristotle, one of three 'theoretical sciences'. The other two are (1) 'theology', which is the same thing as 'first philosophy', and (2) the 'philosophy of Nature' (φυσική), which we may generally render by 'physics'.

The importance of a proper understanding of the mathematics in Aristotle lies principally in the fact that most of his illustrations of scientific method are taken from mathematics. He was evidently not a mathematician by profession, but he was abreast of the knowledge of his day as far as elementary mathematics is concerned; and the historian of mathematics can glean from his treatises valuable hints as to the contents of the text-books in use immediately before the time of Euclid. The particular text-book used in the Academy was probably that attributed to one Theudius. But Aristotle was aware of the important discoveries of Eudoxus which affected profoundly the exposition of the *Elements* by Euclid. One allusion clearly shows that Aristotle knew of Eudoxus' great Theory of Proportion which was expanded by Euclid in his Book V, and recognized the importance of it. Another passage recalls the fundamental assumption on which Eudoxus based his 'method of exhaustion' for measuring areas and volumes; and, of course, Aristotle was familiar with the system of concentric spheres by which Eudoxus and Callippus accounted theoretically for the independent motions of the sun, moon, and planets. But it does not appear that Aristotle had given any attention to higher mathematics. We find in his works no allusion to conic sections,[1] to the doubling of the

---

[1] The only place in the Aristotelian corpus where the expression κώνου τομή, section of a cone, occurs appears to be *Problems* XV. 7. 912ª13, where it is said that if the circle bounding the portion of the moon lit up at any time by the sun is placed obliquely (ἐκκλινέστερον) to our line of vision the circle seems to be like a section of a cone (ὁ κύκλος κώνου τομῇ ἐμφερὴς ἐγένετο); that is to say, when we look at a circular circumference obliquely and not in a direction perpendicular to the plane of a circle, it has the appearance of an ellipse. In one other passage in the *Problems* (XVI. 6. 914ª35) the author speaks of an oblique section (λοξὴ τομή) of a cylinder (actually a scroll, βιβλίον), but says nothing of the nature of the curve so formed on the plane of section, which is, of course, an ellipse.

cube, or to the trisection of an angle. The problem of squaring the circle is mentioned in connexion with the attempts of Antiphon, Bryson, and Hippocrates to solve it: but there is nothing about the curve of Hippias, later known as the *quadratrix*, which was used first for trisecting or dividing in any ratio any given angle, and then for squaring the circle.

The incommensurable is mentioned over and over again, but the only case mentioned is that of the diagonal of a square in relation to its side; there is no allusion to the extension of the theory to other cases by Theodorus and Theaetetus[1] (for the expression in *Metaph. Δ.* 1021^{a}5 'according to a number that is not commensurable' (κατὰ μὴ σύμμετρον ἀριθμόν) is too vague to base any argument upon).

Even in the case of Eudoxus' system of concentric spheres, it may well be doubted whether Aristotle followed out the mathematics which established the shape of the actual path described by a planet. It is to Simplicius that we owe the information that a planet describes a curve on a sphere which Eudoxus himself called a *hippopede* or horse-fetter (like a figure of eight); and Aristotle's allusions to motion in a helix or spiral[2] and to 'spirals in the heaven'[3] are too vague to enable any certain inference to be drawn.

Some light on Aristotle's attitude to mathematics is afforded by his account of the evolution of science and the classification of sciences.

Aristotle gives his views on the origin and evolution of science in the first chapter of Book *A* of the *Metaphysics*. 'All men by nature desire to know—this is indicated by the pleasure we take in our senses. This pleasure is independent of their utility: we delight in them for their own sake and particularly in the case of sight.... Sense represents the first stage. Next comes memory in the case of the animals which have it. In man memory leads up to experience; many memories of the same thing occurring come in the end to have the force of a single experience. Science and art come to men through experience. An art arises when from many notions derived from experience one universal judgement about a class of like things is produced. Experience, like action and production, has reference to the individual; art, on the other hand, is knowledge of the universal. Sometimes the person who possesses the art and knows the universal may fail for want of the necessary experience. The art of medicine

---

[1] Some of the other irrationals, discovered and discussed by Theaetetus and others (especially Euclid in Book X), are indeed mentioned in the tract *On Indivisible Lines*; but this was written not by Aristotle but by Theophrastus or some later person.

[2] *Phys. E.* 4. 228^{b}24.   [3] *Metaph. B.* 2. 998^{a}5.

teaches the doctor how to cure a certain type of case: but he may fail to cure Callias for want of experience, i.e. the knowledge of Callias as a member of the class.

'Nevertheless the art represents, in our judgement, a knowledge and understanding superior to that of mere experience: we regard the man who possesses the art as wiser than the man who only has experience, which implies that wisdom, in all cases, accrues in virtue of knowledge, that is, knowledge of the cause, which the man of mere experience is without.'[1]

Aristotle goes on:[2]

'In the first instance, therefore, it is probable that the man who invented any art whatever which went beyond the common sensations was admired by his fellow men, not merely because of the utility of any particular discovery of his, but because he was regarded as wise and so superior to others. Next, when more and more arts were being discovered, some of which looked to the necessities of life and others to its enjoyment, the inventors of the latter were always conceived to be wiser than those of the former because their sciences did not look to use or profit. Hence, when all such arts had been established, those of the sciences which are directed neither to pleasure nor to the necessities of life were in their turn discovered, and this happened first in those places where men enjoyed leisure. This is why the mathematical arts first took shape in Egypt: for there the priestly caste was privileged to have leisure.'

In all this we see the characteristic Greek spirit and outlook. Knowledge for its own sake and apart altogether from its uses or applications; knowledge of the universal rather than of the particular; knowledge of the *cause*: such is the intellectual ideal. Further remarks in the same strain follow. Having argued the thesis that Wisdom or Philosophy is the science which investigates first principles and causes, Aristotle goes on:[3]

'It was owing to wondering that men began and still continue to philosophize. At the beginning they wondered at the most obvious things that present difficulty; proceeding in this way, by short steps, they probed [or "puzzled over"] the difficulties arising on the greater subjects; for example, with regard to the phenomena of the moon, the facts about the sun and the stars and about the genesis of the universe. Now the man who feels a difficulty and wonders thinks himself ignorant —thus, even the lover of myths is in some sort a "lover of Wisdom" (philosopher), for a myth is made up of wonders—hence, granted that they philosophized because they would leave ignorance behind them, it is manifest that they were pursuing science because of the knowledge it brought and not for the sake of any application of it. There is evidence for this in what actually happened; for it was when practically all the

---

[1] *Metaph. A.* 1. 980ᵃ21—981ᵃ28.   [2] 981ᵇ13–25.   [3] *A.* 2. 982ᵇ12–28.

arts needful to make life easy and enjoyable were already at men's disposal that the knowledge of which we have been speaking began to be sought. It is clear then that we do not seek it because of any other use to which it can be put: but, just as we say that a man is free who exists for the sake of himself and not for another, so we pursue this as the only free science; for it alone exists for itself.'

The wonder of which Aristotle speaks as being the incentive to philosophy is, as he explains in another passage, due to ignorance of the cause :[1]

'Everyone begins, as we said, with wondering that a certain thing should be so, as for example one does in the case of the puppet theatre (if one has not yet found out the explanation), or with reference to the solstices or the incommensurability of the diagonal. For it must seem to everyone matter for wonder that there should exist a thing which is not measurable by the smallest possible measure. The fact is that we have to arrive in the end at the contrary and the better state, as the saying is. This is so in the cases just mentioned when we have learnt about them. A geometer, for instance, would wonder at nothing so much as that the diagonal should prove to be commensurable.'

The incommensurability of the diagonal is one of Aristotle's favourite illustrations. We shall give, later, the main connexions in which he uses it. Aristotle's ideas of 'science' ($\dot{\epsilon}\pi\iota\sigma\tau\dot{\eta}\mu\eta$) and the classification of sciences may be illustrated from the following passages.

'All teaching and all learning in the intellectual sphere start from pre-existing knowledge. This is manifest when we consider the matter in all the specific cases; thus, the mathematical sciences as well as each of the other arts are brought into being by this means.'[2]

'Knowledge and understanding in all systematic studies in which there are principles or causes or elements arise from knowing *these* (for we consider that we know a particular thing whenever we know the first causes and the first principles going as far back as the elements).'[3]

'We think we know a particular thing in an unqualified sense, as opposed to the accidental sense in which the sophist knows, when we think we know, regarding the cause of the existence of the thing, that it is the cause of the said thing, and that the fact could not be otherwise.'[4]

'In other matters too, admitting of proof, we think that we have knowledge of a particular thing when we know *what* it is ($\tau\acute{\iota}$ $\dot{\epsilon}\sigma\tau\iota$), e.g. when we know of "squaring" that it is the finding of a mean proportional.'[5]

The following passages on the classification of sciences are especially relevant to our subject.

'Of the sciences the most exact are those which are most concerned

[1] 983ᵃ12–20.   [2] *An. Post. A.* 1. 71ᵃ1–4.   [3] *Phys. A.* 1. 184ᵃ10–14.
[4] *An. Post. A.* 2. 71ᵇ9–12.   [5] *Metaph. B.* 2. 996ᵇ18–21.

with first principles; those sciences which are based on fewer principles are more exact than those which are more conditioned: thus arithmetic is more exact than geometry.'[1]

'One science is more exact than and prior to another. First, a science which, being one and the same, combines knowledge both of the fact and of the cause is the more exact and prior, not the science of the fact separated from that of the cause. Secondly, the science of things which are not predicated of a substratum is prior to the science of things which have a substratum; thus, arithmetic is prior to harmonic. Thirdly, the science that is based on fewer (assumptions) is prior to that which introduces further conditions; thus, arithmetic is prior to geometry. What I mean by introducing further conditions is this: the unit, for instance, is a substance without position, a point is a substance which has position; it is the point which has the further condition attached.'[2]

'In proportion as the things dealt with are prior in the order of thought and simpler, the science dealing with them is more exact, and exactness means simplicity. Hence, the science is more exact if the things dealt with are without magnitude than if they have magnitude, and most exact of all if they have no movement.'[3]

'Prior in the order of thought' is to be understood in this last passage with reference to a distinction drawn elsewhere:

'Now "prior" and "better known" have two meanings; for prior and better known in the order of nature and prior relatively to us are not the same thing. I call prior and better known relatively to us the things which are nearer to sense, and absolutely prior and better known the things which are farther from it. Now what is farthest from sense is the most universal things, what is nearest is particulars, and these are opposed to one another.'[4]

'And if the things dealt with have magnitude, the science is most exact when they have no movement, while if they have movement the science is more exact when the movement is of the primary kind, that being the simplest, and especially when the movement is uniform.'[5]

'There is a science which investigates being as being and the attributes belonging to it as such (or in virtue of its own nature). This science is not identical with any of the so-called special sciences; for none of the latter concerns itself generally with being *qua* being, but each of them separates off some part of being and investigates the properties appertaining to this part; this is the case, for example, with the mathematical sciences.'[6]

Mathematics is one of the 'theoretical sciences', as Aristotle calls them in contradistinction to the productive and practical arts. The 'theoretical sciences' are three in number: mathematics, physics, and what he calls 'theology' (first philosophy or metaphysic).

[1] *Metaph. A.* 2. 982[a]25-8.
[2] *An. Post. A.* 27. 87[a]31-7.
[3] *Metaph. M.* 3. 1078[a]9-12.
[4] *An. Post. A.* 2. 71[b]33—72[a]5.
[5] *Metaph. M.* 3. 1078[a]12-13.
[6] *Metaph. Γ.* 1. 1003[a]21-6.

'Every science', says Aristotle,[1] 'based upon thought or involving thought to any extent, is about causes and principles more exact or more simple as the case may be; but all these mark off some particular kind of being, some genus, and study this, and not being simply or *qua* being; nor do they give account of the essential nature, the What, of their subject matter; but, starting from the essence, some sciences make it manifest by means of sense, others assume it as an hypothesis, and, beginning in this way, both classes then demonstrate more or less cogently the essential attributes of the genus with which they deal respectively. . . . Similarly they say nothing of whether the genus with which they deal exists or does not exist,[2] because it belongs to the same department of thought to make manifest both what it is and that it is. Now the science of nature is concerned with a particular genus of being (namely with the kind of substance which contains in itself the principle of motion and rest), and it is manifest that this science is neither practical nor productive. In the productive sphere the principle resides in the producer, whether it is reason or art or any other faculty, while in the sphere of action it is in the doer, and consists in volition, for that which is done and that which is willed are the same thing. If, then, all thought is practical or productive or theoretical, it follows that physics is a theoretical science but theorizes about a genus of being which is capable of being moved, and about a kind of substance regarded as form for the most part only as inseparable from matter. But we must not fail to notice how it is with regard to the essence and the definition, since, without this, inquiry is futile.

'Now, of things defined or essences, some are like "snub", others like "hollow". The difference between them is that "snub" is bound up with matter, for the snub is a hollow *nose* whereas hollowness is independent of perceptible matter. Granted then that all natural objects are analogous to snub, like nose, eye, face, flesh, bone, and animal generally, or leaf, root, bark, and plant generally (in none of them is the notion independent of movement, but all of them have matter), it is manifest how we must, in the case of natural objects, seek out and define the What.'[3]

'It is manifest then, from these considerations, that physics is a theoretical science. Whether it deals with immovables and separables is not so far clear; it is, however, manifest that some branches of mathematics investigate objects *qua* immovable and *qua* separable (from matter).

'But if there is anything eternal, immovable, and separable, it manifestly belongs to some theoretical science to know it, not, however, to physics (since physics is concerned with a certain class of movable objects), nor to mathematics, but to some science prior to both. For physics is concerned with things separable but not immovable, while some branches of mathematics are concerned with things immovable but probably not separable, being, as it were, contained in matter. But the first science relates to things which are both separable and

---

[1] *Metaph. E.* 1. 1025^{b}6–13.   [2] 1025^{b}16.   [3] 1025^{b}30–1026^{a}5.

immovable. Now, all causes are necessarily eternal, but, most of all, those now in question, since they are the causes of so much of the divine as is manifest to us. Hence there must be three theoretical philosophies, mathematics, physics, theology.'[1] 'Physics is also a kind of Wisdom but it is not the first kind.'[2] 'The physicist takes account both of the matter of a thing and of its form. He deals with all the active properties or passive affections belonging to body of a given sort and the corresponding matter. . . . The attributes which, though inseparable, are not regarded as properties of bodies of a given sort but are reached by abstraction, fall within the province of the mathematician, while attributes which are regarded as having separate existence fall to the first philosopher (or metaphysician).'[3]

How 'first philosophy' (or metaphysics) and 'theology' come to be, with Aristotle, convertible terms is well explained by Joachim.[4]

'The metaphysician studies reality as a whole and the various kinds and forms of the "real" with a view to determine what is implied in the being of anything which in any sense "is", and to distinguish the kinds and degrees of reality possessed by the various departments and forms of the "real". . . . The substance which is sheer actuality is alone *absolutely* real. It is the primary "real", the standard and measure of reality. . . . It is the metaphysician who examines and develops the conception of the primary "real", the absolutely substantial or self-subsistent. This, as he shows, is a substance which is through and through actual—a substance which is actuality or life, not a substance which has life or manifests activity. . . . It *is* timeless or eternal life, a life which is activity without change and rest without stagnation. And this eternal life Aristotle identifies with God. . . . God—the eternal life of mind, the pure spiritual actuality in which mind is self-expressed, is thus the primary "real" or the central object of the metaphysician's speculation. And metaphysics, since it is concentrated in the *primary* "real", is itself the *first* of the speculative sciences; and since that "real" is God, metaphysics is the "philosophy of God" or "theology". . . .

'Hence finally [continues Joachim], the metaphysician traces out the divinity in things, i.e. exhibits the degree or kind of reality which belongs to the various departments of "being". It is, therefore, a part of his task to determine, in what precise sense the "composite substances" —the perceptible bodies, animate and inanimate, which constitute the world of nature—are real; and again to show what kind of being is to be attributed to the mathematical things, e.g. to the solids and plane figures of the geometer, and to the numbers of the arithmetician. Thus the metaphysician discusses and explains what the natural philosopher and the mathematician take for granted, viz. the 'being' or reality of the subject-matters.'

[1] *Metaph. E.* 1. 1026ᵃ6–19; cf. *Metaph. K.* 7, esp. 1064ᵇ1–14.
[2] *Metaph. Γ.* 3. 1005ᵇ1–2.   [3] *De an. A.* 1. 403ᵇ8–16; cf. *Γ.* 7. 431ᵇ15–16.
[4] *De gen. et corr.*, Introd., pp. xvi–xviii.

In c. 2 of *Metaph. B* Aristotle discusses the question under what
science, or sciences, if any, the 'principles of demonstration' come,
where by 'principles of demonstration' he means the 'common
opinions' or axioms, which are the starting-point of all demonstrations, namely, such propositions as that 'Everything must either be
affirmed or denied' (Law of Excluded Middle), or 'A thing cannot
at the same time both be and not be' (Law of Contradiction). The
science of these principles cannot be any one of the special sciences,
e.g. geometry, for why should they come under any one of these
sciences rather than another? Therefore they must come under all
or none of these sciences. The former of these hypotheses is impossible: for all sciences assume these axioms and the same genus
cannot be subject-matter for different sciences. Do they then belong
to a separate science, and if so, is that the same science as the
science of substance? If not the same, is it more authoritative or
prior? Having stated the ἀπορίαι fully in the chapter quoted,[1]
Aristotle gives his solution in a later passage as follows:

'We have now to consider whether it belongs to one science or to
different sciences to inquire into what mathematicians call axioms and
into substances. It is manifest that the inquiry into these axioms belongs to one science and that the science of the philosopher; for they
hold good for all existing things, and not for some one genus in particular
to the exclusion of others. Everyone makes use of them because they
belong to being *qua* being, and each genus is (part of) being. Men use
them, however, just so far as is sufficient for their purpose, that is, so
far as the genus, to which the demonstrations they offer have reference,
extends. Since then it is clear that they hold good for all things *qua*
being (for this is what they have in common), the person who knows
about being *qua* being must investigate these axioms too. This is why
none of those who study the special sciences tries to enunciate anything
about them, their truth or falsehood; neither the geometer, for instance,
nor the mathematician does so, though it is true that some of the
physicists have made the attempt, and not unnaturally seeing that they
supposed that the inquiry into the whole of nature and into being
belonged to them alone. But since there is a class of inquirer above
the physicist (nature being only one particular genus of being) it is for
the thinker whose inquiry is universal and who investigates primary
substance to inquire into these axioms as well.[2]

'Again since the mathematician, too, uses the common axioms in
a particular application, it must be the business of first philosophy to
investigate the principles of mathematics also. For that when equals
are subtracted from equals the remainders are equal is true of all
quantities alike, but mathematics separates off some part of its proper
subject-matter and investigates that, as for example lines, or angles,

---

[1] 996^b26—997^a34.
[2] *Metaph. Γ*. 3. 1005^a19–^b1; cf *K*. 1. 1059^b14–21.

or numbers, or some one of the other kinds of quantity—not, however, *qua* being, but in so far as each of them is continuous one way, two ways, or three ways. Philosophy, on the other hand, does not inquire into special subjects in so far as each of them separately has attributes, but investigates each of such things so far as each of them *is*. And as with mathematics so with physics; for physics investigates the attributes and the principles of things which are, but *qua* moved and not *qua* being, whereas the first science, as we have said, treats of these things in so far as the underlying subjects are existent but not *qua* anything else. Therefore we must hold both physical and mathematical science to be parts of wisdom.'[1]

(b) Physics and Mathematics

I shall, in general, use the word *Physics* for what Aristotle calls φυσική (sc. ἐπιστήμη or φιλοσοφία) because the term is short and convenient and because we use it as the title of his work the Φυσικὴ Ἀκρόασις. No doubt a more exact translation would be 'natural philosophy' or the 'science of nature'; and φυσική is not coterminous with our 'physics'. But, if this qualification is remembered, the use of the word 'physics' as a rendering is not likely to lead to any confusion.

Joachim has given a succinct account of the content of the Aristotelian physics. The treatise under that name, the *Physics*, has for its subject the 'natural' body (φυσικὸν σῶμα) in general, a 'natural' body being one which contains, innately inherent in it, 'an originative source of motion and rest' (ἀρχὴ κινήσεως καὶ στάσεως)[2] or an impulse to change (ὁρμὴ μεταβολῆς ἔμφυτος).[3] This ἀρχή is the 'nature' (φύσις) of the body.[4] In one aspect φύσις is the primary matter underlying each of the class of objects which have inherent in them the ἀρχή of motion and rest.[5] In another aspect the φύσις of a body is its 'shape' or form in the sense of its 'notion',[6] the form being inseparable from the body except logically.[7] The physicist has to consider not only the matter but the form as well.[8]

The distinction between physics and mathematics and between their respective subject-matters is well brought out in the following passages:

'The science of nature seems, we may say, for the most part to be concerned with bodies and magnitudes, their properties and their movements, and again with each and every one of the principles of this sort of substance. For, of the things constituted by nature, some are bodies

[1] *Metaph.* K. 4. 1061ᵇ17–33; with 1061ᵇ28–32, cf. 1061ᵇ4–7.
[2] *Phys.* B. 1. 192ᵇ14.   [3] 192ᵇ18.   [4] 192ᵇ20–3.   [5] 193ᵃ28–30.
[6] 193ᵃ30—ᵇ4.   [7] 193ᵇ4–5.   [8] *Metaph.* Z. 11. 1037ᵃ16–17.

and magnitudes, some have body and magnitude, and a third class are the principles of the things which possess these.'[1]

'Having distinguished in how many senses we speak of nature, we must next consider wherein the mathematician differs from the physicist. For of course physical bodies contain planes, solids, lengths, and points, which are what the mathematician investigates. Again, astronomy is either different from or a part of physics; for it is absurd to suppose that it is the business of the physicist to know what the sun and moon are, but not to know any of their essential attributes, especially when we see that those who discuss nature do, in fact, also discuss the shape of the moon and sun and the question whether the universe and the earth are spherical or not. Now, the mathematician also studies these (figures) but not *qua* limits or boundaries in each case of a natural body. Nor does he investigate their attributes *qua* attributes of such (physical) bodies. In fact, therefore, he treats them as separate; for they are in thought separable from motion and the separation introduces no error. (The partisans of Forms equally do this, but without knowing it; for they postulate separate physical objects which are less susceptible of separation than mathematical objects.) This can be made manifest if we try to frame the definitions of the objects themselves and of their attributes respectively. For the odd, the even, the straight, the curved, as well as number, line, and figure are independent of motion, whereas flesh, bone, man, are not so, the latter terms being analogous to a snub nose, not like the term "curved". Other evidence is also furnished by the more physical branches of mathematics such as optics, harmonics, and astronomy. These stand to geometry in a sort of inverse relation. For geometry investigates a physical line but not *qua* physical, whereas optics considers a mathematical line not *qua* mathematical but *qua* physical. And since nature means two things, the form and the matter, we must study it in the way in which we should consider the definition of snubness. That is to say, we must consider natural objects neither without reference to matter nor exclusively with reference to matter.[2]

'This is like the mathematician's study of abstractions; for in this study he eliminates all sensibles, as, for example, lightness, hardness, and its contrary, heat, too, and cold and all the other sensible contrarieties, and leaves only the quantitative and continuous, some things being continuous one way, some two ways, and some three ways: studying the attributes of these things in so far as they are quantitative and continuous but with reference to nothing else, and investigating in the case of some of them their positions relatively to one another and the facts which follow therefrom, in other cases their commensurabilities and incommensurabilities, in others their ratios: nevertheless we lay it down that it is one and the same science which deals with all these things, namely geometry. So it is with being also; for the investigation of its attributes *qua* being and the contrarieties in it *qua* being is the business of no other science than (first) philosophy, for it

[1] *De caelo* A. 1. 268ᵃ1-6.   [2] *Phys.* B. 2. 193ᵇ22—194ᵃ15.

is to physics that one would assign the investigation of things *not qua* being but *qua* partaking of movement (or change).'[1]

'By mathematical objects we mean things reached by abstraction (τὰ ἐξ ἀφαιρέσεως); physical objects have other attributes in addition (ἐκ προσθέσεως).'[2]

Note. The distinction between snub (σιμόν) and hollow or concave, κοῖλον, is a favourite illustration of the distinction between the objects of physics and of mathematics. Cf. *De anima Γ* 7. 431ᵇ12–16:

'But the abstractions of mathematics, as they are called, the mind thinks of as it might conceive the snub-nosed; *qua* snub-nosed it would not be conceived apart from flesh, whereas *qua* hollow, if anyone ever had actually so conceived it, he would have conceived it without the flesh in which the hollowness resides. So too when we think of mathematical objects we conceive them, though not in fact separate from matter, as though they were separate.'

(c) Mathematics and Applied Mathematics

We have seen how optics, harmonics, and astronomy are called the more physical branches of mathematics.[3] But there are 'parts', or branches, even of pure mathematics: there is a 'first' and 'second' science in mathematics and others again in order. As Joachim says:[4] 'the order of these successive mathematical sciences appears to be determined by the increasing complexity of the mathematical things whose being is taken for granted. Arithmetic is prior to geometry in the series because the mathematician assumes the being of the unit, substance without position, whereas the geometer assumes the being of the point, i.e. unit *plus* position'.[5]

Applied mathematics, or the 'more physical branches of mathematics', come under 'mathematics' because they use mathematics for their proofs. The following passages are relevant:

'It is not for one science to prove something belonging to a different science, except when the things are so related that one is subordinate to the other, that is to say, as e.g. theorems in optics are to geometry, and theorems in harmonics to arithmetic.'[6]

'The same is true of harmonics and optics: neither considers its objects *qua* sight or *qua* voice but *qua* straight lines and numbers, which latter are proper attributes of the former; similarly with mechanics.'[7]

---

[1] *Metaph. K.* 3. 1061ᵃ28 –ᵇ7.   [2] *De Caelo Γ.* 1. 299ᵃ15–17.
[3] *Phys. B.* 2. 194ᵃ7–8.
[4] *Aristotle: On Coming-to-be and Passing-away,* p. xxi.
[5] *An. Post. A.* 27. 87ᵃ31–7.
[6] *An. Post. A.* 7. 75ᵇ14–17; cf. *A.* 9. 76ᵃ9–13, 22–5.
[7] *Metaph. M.* 3. 1078ᵃ14–17.

Similarly, Aristotle speaks of mathematicians proving facts in astronomy[1] and of the contributions of mathematicians to astronomy.[2]

Again,

'the Why and the What differ in another way, namely in respect that their investigation belongs to different sciences. This is the case where the two things are so related that one falls under the other; this is the relation in which optics stands to geometry, mechanics to solid geometry, harmonics to arithmetic, and phenomena to astronomy. (Some of these sciences in practice bear the same name, e.g. mathematical and nautical astronomy, mathematical and audible harmonics.) For here it is for the practising observer to know the fact, but for the mathematician to know the cause; it is the mathematicians who are in possession of the demonstrations of the cause, and in many cases they do not even know the fact, just as those who investigate the universal often do not know some of the particular cases coming under it because they have not specially considered them. . . .'[3]

Again,

'as optics is related to geometry, so is another science related to optics, namely the theory of the rainbow; it is for the physicist to know the fact as regards the rainbow, whereas to know the cause is for the student of optics, either simply as such or so far as he is concerned with the mathematics of it. There is the same relation between many sciences which are not subordinate to one another. For example medicine is so related to geometry: it is for the physician to know the fact that round wounds heal more slowly, the cause is for the geometer.'[4]

Astronomy occupies a special position. The objects of mathematics are in general without motion; the only exception is those of astronomy.[5] Astronomy is 'the nearest to philosophy of all the mathematical sciences, since it studies substance which is sensible but eternal, whereas the others are concerned with no kind of substance, e.g. the sciences of arithmetic and geometry'.[6]

(d) Astronomy and Physics

The parts assigned to astronomy and physics, respectively, in the investigation of the heavenly bodies are not well distinguished by Aristotle. Astronomy studies substance which is sensible but eternal, physics substance which is sensible but subject to change. Yet physics studies the heavenly bodies, too, though eternal: it is the business of the physicist to know the τί ἐστι of the sun and moon and the rest, and not only that; it would be absurd that he should

---

[1] *De part. an. A.* 1. 639ᵇ7.   [2] *De caelo B.* 14. 297ᵃ3.

[3] *An. Post. B.* 13. 78ᵇ34—79ᵃ6.   [4] 79ᵃ10–16.

[5] *Metaph. A.* 8. 989ᵇ32.   [6] *Metaph. Λ.* 8. 1073ᵇ4–8.

not also discuss their essential attributes and in fact 'we find' (says
Aristotle) 'physicists discussing the shapes of the sun and moon
and the question whether the earth and the universe are spherical
or not'.[1] The latter subjects would naturally be thought to be the
province of astronomy. What then is the function of astronomy as
distinct from that of physics?

In the absence of clearer explanations by Aristotle himself, we
naturally turn first to the Greek commentators. Simplicius has a
long passage on this subject.[2] 'If', he says, 'the physicist investigates
both the substance of the stars and their attributes, while the
astronomer deals with the attributes only, astronomy would appear
to be a part of physics.'[3] Consider first the case of mathematics and
physics. The physicist takes account not only of the attributes of
physical bodies but of their matter; though he speaks of planes
and lines and points, he speaks of these only as limits or extremities
of a physical and movable body. The mathematician says nothing
of matter; his planes, lines, and points are the result of abstraction
and are considered apart altogether from physical bodies and from
motion or change of any kind; therefore the mathematician is not
a physicist nor is mathematics a part of physics.

'Nor is astronomy a part of physics; for while it investigates the
attributes of physical bodies, it considers them as attributes not of
physical bodies as such but of any kind of bodies whatever possessed
of form and moving; so that the astronomer, even when he speaks of
the essential attributes of physical bodies, does not investigate them
qua attributes of such bodies, and he does not prove that such-and-such
forms, such-and-such sizes, and such-and-such motions are appropriate
to such bodies. Thus in the case of the body of the heavens, when it is
a question of proving that it is spherical, the physicist proceeds on the
basis that that particular form of solid body is alone primary, simple,
perfect, and uniform (whereas rectilinear figures are compounded of
a number of separate parts and are therefore secondary) and argues
that for this reason the spherical shape is appropriate to the first of
bodies, as Aristotle shows;[4] the astronomer, on the other hand, draws

---

[1] *Phys. B.* 2. 193^{b}28–30.   [2] *Phys.* ed. Diels, 290–1.   [3] 290. 21–4.
[4] In the *De caelo* (II. 4) Aristotle gives the physicist's reason for the sphericity
of the heaven. The sphere is the first of solid figures as the circle is of plane
figures. The circle is bounded by one line, the sphere by one surface, while
rectilineal figures are bounded by several. You can add to a straight line but not
to the circumference of a circle. The circle, therefore, is complete among plane
figures and the sphere is complete among solids. 'The sphere, then, is the first
solid figure. Now the first figure belongs to the first body; the first body is that
at the extremity of revolution' (287^{a}2–5), i.e. the heaven, therefore the heaven
is a sphere. Aristotle does not state the astronomer's reason, according to
Simplicius, viz. that the sphere is the figure which with a given extent of surface

his argument from the fact that of all solid bodies having equal contour, the sphere is the greatest in spatial content.'[1]

Simplicius[2] proceeds to give after Alexander a word-for-word quotation from Geminus' summary of or commentary on Posidonius' *Meteorologica*, observing that herein Geminus took his cue from Aristotle.

'It is the part of physical inquiry to investigate the substance of the heaven and the stars, their force and quality, their coming to be and their passing away; nay, physics can even prove the facts about their size, form, and arrangement. Astronomy, on the other hand, does not attempt to discuss anything of this kind;[3] but demonstrates the arrangement of the heavenly bodies on the basis of the declaration that the universe is really and truly a Cosmos, and discusses the shapes, sizes, and distances of the earth, the sun, and the moon, eclipses and conjunctions of the heavenly bodies, and the quality and quantity of their motions. Hence the astronomer, when he attacked the question of quantity, size, and quality in respect of figure, naturally came, in this way, to require arithmetic and geometry. And, with regard to those things of which alone he promised to give an account, he is able to compass his proofs by means of geometry and arithmetic. The astronomer and the physicist then will often set out to prove one and the same point, e.g. that the sun is of great size, that the earth is spherical in shape, but they will not proceed by the same roads. The physicist will prove each item from the consideration of substance, of force, or of

contains the most room; but he has what is almost the equivalent of this. 'Since the whole universe revolves in a circle and it has been proved that there can be no void or place outside the limits of the revolution, the heaven must on this account too be spherical. But if the heaven had the shape of a rectilinear solid there would have to be place and body and void outside it. For in turning in a circle the rectilinear solid will never occupy the same room, but where there was formerly body there will now be none, and where there is now none there will again be body because of the overlapping of the angles. Similarly if the universe had any figure with radii not all equal, e.g. lentiform or oviform' (287ª11–20). (The latter figure would always occupy the same place if the revolution were about the one axis of symmetry, but the sphere alone may revolve about *any* diameter without changing its place.)

---

[1] 291. 7–18. [2] 291. 21–292. 29.

[3] περὶ τοιούτου μὲν οὐδενός must apparently refer to the first portion only of the description of the function of physics (the investigation of the substance, power, and quality of the heavenly bodies, their coming to be and their passing away). The second part καὶ νὴ Δία τούτων περὶ μεγέθους καὶ σχήματος καὶ τάξεως ἀποδεικνύναι δύναται looks like a kind of afterthought-parenthesis: this is probably why the editor (Bale) of Posidonius' fragments wrote νὴ Δία διὰ τούτων, namely, in order to save the sense by making the physicist's discussion of the form, size, and arrangement a mere appendage or incident not forming part of his proper subject.

the fact that it is better that it should be so, or again, from the processes of coming to be or change: the astronomer will prove his propositions from the attributes of figures or magnitudes or from the quantity of motion or the time appropriate to it. The physicist, again, will often touch on the cause, looking to creative force; but the astronomer, when he bases his proof on external attributes, does not thereby become a competent observer of the cause, as when, for example, he declares the earth or the heavenly bodies to be spherical in shape; nay, in some cases he does not even aspire to study the cause, as when he speaks of eclipse; at other times he discovers by way of hypothesis and states certain expedients by the assumption of which the phenomena will be saved. Why, for instance, do the sun, the moon, and the planets appear to move irregularly? We may answer that, if we assume that their orbits are eccentric circles or that the stars describe an epicycle, their apparent irregularity will be saved; and it will be necessary to go farther and examine in how many different ways it is possible for these phenomena to be brought about, so that we may bring our theory concerning the planets into agreement with that explanation of the causes which follows an admissible method.

Accordingly we actually find someone coming forward and saying that even on the assumption that the earth moves in a certain way while the sun is in a certain way at rest, the apparent irregularity with reference to the sun can be saved. For it is no part of the business of an astronomer to know what is by nature suited to a position of rest, and what sort of bodies are apt to move, but he introduces hypotheses under which some bodies remain fixed, while others move, and then considers to which hypothesis the phenomena actually observed in the heaven will correspond. But he must go to the physicist for his first principles, namely, that the movements of the stars are simple, uniform, and ordered, and, by means of these principles he will then prove that the rhythmic motion of all alike is in circles, some being turned in parallel circles, others in oblique circles.'[1]

The general inference to be drawn from the above distinctions appears to be this. It is the business of the physicist to consider the substance of the universe and all that it contains, the constitution of the heavenly bodies and their essential attributes as physical bodies and *qua* endowed with motion: he does not exclude the consideration of their shape, but when he maintains, for example,

---

[1] I have explained elsewhere (*Aristarchus of Samos*, 279–83, and *Greek Mathematics*, ii. 231–2) that the phrasing of this sentence with τις, 'some one' or 'a certain person', makes it certain that 'Ηρακλείδης ὁ Ποντικός is an interpolation by some glossarist. The sentence runs quite naturally without the words but very awkwardly with them. It is clear that the reference in τις was really to Aristarchus of Samos and the gloss was inserted in error by someone who was not well informed.

that the earth and the universe, the sun and the moon are spherical in shape, he gives quasi-physical reasons. Motion is either in a straight line or circular; the proper motion for the elements is in a straight line, for the ether it is circular motion, and for bodies endowed with circular motion the spherical shape is the appropriate one. He can also take cognizance of facts, e.g. the size and arrangement of the heavenly bodies.

Farther than this the physicist cannot go. When it comes to the question of accounting for the phenomena, disentangling the different motions, comparing their speeds, and estimating their effects with reference to producing the phenomena, the physicist has to give way to the astronomer. The astronomer's business is to use mathematical considerations in order to formulate a theory which shall save the phenomena. He starts with a set of facts ascertained by observation: as Aristotle says elsewhere,[1] 'it is astronomical experience (ἐμπειρία)—i.e. observations—which supply the principles of astronomical science, for it was after the phenomena had been sufficiently ascertained (by observation) that astronomical proofs were discovered'.

[1] *An. Pr. A.* 30. 46ᵃ19–21.

II

CATEGORIES

(a) Squaring of the circle

Categ. 7. 7^b27–33

'Again destruction of the knowable carries with it destruction of knowledge, but the destruction of knowledge does not involve destruction of the knowable. For if the knowable does not exist, there can be no knowledge—since there will no longer be knowledge of anything—but the non-existence of knowledge is no obstacle to the existence of the knowable. Thus it is, for example, with the squaring of the circle, assuming that it is knowable: knowledge of it does not, it is true, yet exist, but the thing itself is knowable (or an object of knowledge).'

This is part of a passage in which Aristotle explains that in general it is true to say that relatives are naturally concomitant and inseparable. You cannot have double without a half or a slave without a master. But this does not appear to be true of all relatives: for it would appear that the knowable is prior to knowledge. For the most part it is of things pre-existing that we acquire knowledge, and you can point to few cases (if any at all) where knowledge of a thing comes into existence simultaneously with its object (7^b15–27).

Simplicius tells us[1] that Archytas the Pythagorean was the first to lay down a doctrine like that of the *Categories*, that in a work on the 'All' or the 'Universal' Archytas made the same division of things into ten classes (γένη), that his description of them and distinctions between them were reproduced in a work by Iamblichus, and that Aristotle evidently tried to follow Archytas throughout. A passage from Archytas on the point taken by Aristotle about the relation between the knowable and knowledge is quoted word for word by Simplicius. 'Some relatives', he said,[2] 'are not reciprocally related. So it is with knowledge and the knowable: knowledge is said to be of the knowable, and sense of the sensible; but the knowable is not described in terms of knowledge, nor the sensible in terms of sense-perception. The reason of this is that the knowable and the sensible may exist without the sense-perception and the knowledge of them severally, but the knowledge and the sense-perception cannot exist without the knowable and the sensible in each case.'

Simplicius illustrates first by the case of eclipses. Their occurrence

---

[1] 2. 15–25 Kalbfleisch.　　　　　　　[2] 182. 25–183. 2 K.

had been observed 'by certain barbarians',[1] but 'the knowledge of the eclipse came to the Greeks later, through Thales;[2] the eclipse itself, the "knowable" thing, was pre-existent'. This is, of course, an allusion to the story that Thales predicted a solar eclipse which took place during a battle between the Lydians and the Medes (probably the eclipse of May, 585 B.C.). The explanation of the prediction is, no doubt, that Thales had learnt directly or indirectly from the Babylonians the period of 223 lunations after which eclipses recur, which period had been discovered by the Babylonians as the result of observations of eclipses through long centuries. (It is curious that in the passage of Simplicius about 'certain barbarians' it is eclipses of the *moon* which are spoken of as having been 'known' to them but unknown to the Greeks before Thales.)

The case of eclipses is an even better illustration of the truth enunciated by Aristotle than his own, namely, that of the squaring of the circle, inasmuch as the occurrence of eclipses must have been a matter of common observation from time immemorial, whereas the squaring of the circle was a problem which had not to Aristotle's knowledge yet received its solution, and it was therefore necessary for him to add the proviso 'assuming that it (the squaring) is knowable'. The passage, however, furnished the occasion for an historical note by Simplicius about the squaring of the circle which is of interest to the historian of mathematics.[3] 'The squaring of the circle', he says, 'is effected when we construct a square equal (in area) to a given circle. Now this (squaring), it would seem, was not yet known to Aristotle. But Iamblichus says that it had been discovered in the Pythagorean school, "as is clear from the proofs given by Sextus the Pythagorean, who learnt the method of proof by tradition handed down by his predecessors. Later", he says, "Archimedes (effected the quadrature) by means of the spiral-shaped curve (ἑλικοειδοῦς), Nicomedes by means of the curve which is called by the special name *quadratrix* (τετραγωνίζουσα), Apollonius by means of a certain curve which he himself calls 'sister of the cochloid', but which is the same as the curve of Nicomedes, and finally Carpus by means of a certain curve which he simply calls 'that arising from a double motion'; and many others made the construction in various ways." So says Iamblichus.' Simplicius adds: 'No doubt some mechanical device was invented for the solution of the problem, and not a theoretical proof.'[4]

There are some difficulties connected with this passage which I have fully discussed elsewhere.[5] Now Archimedes (287–212 B.C.),

[1] 194. 13 K.   [2] 191. 6–7 K.
[3] Simpl. on *Categ.* c. 7, 192. 15–30 K.   [4] 192. 29–30 K.
[5] Heath, *Greek Mathematics*, i. 225–6, 231–2.

Apollonius (born, say, 252 B.C.), and Nicomedes were all later than Aristotle. The only attempts to square the circle mentioned by Aristotle are those of Antiphon the Sophist, Bryson, and Hippocrates of Chios; the passages dealing with these will be discussed later; it is noteworthy that he makes no mention of Hippias of Elis, who as early as (say) 420 B.C. invented the curve known as the *quadratrix*. It may be that we have here a confirmation of the supposition that Hippias used his curve for the trisection of an angle and not for the squaring of the circle, and that Nicomedes was the first to use it for the circle. Pappus, too, confirms the statement of Iamblichus, for he says that Dinostratus and Nicomedes used the curve which they called *quadratrix* for squaring the circle.[1]

(b) *Figure*

Categ. c. 8. 10ª11–24

'A fourth kind of quality is figure and the shape connected with each thing, and again, in addition to this, straightness and curvedness and anything of the like sort. For in each of these cases a certain quality is asserted; in virtue of a thing being triangular or square a certain quality is asserted of it; so with straight or curved; each particular thing, according to its shape, is described as a certain quality. The rare and the dense, the rough and the smooth, would appear to point to a certain quality; and yet such things seem to be foreign to the class we distinguish as quality, for each of these terms seems rather to indicate a certain relation of position between the parts of the thing. A thing is dense by reason of the parts being in close contact with one another, and rare by reason of their being spatially separated from one another. And a thing is smooth by reason of its parts lying as it were in a straight line; rough by reason of one part standing out and another falling short.'

In this passage 'figure' seems to mean 'shape' simply; it is put on a par with straightness and curvedness, whereas in *Physics* A. 5. 188ª25, 'straight' and 'circular' along with 'angle' are said to be genera of 'figure'.

Figures according to Aristotle differ from the generality of qualities in that they do not admit of more and less. 'The triangular and the square are not thought to admit of more (and less), nor does any other figure. Things which satisfy the definition of a triangle or that of a circle are all equally triangles or circles respectively, while of those which do not satisfy the definitions no one will more than any other be spoken of as the thing defined; the square is no more a circle than the oblong is, for neither satisfies the definition of a circle.'[2]

---

[1] Pappus, iv. 250. 33–252. 2 Hultsch.   [2] *Categ.* c. 8. 11ª5–12.

Aristotle's views on mathematical 'figure' will be found elsewhere: see especially my note on *Topics* vi. 6. 143^{b}11–144^{a}4 (pp. 88–91).[1]

(c) *Gnomon*

Categ. c. 14. 15^{a}29–33

'But there are some things which are increased without being altered; for example, a square is increased (i.e. enlarged) when a gnomon is placed round it, but it is not any the more "altered" (i.e. changed in shape) thereby, and so in other similar cases.'

The term *gnomon* has a history. It was originally the upright stick acting as the 'pointer' in a sundial with plane or hemispherical base. This explains Oenopides' name for a perpendicular, which he

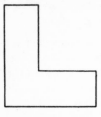

called 'a line drawn gnomon-wise' (κατὰ γνώμονα). In Theognis it appears as an instrument for drawing right angles, shaped like a carpenter's square. Next comes the Pythagorean use of the term to describe the figure which, when placed round a square, produces a larger square. This is the common use, as here. Euclid gives it the extended sense of the figure which is similarly related to any parallelogram. Later still, Heron of Alexan-

FIG. 1

dria defines a gnomon as that which, when added to anything, number or figure, makes the whole similar to that to which it is added.

The numerical use is first found in the Pythagorean theory of numbers, which dealt largely with *figured*

FIG. 2

numbers. The gnomon in relation to square numbers will be seen in the annexed diagram where units are represented by dots. 1 being taken as the first square number, 3 dots placed round it as shown make up 4, the second square number, 5 dots round the 4 make up 9, the next square number, and so on. Accordingly the successive odd numbers 3,

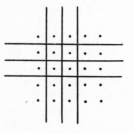

FIG. 3

5, 7, 9, ... were called gnomons. Simi-

[1] Also *The Thirteen Books of Euclid's Elements* (hereinafter referred to as *H.E.*), vol. i, pp. 182–3.

larly the other figured numbers, triangles, pentagons, hexagons, etc., had their series of gnomons. In the case of triangles the gnomons are 2, 3, 4, etc. (the series of all natural numbers), for pentagons they are 4, 7, 10, ..., each exceeding the one before by 3; for hexagons

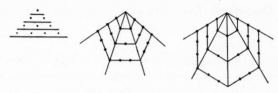

FIG. 4

they are 5, 9, 13, ..., the common difference being 4. In general, if a polygonal number has n sides, the gnomons have $n-2$ for their common difference.

A more difficult question as regards gnomons in numbers arises on a passage of the *Physics*,[1] which will be dealt with later, pp. 101-2.

[1] III. 4. 203ª10-15.

III

PRIOR ANALYTICS

(a) *Incommensurability of the diagonal (of a square with its side)*

An. Pr. I. 23. 41ᵃ23-7

'All who reach a conclusion *per impossibile* infer by syllogism what is false, proving by a hypothetical argument the original proposition, when something impossible results from assuming its contradictory; e.g. they prove that the diagonal of a square is incommensurable with its side by showing that, if it is assumed to be commensurable, odd numbers will be equal to even.'

There is another reference to the case in practically the same terms:[1] 'in this case (proof *per impossibile*) we accept the reasoning even without any preliminary agreement because the absurdity proved is manifest, as when, for example, on the assumption that the diagonal of a square is commensurable with its side, it is proved that odd numbers are equal to even'.

The allusion is clearly to the well-known proof of the incommensurability of the diagonal which appears in our text-books. It is given in practically the same form (1) by Alexander in his note on this passage, and (2) in a proposition interpolated as Prop. 117 in Euclid's Book X. There can be no doubt that it goes back to the Pythagoreans, who were the first to discover the incommensurable.

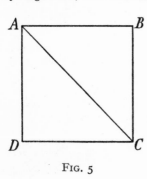

FIG. 5

Suppose AC, the diagonal of the square $ABCD$, to be commensurable with AB, the side.

Let $a:\beta$ be the ratio between them expressed in the smallest possible integers.

Then $a > \beta$, and therefore necessarily $a > 1$.

Now $AC^2 : AB^2 = a^2 : \beta^2$.

But (Euclid I. 47) $AC^2 = 2AB^2$.

Therefore $a^2 = 2\beta^2$.

Therefore a^2 is even, so that a is also even.

Since $a:\beta$ is in its lowest terms, β must be *odd* (otherwise both a and β would be divisible by 2, and $a:\beta$ would not be in its lowest terms).

[1] *An. Pr.* I. 44. 50ᵃ35-8.

Suppose then that $\qquad a = 2\gamma.$

Therefore $\qquad a^2 = 4\gamma^2 = 2\beta^2,$

whence $\beta^2 = 2\gamma^2$, so that β^2, and therefore β, must be *even*.

But β was also odd: which is impossible.

Of many allusions by Aristotle to the incommensurability of the diagonal two others may be mentioned. In *An. Post.* I. 33. 89ª29 we are told that 'the idea that you can have a true opinion that the diagonal is commensurable is absurd'. In *Metaph.* A. 2. 983ª15 the incommensurability of the diagonal is mentioned along with the solstices as one of the things at which the uninstructed person would feel 'wonder', until he learnt the 'cause'.

(b) Euclid I. 5—Aristotle's Proof

An. Pr. I. 24. 41ᵇ13–22

Aristotle has just said that in order that a syllogism may be valid, one of the premisses must be affirmative and one must be universal (41ᵇ6). He illustrates by a syllogism directed to proving that 'pleasure in music is good' and proceeds:

'This is more manifest in geometrical propositions, e.g. the proposition that the base angles of an isosceles triangle are equal. Suppose the straight lines A, B have been drawn to the centre. Then, if one should assume that the angle AC is equal to the angle BD without having claimed generally that the angles of semicircles are equal, and again, if one should assume that the angle C is equal to the angle D without making the additional assumption that every angle of a segment is equal to the other angle of that segment, and if one should then, lastly, assume that, the whole angles being equal and the angles subtracted being equal, the remaining angles E, F are equal, he will beg the question unless he assumes (generally) that "if equals be subtracted from equals the remainders are equal".'

We have here what is obviously a pre-Euclidean proof of the proposition of Euclid I. 5, which shows remarkable differences from Euclid's method and suggests therefore that Euclid's proof was his own. The only difficulty in the interpretation of the passage is how to show the lettering on the supposed figure. It is clear that the isosceles triangle is that formed by two radii of a circle and the chord joining their extremities. Again, it is clear that the angle 'AC'

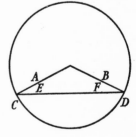

FIG. 6

(and the angle 'BD') is, not a rectilineal angle, but the 'angle *of* a semi-circle', which is the 'mixed' angle formed by the circumference of a semicircle and the diameter, at either end of the diameter; again, the angles C, D are 'mixed' angles, namely, the 'angles *of* the (smaller) segment' of the circle subtended by the base of the triangle, i.e. the 'angles' formed by the circumference and the chord, at either end of the chord. Such 'mixed angles' were recognized in early Greek geometry, as is proved by their survival in Euclid III, first in Def. 7, where the angle *of* a segment is defined, and then in Prop. 16, where it is proved that 'the angle *of* a semicircle is greater, and the remaining angle [its "complement"] less, than any acute rectilineal angle'.

I formerly[1] placed A, B at the extremities of the base, and C, D inside the corners of the segment respectively. This meant that A, B were taken to be the base angles of the isosceles triangle and hence AC, BD had to be taken as $A+C$ and $B+D$ respectively. This made Aristotle speak of 'drawing' for joining *angles* [A, B] to the centre, and had the further awkwardness that A, B were the same angles as the angles afterwards called E, F. I now think it better to place the letters as shown on the figure on p. 23. A, B are for Aristotle obviously the two equal *sides* respectively. C, D have then to be shown in such a way as to make 'AC', 'BD' appear in the figure as reasonable descriptions of the angles *of* the semicircle. But C, D must also be put in places whereby they may reasonably appear to denote the angles *of* the segment respectively. These objects are, I think, both secured by placing A, B as in the figure and putting C, D *outside* the arc of the segment but fairly near the corners as I have done; for 'AC', 'BD' are hardly natural descriptions of the angles *of* the semicircles if C, D are within the segment. My figure is then very like that of Pacius, the only difference being that he puts C, D outside the circle but *at* the corners of the segment. Aristotle's own lettering was no doubt rough and informal and we can hardly hope to restore it to a form which will show no anomalies; but the present suggestion seems to reduce them to a minimum.

The proof is, as I have said, interesting for its use of 'mixed' angles; but it is even more remarkable because the equality of the two 'angles' of a semicircle, and of the two 'angles' of a segment, is *assumed* as a means of proving the equality of the two rectilineal angles at the base of an isosceles triangle, though *a priori* these assumptions would seem no more obvious, or even less obvious, than the proposition to be proved; indeed they could hardly have been held to be justified without some kind of proof, e.g. by superposition.

[1] *Greek Mathematics*, i, 338; *Manual of Greek Mathematics*, p. 196.

(c) Observational astronomy—phaenomena

An. Pr. I. 30. 46ᵃ17–21

'Now most of its principles are peculiar to the particular science. Hence it is the business of experience to furnish the principles in each subject. For example, astronomical experience must furnish the principles of astronomical science; it was only when the phenomena had been adequately grasped that astronomical demonstrations were discovered.'

'Phaenomena' is the technical term for observed appearances in the heavens, e.g. that the sun and the stars rise and set every day, that the meridian height of the sun in these latitudes is greater in summer than in winter, that the moon shows phases, etc. Hence books on observational astronomy were called 'Phaenomena' in contrast to works on theoretical astronomy (sometimes called ἀστρολογία, sometimes σφαιρική); cf. the *Phaenomena* of Aratus, Eudoxus, Euclid; Hipparchus' *Commentary on the Phaenomena of Aratus and Eudoxus*, and Geminus' *Introduction to Phaenomena*.

In *An. Post.* I. 13. 78ᵇ35–9, Aristotle explains that observational astronomy is subordinate to astronomy (ἀστρολογική) in the same way as optics to geometry, mechanics to solid geometry, and harmonics to arithmetic; that is, astronomy supplies the theoretical proofs, and the explanation of the causes, of the phenomena.

(d) Syllogism: forms of terms. The sum of the angles of a triangle is equal to two right angles

An. Pr. I. 35. 48ᵃ29–39

'We need not always seek to set out the terms in a single word for each; for we shall often meet with descriptions which have no single name assigned to them. This is why it is difficult to reduce the syllogisms in such cases to the proper form. Sometimes the effort to find such a single word will actually result in our deceiving ourselves; e.g. that there may be a syllogism about things which have no middle term. Let *A* be two right angles, *B* triangle, *C* isosceles. Then *A* is an attribute of *C* because of *B*, but it is not an attribute of *B* because of any other middle term; for it is of its own nature that a triangle has (its angles equal to) two right angles, so that there will be no middle term between *A* and *B*, though their relation is matter for demonstration. It is manifest, therefore, that the middle term must not always be assumed to be a particular thing, but it may sometimes be a statement or description, as happens in the case mentioned.'

Alexander and Philoponus explain how, in such a case, an argument or a statement of fact takes the place of a single word denoting a middle term. For in the Pythagorean and Euclidean proofs of Eucl. I. 32 it is shown that the three angles of a triangle are together equal to the sum of the two 'adjacent' angles made by a certain straight line in the figure standing on another straight line passing through its extremity, and it has been proved (as in Eucl. I. 13) that in any such case the two adjacent angles are together equal to two right angles. We may therefore put the argument thus: (1) the sum of the three angles of any triangle is equal to the sum of the two 'adjacent' angles as drawn, (2) every sum of two such 'adjacent' angles is equal to two right angles, therefore (3) the sum of the three angles of any triangle is equal to two right angles.

For a comparison between the Pythagorean and the Euclidean proofs of the two-right-angles property of any triangle see my notes on *An. Post.* I. 5. 74^{a}16-^{b}4; on *Metaph.* Θ. 9. 1051^{a}21-31; and on *An. Pr.* II. 16. 65^{a}4-9.[1]

Notwithstanding Aristotle's warning there were apparently those who tried to put Euclid into syllogisms. There are two references in Riccardi's *Bibliografia Euclidea*: on p. 98, '1845—Euclid's (sc. Elements) in syllogisms'; this purports to contain the first six books and the first twenty-one propositions of the eleventh book from the text of Simson 'with the planes shaded. *London, Bogue*'; and on p. 101, '1848. Euclid in syllogisms with diagrams and symbols in colours. By O. Byrne. *London, Pickering*'.

(e) *The geometer's hypotheses*

An. Pr. I. 41. 49^{b}33-7, 50^{a}1-4

'We must not suppose that anything absurd results through our setting out terms; for we make no use of the existence of a particular thing. We are in the position of the geometer who calls this line a foot long, and that line straight and breadthless, when it is not; he does not, however, use this assumption in the sense that his argument depends upon it. . . . We in fact use the method of setting out terms as we do that of presentation to sense, with reference, that is, to the learner; we do not use the terms with any implication that the demonstration cannot be effected without them; they are not like the actual premisses out of which the syllogism is constructed.'

An. Post. I. 10. 76^{b}39-77^{a}3

'Nor does the geometer make hypotheses which are false, as some have said, I mean those who maintain that, although you should

[1] pp. 41-4, 27-30.

not make use of what is false, the geometer is guilty of falsehood in saying that the line which he has drawn is a foot long when it is not, or straight when it is not straight. The fact is that the geometer bases no conclusion on the particular line which he has drawn being what he has described, but he refers to what his diagrams denote.'

That is to say, the truth of a geometer's argument does not depend on the accuracy or inaccuracy of the figures that he draws; he does not argue about the lines etc., that he has drawn but about the lines etc., which they *represent* or symbolize, the (ideal) lines etc., about which he *thinks*. Similarly Plato says[1] that geometers 'use visible kinds' (i.e. visible squares, etc.) 'and frame their arguments about them, though they are not thinking of the particular figures but of those which they resemble: I mean that they are arguing about the square itself and the diagonal itself (the ideal figures), not that which they draw, and so in all other cases'.

(*f*) *Parallel straight lines—petitio principii*

An. Pr. II. 16. 65ª4–9.

Aristotle is speaking of *petitio principii*, which, he says, may take two forms. It may be immediate or mediate. You may either directly assume the proposition to be proved, or assume as true another proposition which falls to be proved by it.

'This is what happens with those who think they draw parallels' [or, possibly, 'establish the theory of parallels', for this is a possible translation of τὰς παραλλήλους οἰόμενοι γράφειν]; 'for they unconsciously assume things which it is not possible to demonstrate if parallels do not exist. The result is that persons so arguing merely say that a thing is *if* it is: and on this basis everything must be known by means of itself [i.e. must be self-evident]: which is impossible.'

This difficult passage, which none of the commentators has succeeded in explaining satisfactorily, seems to imply that the theory of parallels current in Aristotle's time involved some *petitio principii*, whatever it was (for his words are quite general, 'those who think that they draw parallels').

Something depends on what we may take to have been Aristotle's definition of parallels. Euclid, of course, defines them as 'straight lines which, being in the same plane and being produced without limit (εἰς ἄπειρον) in both directions, do not meet in either direction'. It would seem from other passages in Aristotle that the main characteristic of parallels in his mind was that of their *not meeting*. In *An. Post.* I. 5[2] he alludes to a proof that, if a straight line meets

1 *Rep.* 510 D.　　　　2 74ª13–15.

two other straight lines in such a way that the interior angles made with them in either direction *taken together* are equal to two right angles, the two straight lines will not meet if produced. Now this is the proposition proved in the second part of Eucl. I. 28. Again, in *An. Prior*. II. 17. 66ª11–15, he says that we might conclude that parallels meet if we made either of two assumptions: (*a*) that the interior angle (on one side) is greater than the exterior angle (on the same side), or (*b*) that the sum of the three angles of a triangle is greater than two right angles. The statement of (*a*) clearly implies that, in Aristotle's view, the true criterion of parallelism is that the interior angle is not greater than the exterior angle (or less either, presumably) but *equal* to it, which is precisely the theorem proved in the first part of Eucl. I. 28. (It should be noted that both parts of I. 28 are proved by reduction to the preceding proposition I. 27 to the effect that 'if a straight line falling on two straight lines make the alternate angles equal to one another, the two straight lines are parallel'.)

We may reasonably infer that Aristotle's view of parallels would be substantially that of Euclid. Where then is the supposed *petitio principii* committed, according to Aristotle, by 'some who think they draw parallels (or write on parallels)'?

If a general theory of parallels is here alluded to, we infer that it was on the lines of Euclid's propositions on the subject, but that, at some point, it tacitly assumed something equivalent to the very thing to be proved. It is a fair inference that Euclid was the first to get rid of a *petitio principii* in some earlier text-books, by himself formulating the famous Postulate 5.

The commentators throw little light on the subject, but Philoponus has a note which may hint at the existence of an alternative theory of parallels, something of the nature of the *direction*-theories of parallels which have appeared in modern text-books.[1] Philoponus says: 'The same thing is done by those who draw parallels, namely begging the original question; for they will have it that it is possible to draw parallel straight lines from the meridian circle, and they assume, so to say, a point falling on the plane of that circle, and thus they draw the straight lines. And what was sought is thereby assumed; for he who does not admit the genesis of the parallels will not admit the point referred to either.' What is meant seems to be something of this kind. Let it be required to draw, through a given point, a straight line parallel to a given straight line. Suppose the given straight line to be placed (horizontally) in the plane of the meridian. Then through the given point draw another straight line 'in the plane of the meridian' (strictly speaking it would have to be drawn in a plane parallel to the meridian plane but very close

[1] See *H.E.* i, pp. 191–2.

to it). But the plane of the meridian would be of no practical use for enabling us to draw the line required; we might as well be told at once to draw a straight line *in the same direction* as the given straight line, which again is as good as telling us to draw a line *parallel* to the given one. And herein is the *petitio principii*.

We have still to consider how, in Aristotle's time, the false conclusion that parallels meet would be drawn from either of the hypotheses mentioned in 66ª11–15.

(1) Suppose that the 'interior angle is greater than the exterior'. If a transversal *EF* cuts the two parallel lines *AB, CD* in *G, H* respectively, *EGB* is one of the 'exterior' angles and *GHD* the corresponding 'interior' angle. Now it is proved in the theory of parallels that, if *AB, CD* are parallel the exterior angle *EGB* will be equal to the interior and opposite angle *GHD* (cf. Eucl. I. 27–9). If then, says

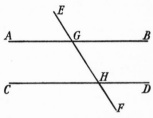

Fig. 7

Aristotle, the angle *GHD* is greater than the angle *EGB*, the straight lines *AB, CD* will meet. To prove this, we add the angle *BGH* to each. Then the sum of the angles *BGH, GHD* must be greater than the sum of the angles *EGB, BGH*. The latter, being 'adjacent' angles, are together equal to two right angles (Eucl. I. 13). Therefore the angles *BGH, GHD* (the two interior angles on one side of *EF*) must be together greater than two right angles. It follows that the angles *AGH, GHC*, the interior angles on the other side of *EF*, must be together *less* than two right angles. (This was probably the accepted criterion for two straight lines meeting, however it was supposed to be proved, even before Euclid laid down his Post. 5.)

(2) The theorem that the angles of a triangle are together equal to two right angles depends upon the Euclidean theory of parallels. There are two traditional proofs, the Pythagorean, handed down by Proclus on the authority of Eudemus, and the Euclidean (I. 32).

Given a triangle *ABC*, in the Pythagorean proof a straight line *DAE* is drawn through *A* parallel to *BC*; Euclid produces *BC* to *D* and draws through *C*, in the angle *ACD*, a straight line parallel to *BA*.

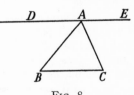

Fig. 8

In the former case it is shown that the angles *B, C* are equal to the angles *DAB, EAC*, the alternate angles, respectively; hence the three angles together are equal to the sum of the three angles about A, which sum is equal to two right angles (I. 13).

In the second case the angle A is proved equal to the alternate angle ACE, and the angle B to the exterior angle ECD, and hence the sum of the three angles A, B, C is equal to the sum of the three angles about C, which sum again is equal to two right angles (I. 13).

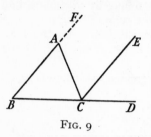

FIG. 9

The proof known to Aristotle was that of Eucl. I. 32, as we gather from the wording of another passage (*Metaph. Θ.* 9. 1051ᵃ24).

If now, in Euclid's figure, the three angles of the triangle are together greater than the sum of the three angles at C, either the angle A must be greater than the alternate angle ACE, or the angle B must be greater than the exterior angle ECD, or both. Suppose the angle A to be greater than the angle ACE. Then, if we produce BA to F, the angles FAC, ACE are together less than the sum of the angles BAC, FAC, and therefore less than two right angles. Hence, as before, the supposed parallels BF, CE will meet beyond F, E.

The hypothesis that the angle ABC is greater than the angle ECD has already been dealt with.

(g) *Incommensurability of diagonal and Zeno's bisection. Chrystal's proof*

An. Pr. II. 17. 65ᵇ16–21

'To assign the not-cause as cause is just this: suppose, for example, that a person wishing to prove that the diagonal is incommensurable should attempt to apply the argument of Zeno that motion is impossible, and should reduce the impossibility (that the diagonal should be commensurable) to *this*; for the false conclusion (of Zeno) is not connected in any way whatever with the original assumption.'

The Greek commentators do not throw much light on this passage. The text of Philoponus is unsatisfactory,[1] and I do not see how any proper sense can be extracted from Wallies's version of it, in which he inserts ⟨ἐλέγχων⟩ after τὸν Ζήνωνος λόγον. Aristotle's words afford, I think, no support for this, and it would make Philoponus say: 'It is as if any one should wish, in refuting the argument of Zeno that motion is impossible, to assume that the diagonal is incommensurable (with the side).' What Aristotle cites as an

---

[1] p. 458. 1–10 Wallies.

example is *not* a man trying to disprove Zeno's argument by *assuming* that the diagonal is incommensurable, but a man who is trying to *prove* the incommensurability by applying, in some way, Zeno's line of argument. To prove the incommensurability by *reductio ad absurdum* one has to assume that the diagonal is commensurable, not that it is *in*commensurable (which is the very thing to be proved).

I think that Aristotle's remark may point to some genuine attempt to prove the incommensurability of the diagonal by means of a real 'infinite regression' of Zeno's type. Euclid, in fact, succeeded in proving (in Book X) the property of the incommensurable by an 'infinite regression', but found the correct result whereas Zeno deduced an incorrect one. Euclid proves in his Prop. 2 of Book X that, if we apply to two incommensurable magnitudes the process of finding the greatest common measure, the process will never come to an end. His proof by *reductio ad absurdum* shows that, if the process *did* come to an end, the magnitudes would be commensurable and not incommensurable. It seems, therefore, as if the argument referred to by Aristotle, beginning with the assumption that the diagonal is commensurable with the side of a square, revealed some 'infinite regress', and it was then inferred that Zeno's argument, as, for example, in the *Achilles*, to prove that motion is impossible (which is, of course, absurd), would apply in this case. An anonymous scholium to the passage[1] may be thought to hint at some idea of this kind.

'If then any one wishing to prove that the diagonal of a square is incommensurable with its side should first assume the contrary, namely, that it is commensurable, should next tack on to this proposition, in addition, the said argument of Zeno, and should then conclude that motion is impossible, which is absurd—we shall reply to him that he must find another proof; for the impossibility does not follow as a consequence of the hypothesis. Even if the hypothesis [that the diagonal is commensurable with the side] be destroyed, the same absurdity [namely that motion is impossible] will be inferred on the ground of Zeno's fallacious argument (alone).'

No doubt Aristotle himself might say, as Pacius suggests, that the hypothesis itself is purely mathematical, but the conclusion is 'physical'; the former is independent of motion, the latter asserts something about motion; hence the two things have no connexion with one another.

As we have said, Euclid's general test of the incommensurability of two magnitudes with one another is this: two magnitudes are incommensurable when, in continuing the process of finding their

[1] Brandis, p. 192^{b}46–193^{a}5.

greatest common measure, it is found that 'no remainder ever measures the one before it', i.e. the process will never come to an end. This is easily proved theoretically; the difficulty would be how to apply the principle in a particular case such as that of the diagonal and the side of a square.

A modern proof on this principle is given in G. Chrystal's *Text-Book of Algebra*;[1] it is true that it could hardly have been discovered by the Greeks in that form, since it is a case of the application of Fermat's method of 'diminution without limit' (*descente infinie* or *indéfinie*).

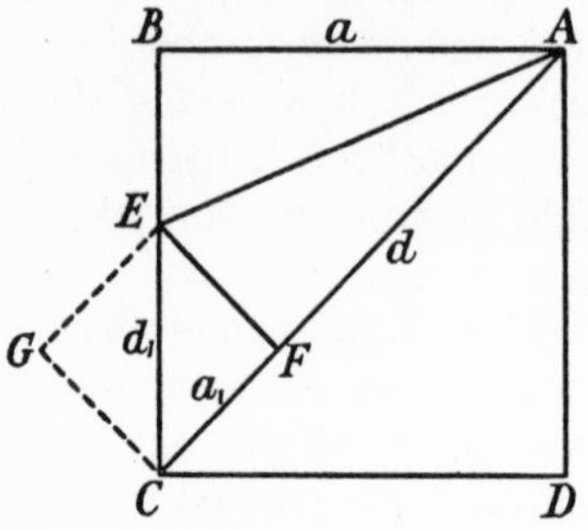

FIG. 10

Let d, a be the diagonal and the side respectively of a square $ABCD$. Along AC mark off AF equal to a.

Draw FE at right angles to CA meeting CB in E. Join AE.

Then $AE^2 = AB^2 + BE^2$,

and $AE^2 = AF^2 + FE^2$,

since the angles at B, F are right angles.

But by construction $AF = AB$, and therefore $AB^2 = AF^2$.

Therefore the remainders BE^2, FE^2 are equal, whence

$$BE = EF$$

Since CFE is a right angle, each of the angles ECF, CEF is half a right angle, and therefore the angles ECF, CEF are equal.

Therefore $EF = FC$.

so that BE, EF, FC are all equal.

Now $\qquad CF = CA - AB = d - a \qquad$ (1)

and $\qquad CE = CB - EB = a - (d - a)$

$$= 2a - d \qquad (2)$$

Suppose, if possible, that a, d are commensurable.

If d, a are both commensurably expressible in terms of any finite unit, each must be an integral multiple of the same unit.

But from (1) it follows that CF, and from (2) that CE, is an integral multiple of the same unit.

And CF, CE are the side and diagonal respectively of a square $CFEG$ with side CF ($= BE$), which is *less than half the side of the original square*. Let a, d, be the side and diagonal respectively of the square $CFEG$.

Then $\qquad a_1 = d - a,$

$\qquad\qquad d_1 = 2a - d.$

Similarly we can construct a square with side a_2 and diagonal d_2,

[1] Part i[5], p. 270.

which are less than $\frac{1}{2}a_1$ and $\frac{1}{2}d_1$ respectively, and a_2, d_2 must (for the same reason as before) be integral multiples of the same unit, while

$$a_2 = d_1 - a_1,$$
$$d_2 = 2a_1 - d_1.$$

This process may be continued indefinitely until (Eucl. X. 1) we have a square as small as we please, the side and diagonal of which are nevertheless integral multiples of a finite unit: which is absurd.

Therefore a, d cannot both be measured by any finite length, however small: therefore they are incommensurable.

The above proof is of special interest because the procedure of constructing a series of smaller and smaller squares in accordance with a certain formula is precisely the reverse of that followed by the Pythagoreans for the purpose of finding the series of pairs of 'side-and-diagonal-numbers' which give closer and closer arithmetical approximations to the value of the ratio ($\sqrt{2}$) of the diagonal of a square to its side; the Pythagoreans passed from the original square to larger and larger squares instead of to smaller and smaller. Our authority is Theon of Smyrna.[1]

(h) The squaring of the circle by means of lunes

An. Pr. II. 25. 69^{a}20–5, 30–4

'*Reduction* is effected (1) when the first term is clearly an attribute of the middle term, whereas that the middle term is an attribute of the last term is, though not actually clear, at all events equally probable or more probable than the conclusion is; or (2) when the terms intermediate between the last and the middle are few; the result in any case is that we are nearer to knowledge.... For example, suppose D means 'being squared', E a rectilineal figure, F a circle; then if between E and F there is only one intermediate term, namely that the circle together with (certain) lunules is equal to a rectilineal figure, we should be near to knowing [how to square the circle itself].'

The squaring of *lunules* [μηνίσκοι] or lunes of different kinds is a subject specially associated with the name of Hippocrates of Chios (fl. perhaps about 450–430 B.C.), who squared certain lunes, presumably in the hope that this investigation would ultimately lead to the actual squaring of the circle. There are two other passages in Aristotle containing similar allusions, one of which is certainly to Hippocrates, because he is mentioned by name. (1) In *Soph. El.*

[1] pp. 43–4 (Hiller); Heath, *Greek Mathematics*, i. 91–3; *Manual of Greek Mathematics*, 53–5.

11. 171^{b}15 Aristotle speaks of 'the (fallacy) of Hippocrates or the quadrature by means of lunes', where most probably (I think) the 'or' only indicates another description of the same thing (cf. 172^{a}3). (2) In *Phys.* I. 2. 185^{a}16–17 he says: 'Thus it is for the geometer to refute the (supposed) quadrature (of the circle) *by means of segments*, but it is not the business of the geometer to refute the argument of Antiphon.' It seems most probable that here too the reference is to Hippocrates, and that the word 'segments' is loosely used for what are not technically segments, but are really *lunes*; the point does not seem important because segments are used in the proofs of all the propositions.

In the present passage, however, where Aristotle speaks of the quadrature of a circle *together with* certain lunes, it seems certain that the quadrature is one of two of the kind in question which are on record. The first is a case where certain lunes are formed by describing semicircles on the sides of a regular hexagon inscribed in a circle, and it is proved that three of such lunes with a semicircle (of the same size as those constructed on the sides of the hexagon) make up an area equal to the trapezium which is half of the regular hexagon. The other is a case where Hippocrates proved that *one* lune of a certain type together with a circle related to it in a certain way is equal to the sum of the isosceles triangle inscribed in the segment containing the lune *plus* the hexagon inscribed in the circle.

The fallacy connected with the first case only arose when its presumed author (or someone else) assumed that the lunes described on the sides of the regular hexagon were squarable by themselves (which they are not). The second case is one of the genuine cases discovered by Hippocrates himself, as is known from the invaluable citation from Eudemus' *History of Geometry* given by Simplicius[1] on *Phys.* I. 2. 185^{a}14–17; but this could not reasonably be called 'the fallacy of Hippocrates', unless Hippocrates had stated, or allowed it to be supposed that he thought, that by means of this particular quadrature he had made it possible to square the circle itself. This is, however, inconceivable; it would only have been possible if the particular lune in question had been proved to be, by itself, equal to some rectilineal figure, and a geometer so able as Hippocrates would have been the last person to assume or imply this. For this reason, and for the reason stated by Ross,[2] namely, that Aristotle speaks of the quadrature of a circle plus lunes (in the plural, not the singular), it seems clear that he is alluding to the first case, the quadrature of a circle *plus* the lunes on the sides of a regular hexagon inscribed in a circle of twice the radius.

[1] Simpl. in *Phys.*, pp. 60. 22–68. 32 Diels.
[2] Aristotle, *Physics*, p. 465.

I have elsewhere[1] set out at length all the quadratures of lunes that are on record; first, the two cases which alone Simplicius found described by Alexander, and, secondly, the four which he quotes textually from Eudemus, and which therefore may with certainty be taken to be the only cases included in the genuine work of Hippocrates himself. The latter cases hang together perfectly; the first three correspond exactly to the summary statement (whether due to Simplicius or to Eudemus himself) that Hippocrates 'squared every (sort of) lune (πάντα μηνίσκον) *in the sense* that (εἴπερ καί) he squared that which has a semicircle for its outer circumference and those which have for their outer circumference an arc greater than, and an arc less than, a semicircle respectively'; and the last, that of the lune ·*plus* the circle, was added by Hippocrates as an additional interesting case, without any statement or implication by Hippocrates himself that he had, by means of that case or otherwise, succeeded in squaring the circle itself.

We are driven to the conclusion (indicated by Ross[2]) that Aristotle was not well informed as to what Hippocrates had actually done, and his strictures on the 'fallacy' of Hippocrates were due to a simple misapprehension on his own part and were unjustified in fact. It would seem that neither Aristotle nor Alexander knew of any quadratures other than the two described by the latter, which must in Aristotle's time have gained currency and been somehow wrongly ascribed to Hippocrates, and that it was left for Eudemus to discover the real facts by independent researches of his own, with the results handed down by Simplicius but evidently unknown to Aristotle and Alexander. The first of the two cases reproduced by Alexander, that of the lunes which are parts of semicircles described on the sides of a square inscribed in a circle, does give the same result as the first of Hippocrates' cases though the figures used are

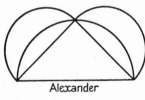

Alexander   Hippocrates

FIG. 11   FIG. 12

different. The other case given by Alexander, that of the lunes described on the sides of a regular hexagon inscribed in a circle, does not correspond to anything in Hippocrates' own exposition, and the

[1] *Greek Mathematics*, i, pp. 183–200.   [2] l.c., p. 466.

false conclusion based upon it (whether by its discoverer or another) has nothing to do with Hippocrates.

FIG. 13

It will be observed that the Oxford translation of our passage needs correction: 'let D stand for squaring' should be 'let D stand for *being squared*' (τετραγωνίζεσθαι), i.e. being *squarable*; again, τὸ μετὰ μηνίσκων ἴσον γίνεσθαι εὐθυγράμμῳ τὸν κύκλον does not mean 'the circle is made equal to a rectilineal figure by the help of lunules' but 'the circle when *taken together* with (certain) lunules can be made equal to a rectilineal figure', i.e. the area which is the sum of the areas of the circle and of the lunules is squarable.

IV
POSTERIOR ANALYTICS
(a) General

An. Post. I. 1. 71ª1–9, 11–21

'Every kind of teaching and learning in the intellectual sphere starts from pre-existing knowledge. This is manifest if we consider it in all the several cases; the mathematical sciences arise in this manner, and so does each of the other arts. Similarly with logical arguments, whether they are by way of syllogism or by way of induction; for it is by means of things previously known that both perform their function of teaching, the former making assumptions which an understanding audience is taken to accept, the latter proving the universal by the method of making the particular case clear. . . .

'The previous knowledge required is of two kinds: (1) as regards some things, we must know beforehand that they exist, (2) as regards others, we must understand the meaning of the term used, (3) in some cases both assumptions are necessary. Thus, that every predicate can be either truly affirmed or truly denied of every subject we must admit as a fact; of a triangle we must know that it means a certain thing; of the unit we must know both, namely what it means (i.e. its definition) and that it exists; for these different things are not equally clear to us. Recognition of a fact may involve some things known before, and others the knowledge of which comes at the same time, e.g. things which come under the universal and are thus implicitly known. The student knew beforehand that every triangle has its angles together equal to two right angles; but that such-and-such a figure in a semicircle is a triangle he recognized (only) as the induction proceeded.'

It is in the above passages that Aristotle first broaches the questions, what are the fundamental principles which must be assumed as the basis of science in general and of the separate sciences respectively, and how they are to be classified. We shall come later to the passage in which he gives the fullest account of the first principles on which mathematics is based, the distinction between axioms, definitions, 'theses', 'hypotheses', etc. This is the passage in *An. Post.* I. 10. 76ª31–77ª4.[1]

Evidently Aristotle is referring to such a figure as may be used

---

[1] On this see my translation below with the notes appended (pp. 50–2).

to prove the theorem that the angle in a semicircle is a right angle.[1]

Suppose that BAC is a semicircle on BC as diameter and A any point on the circumference. Draw AO to the centre O, and join BA, AC. Euclid proves our proposition in this way.

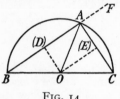

FIG. 14

Produce BA to F. Now the angles OAB, OBA are equal because $OA = OB$. Similarly the angles OAC, OCA are equal.

By addition the whole angle BAC is equal to the two angles ABC, ACB.

But (I. 32) the 'exterior' angle FAC is also equal to the two ('interior and opposite') angles ABC, ACB.

Therefore the angles BAC, FAC are equal.

Therefore each of them is a right angle (I, Def. 10).

The meaning of Aristotle's remark above would seem to be rather that, until the figure was drawn, the attention of the learner had not been directed to the particular case of a triangle inscribed in a semicircle, and he then learnt of its existence as part of an induction. If he only recognized the figure drawn to be a triangle after a certain argument had convinced him, we must suppose some construction made in which, for example, BC was not drawn as one line, but in two parts BO, OC, and that it was only then shown that BOC is one straight line.

Suppose, for instance, that a circle has been drawn passing through three points, A, B, C, so placed that BA, AC form a right angle at A.

To find the centre (O) of the circle, we may bisect BA, AC in D, E respectively and draw perpendiculars from D, E to BA, AC respectively, meeting in O.

Then, since the angles at D are right, the triangles BDO, ADO are equal in all respects; hence $AO = BO$.

Similarly we prove that $AO = CO$; therefore AO, BO, CO are all equal, and O must be the centre of the circle.

Now DO, being at right angles to BA, is parallel to AC; therefore $\angle DOA = \angle OAC$.

But $\angle BOD = \angle DOA$; therefore $\angle BOA = 2(\angle OAC)$.

Similarly $\angle COA = 2(\angle OAB)$.

Therefore by addition $\angle BOA + \angle AOC = 2(\angle BAC) =$ two right angles.

Therefore BOC is a straight line (Eucl. I. 13), and ABC is a *triangle*.

A proof of the proposition that the angle in a semicircle is right,

[1] See Eucl. III. 31.

differing slightly from Euclid's, was interpolated in the text of
Euclid after III. 31. It is rather this proof which Aristotle seems to
have had in mind in a later passage of the *An. Post.* (II. 11. 94ᵃ24–35):
see the note on that passage below (pp. 71–3). Yet another proof
seems to be hinted at in *Metaph.* Θ. 9. 1051ᵃ26, on which see my note
(pp. 216–17).

(b) Essential attributes; primary and universal

In *An. Post.* I. 4. 73ᵃ28–ᵇ5 Aristotle discusses 'essential' (καθ'
αὑτά) attributes. An essential attribute must not only be true of
every instance (κατὰ παντός); it must attach to the very nature of
the subject (the thing *per se, ᾗ αὑτό*). Essential attributes include:
(1) those which are contained in the definition of the thing, and (2)
those which require that the thing itself shall appear in their own
definition. The definition of a line includes 'points', that of a triangle
straight lines. The definitions of straight and curved must include
'line'; those of odd, even, prime, composite, square, and oblong
(as applied to numbers on the analogy of the geometrical figures)
must include 'number'. Aristotle calls an attribute 'universal' when
it not only belongs to every random instance of the subject but also
belongs to that subject *primarily*, i.e. when the subject is the *first*
or *highest* to which it belongs. The property of having its angles
'together equal to two right angles' belongs *primarily* to one class
of rectilinear figure (the triangle), not to every rectilinear figure.
In a square the angles are together equal to four right angles, in
a figure with more than four sides to more; the triangle is the first
rectilinear figure to possess the property. On the other hand,
though a variety of the triangle, e.g. the isosceles, has the property,
it is not the *first* subject to have it: the triangle in general is prior
to it.

Aristotle goes on:

An. Post. I. 5. 74ᵃ4–16

'We must not forget that it often happens that we are mistaken,
and what is proved is really not primary and universal in the way
that it appears to be proved so. We deceive ourselves in this way:
(1) when we cannot find any higher category above a particular case
or cases; (2) when there is such a higher category, but there is no
name for it because the subjects differ in species; (3) when the supposed whole to which a proof applies turns out to be only a part of
a larger whole; for in the latter case the demonstration will apply
to the part and will be true "of every instance", yet the demonstration will not be true of this subject primarily and universally. When
a demonstration is true of a subject primarily and universally, we

mean that it is true of the subject primarily and *as such* (ᾗ αὐτό).
Thus, if anyone were to show that right angles [by which is meant
straight lines each of which is at right angles to one and the same
straight line] do not meet, it might be thought that *this* [the fact
that these straight lines making right angles respectively with the
one transversal are parallel] was the proper subject of the demonstration because it is true of all right angles. But this is not so,
inasmuch as the result does not follow because the two angles are
together equal to two right angles *in the particular way* [i.e. because
each of them is a right angle], but in virtue of their being equal to
two right angles in any way *whatever.*' [i.e. the angles need not be
equal, both being right angles: it is sufficient that their *sum* is two
right angles.]

The allusion here is to the theorem proved in Eucl. I. 28 that, if
a straight line falling on two straight lines makes the interior angles
on the same side equal to two right angles, the straight lines will be
parallel to one another. Euclid's diagram is like that annexed, and
it is proved that, if the angles BGH, GHD (or AGH, GHC) are together

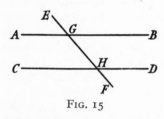

FIG. 15

equal to two right angles, the straight
lines AB, CD are parallel. Now, if
EF had cut AB, CD perpendicularly,
making each of the angles BGH, GHD
right angles, and if it had been proved
in that case, and therefore in all cases
in which AB, CD make right angles
with EF, it might be thought that
this was the proper subject of de-
monstration. But it is not, because the demonstration is not true
of those lines *primarily*. The proposition is true of any straight
lines making with the transversal any angles (equal or unequal)
which are together equal to two right angles, and the class of such
straight lines is more general than, and includes, the class of those
making right angles. It is therefore of the more general class that
the proposition is *primarily* true. The illustration comes therefore under (3) of the possible ways in which we are liable to be
misled.

I dealt with this passage somewhat fully in my note on Euclid
I. 27, to which I may refer.[1] I am clear that αἱ ὀρθαί in 74ᵃ13–14
means right *angles*, not straight lines both at right angles to another,
because there is no alternative to supplying *angles* (γωνίαι) with
ἴσαι two lines farther down ('because *they* are equal in the particular
way')—it would be nonsense to say that the perpendicular *straight
lines* are equal to one another in the particular way. To speak of

[1] *H.E.* i, pp. 308–9.

'right angles meeting' is quite in keeping with Aristotle's shorthand-like manner: cf. his constant use of the expression τὸ δύο ὀρθαῖς, 'the (equality) to two right (angles)', to denote the theorem that the three angles of a triangle are together equal to two right angles.

The Oxford translation takes the other view, making αἱ ὀρθαί 'perpendiculars to the same line'; but the awkwardness is apparent when the translator has to say, in the next sentence, that 'the parallelism depends not on *these angles* being equal to one another . . .' though, on his hypothesis, no angles have actually been mentioned.

I may note that Blancanus takes the same view as I have taken.

(c) *Proposition about parallels*

An. Post. I. 5. 74ᵃ16–ᵇ4

'And, if there had been no triangle but an isosceles triangle, the property that its angles are together equal to two right angles would have been thought to belong to it *qua* isosceles. Another case is the theorem about proportion, that you can take the terms alternately (i.e. *alternando*); this theorem used at one time to be proved separately for numbers, for lines, for solids, and for times, though it admitted of proof by one demonstration. But because there was no name comprehending all these things as one, I mean numbers, lengths, times, and solids, which differ in species from one another, they were treated separately. Now, however, the proposition is proved universally; for the property did not belong to the subjects *qua* lines or *qua* numbers, but *qua* having a particular character which they are assumed to possess universally. Hence, even if we prove with reference to each kind of triangle, either by one demonstration or different demonstrations, that each has its angles together equal to two right angles, that is, if we prove this separately for the equilateral, the scalene, and the isosceles triangle, we do not yet know that *triangle* has its angles together equal to two right angles except in a sophistical sense, nor that triangle universally has this property even if there is no triangle other than the species mentioned. We do not know it *qua* triangle, nor do we know it even of every triangle except in a numerical sense; we do not know it *notionally* (κατ' εἶδος) of every triangle even if there be no triangle which we do not know. When then do we fall short of knowing universally and when do we know without qualification?

'It is clear that had the essence of "triangle" been the same as that of "equilateral triangle", each or all (we should have known in an unqualified sense); if, however, it is not the same but different, and if the (two-right-angles) property belongs (to the equilateral) *qua* triangle, we do not know (without qualification). Does the property then belong to the subject *qua* triangle or *qua* isosceles? And when does it belong to the subject *primarily*? With reference to what subject is the demonstration universal? Clearly we come to this when, in the process of *abstraction* (i.e. elimination of non-essentials), we arrive at the *first* thing to which the property or attribute belongs. For example, the two-right-angles property will belong to a bronze isosceles triangle; but it will continue to belong when you have taken away the characters of being bronze and being isosceles. Not so if you take away "figure" or "boundary". These are not the *first* characters the abstraction of which destroys the attribute. What then *is* the first? If it is clear that this is "triangle", it is "triangle" in virtue of which the property belongs to other things as well, and it is with reference to "triangle" that the demonstration is universal.'

There is a difference of opinion between commentators as to which particular one of the three modes of self-deception mentioned in 74ª7–10 the examples given by Aristotle are intended to illustrate respectively.

With reference to Aristotle's statement that, if there had been no triangle but an isosceles triangle, the '2R' property (as we will call it in future for brevity) would have been thought to belong to it *qua* isosceles, Philoponus takes this case to be an example of mode (1) where we cannot find any higher category above a particular case or particular cases. So does Zabarella, while observing that Aristotle is putting a fictitious case.

Blancanus, however, thinks that we have here a second example of mode (3) where the part is taken for the whole of a class, the first example of this being the straight lines both of which meet a transversal perpendicularly. I agree with Zabarella's view, because, if there *were* none but isosceles triangles, there would be no more comprehensive 'whole'.

In Aristotle's further remark that, if we prove the 2R property separately for three kinds of triangle, the equilateral, scalene, and isosceles, either by one proof or by different proofs, we do not yet know except in a sophistical sense that the property belongs to the *triangle*, Blancanus sees an example of mode (1) of self-deception. Zabarella takes it as a second illustration of mode (2) because, although there is in this case a name for a more comprehensive class ('triangle'), the proofs would be on a par with the partial proofs of the *alternando* theorem in proportions; the case is given, therefore, in order that we may better understand the kind of case in which no name has been found for the more comprehensive class. I incline to Zabarella's view, which is, I think, confirmed by the fact that the illustration comes immediately after the *alternando* illustration of mode (2), and is introduced with the words 'for this reason' (διὰ τοῦτο).

It is worth noting that Eutocius at the beginning of his commentary on Apollonius' *Conics* tells us on the authority of Geminus that the ancients investigated the theorem of the two right angles in each individual species of triangle, first in the equilateral, again in the isosceles, and afterwards in the scalene, and later geometers demonstrated the general theorem that in *any* triangle the three interior angles are together equal to two right angles. This does not seem to be confirmed by any other documentary evidence; and, as we have seen,[1] the first proof known to us, the Pythagorean, handed down by Eudemus, is quite general like that of Euclid in I. 32. It is not easy to make a probable reconstruction of the arguments by which the proof would be given in three stages. It seems possible, therefore, that Geminus' idea might rest on nothing more than the present passage of Aristotle, where the illustration may be entirely hypothetical.

Very interesting is Aristotle's allusion to the theory of proportion, where he says[2] that the theorem that you can transform a proportion *alternando* used at one time to be proved separately for different species of things, numbers, lines, solids, and times, but is now proved universally, since the property did not inhere in the subjects *qua* numbers, lines, etc., but *qua* having a particular character 'which men suppose all of them to possess' (ὃ καθόλου ὑποτίθενται ὑπάρχειν). Euclid, of course, gives in his Book V the great theory of proportion which is applicable to all magnitudes alike, whether commensurable or incommensurable, and the discovery of which is universally attributed to Eudoxus, whereas in Book VII he gives, quite independently, a theory of proportion which applies only to integral numbers. The latter theory, we may assume, was substantially the older theory of proportion, probably Pythagorean, which was generally in use before Eudoxus' time, but became a broken reed as a geometrical method when the discovery of the incommensurable showed that there were an infinity of geometrical magnitudes to which it could not be applied. It may be asked, why did Euclid give the two theories of proportion separately with separate sets of definitions, without saying anything to connect them, even in X. 5, where he has a proportion in which two terms are magnitudes and two are numbers ('commensurable magnitudes have to one another the ratio which a number has to a number')? The probable explanation is that Euclid simply followed tradition and gave the two theories as he found them.

It seems clear that Aristotle was already acquainted with the general theory of proportion due to Eudoxus, and that he is alluding to it here. It is true that Philoponus remarks that, when Aristotle says that the *alternando* theorem was 'at one time' (ποτέ) proved separately for the different species of subjects, but is 'now' (νῦν) proved by one demonstration applying to all, the ποτέ and the νῦν have no reference to different times at all, but the words only imply a difference in the completeness and perfection of the proofs, the ποτέ implying a proof more or less rough and ready (ὁλοσχερέστερον) and the νῦν the rigorous scientific proof (ἀκριβῶς). I cannot believe this, since Aristotle is so careful in the one case to use the imperfect tense and in the other the present: 'it used at one time to be proved separately' (ἐδείκνυτό ποτε χωρίς), but, as there was no name to comprehend numbers, lengths, and solids, 'they used to be taken separately' (χωρὶς ἐλαμβάνετο); 'now, however, they are proved universally' (νῦν δὲ καθόλου δείκνυται).

Aristotle does not say what general term was used in his time to cover the four categories of things; possibly no term had yet been definitely agreed upon, for he merely observes that the common character was 'a certain something which "they" assume to inhere universally' (τοδί, ὃ καθόλου ὑποτίθενται ὑπάρχειν). If he had suggested a term, it would presumably have been ποσόν, quantity, *how much*; for in the *Categories*[1] he says that quantity may be either discrete or continuous, and sometimes it is made up of parts having a position relative to one another in space, sometimes of parts having no local relation, while, as examples of the discrete, he mentions number and ratio, and, as examples of the continuous, line, surface, body, and again, besides these, time and space. Philoponus, too, speaks of the unknown general term as being possibly ποσόν ('whether it is ποσόν or anything else whatever'). Themistius in his paraphrase suggests no name. Euclid, of course, uses the term 'magnitudes' (μεγέθη); and this may have been his personal contribution to the terminology.

(d) General: you cannot to prove a thing pass from one genus to another

An. Post. I. 6–7. 75ª35–ᵇ17

'The middle term then must in virtue of its own nature (δι' αὐτό) belong to the third, and the first term to the middle.

'You cannot therefore when proving a thing pass from one genus to another; e.g. you cannot prove a geometrical proposition by arithmetic. For the things required in demonstrations are three:

[1] c. 6.

(1) the conclusion that is being demonstrated, (2) the axioms—it is the axioms from which (the proof starts), (3) the underlying genus or subject-matter, the properties and essential attributes of which are made clear by the demonstration. Now the things from which the proof starts (the axioms) may be the same (whatever the subject) ; but where the genus is different, say in arithmetic and geometry, it is not possible to apply the arithmetical demonstration to the properties of magnitudes unless the magnitudes are numbers. There are, however, cases where such transfer is possible as will be explained hereafter.

'Now arithmetical demonstration has its own genus, with which it is concerned, and so have the rest of the sciences. Hence it is necessary that the genus should be the same, either absolutely, or in some respect, if the demonstration is to be transferred ; otherwise the transfer is impossible, since the extreme and middle terms must be taken from the same genus.

'If the properties are not essential, they will be accidents. This is why it is impossible to prove by geometry that contraries come under one science, or even that two cubes (make) a cube. Nor can one science prove what belongs to another, save where theorems are so related to one another that one falls under the other, in the way that theorems on optics, for example, are related to geometry and theorems in harmonics to arithmetic.'

When Aristotle says (75^b4) that you cannot use arithmetic to prove the properties of magnitudes 'unless the magnitudes are numbers' he does not express an opinion whether magnitudes *can* be numbers, but the probabilities are that he would not include numbers among magnitudes. Magnitude with Aristotle is generally connected with *body*; it has one, two, or three dimensions,[1] it is 'continuous one, or two, or three ways' ;[2] 'all body has depth, this being the third (kind of) magnitude' ;[3] i.e. a magnitude is a line, a plane, or a body ; two magnitudes cannot be in the same place ;[4] cf. 'If it is not possible that any magnitude can be invisible, but every magnitude is visible at a certain distance'.[5] Magnitude in fact corresponds to one of the two divisions of *quantity*, ποσόν, namely the continuous (as a line, a surface, or a body), whereas a number is *discrete*.[6]

Philoponus observes on 75^b13 that to prove that contraries come under one science is the business of dialectic which, aping *first philosophy*, tries to demonstrate everything, as if all subjects were included in its province. The proposition has of course no relation to geometry, but belongs rather, as Zabarella says, to metaphysics.

---

[1] *De caelo* I. 1. 268ª6-10.
[2] *Metaph. Δ.* 13. 1020ª11.
[3] *De an.* II. 11. 423ª21.
[4] *De gen. et corr.* A. 5. 321ᵇ15.
[5] *De sensu* 3. 440ª26-8.
[6] *Categ.* c. 6.

'Nor that two cubes (are) a cube' (ἀλλ' οὐδ' ὅτι δύο κύβοι κύβος, 75ᵇ13). Since geometry cannot prove this proposition, it is clear that the 'cubes' are not solid figures (for in that case geometry could deal with them), but cube *numbers*. Now no cube number can be the *sum* of two cubes; therefore the *product* of two cubes must be meant, for this is always a cube; e.g. 8, the cube of 2, and 27, the cube of 3, when multiplied together, give 216, which is the cube of 6. Unwary persons have seen in the words an allusion to the famous problem of doubling the cube (as if 'two cubes' meant 'twice a cube'). Thus Philoponus tells the story of the Delians who were told by the Oracle that, if they would get rid of a plague, they must construct an altar double the size of an existing cubical altar while keeping the shape. In despair they appealed to Plato to tell them how this could be done. Plato replied that, in setting them the problem, the god wished to shame them for their neglect of geometry; if, however, he said, two mean proportionals could be found in continued proportion between two straight lines, a cube could be doubled. Plato accordingly referred the problem of the two mean proportionals to his pupils in order that they might solve it. Philoponus thereupon gives the solution attributed to Philon of Byzantium which is the same (though in slightly different form) as those given by Apollonius of Perga and Heron.[1] Philoponus notices the difficulty of supposing that the problem of doubling the cube cannot be dealt with by *geometry*; and he can suggest nothing better than that the problem is one of *stereometry* (solid geometry) rather than geometry. This is mere special pleading, for no one would question that the problem of finding two mean proportionals belongs to geometry, though not to *elementary* geometry (that of the straight line and circle).

The exceptions to the principle that the proofs of one science cannot be applied to the subjects of another are the cases of what we call 'applied' mathematics, where the subjects are 'subalternate' to those of pure mathematics, as optics is to geometry and music to arithmetic. In a later passage[2] Aristotle mentions mechanics also as subordinate to geometry: 'demonstration (in one science) is not applicable to another genus except where geometrical demonstrations are applied to theorems in mechanics and optics, and arithmetical demonstrations to theorems in harmonics'. We have only to compare Euclid's *Optics*, which is purely geometrical, as well as Archimedes' *On plane equilibriums*. The dependence of the musical intervals on numerical ratios between lengths of string at the same tension was discovered by Pythagoras for the octave, fourth, and

[1] See on this, *Greek Mathematics*, i. 262–4, and on the subject generally pp. 244 et sqq.

[2] *An. Post.* I. 9. 76ᵃ22–5.

fifth; and works on music on arithmetical lines were written by
Archytas, Aristoxenus, Euclid, and Ptolemy.

(e) Bryson and the squaring of the circle

An. Post. I. 9. 75ᵇ37–76ᵃ3

'Since it is manifest that it is not possible to prove a fact in any
science except from the principles of that science, if the attribute
proved is to inhere in a thing *as such*, it is not sufficient to constitute
knowledge of it that the proof should be deduced from premisses
that are true, indemonstrable, and immediate. A proof may be
like that of Bryson's quadrature of the circle; arguments of this
kind prove a thing by virtue of some common character which may
inhere in another subject as well; accordingly such arguments will
apply to subjects different in kind. The knowledge therefore that
we acquire is knowledge of an attribute inhering in the thing not
as such but only accidentally; were it otherwise, the demonstration
would not have been applicable to another genus as well.'

Soph. El. 11. 171ᵇ12–18

'The so-called geometrical *Fallacies* (ψευδογραφήματα) are not
eristic (for these paralogisms have reference to things which come
under the particular art), still less is any such fallacy as relates to
a true proposition, like that of Hippocrates, or the squaring of the
circle by means of lunules. But the method by which Bryson tried
to square the circle, were it ever so much squared thereby, is yet
made sophistical by the fact that it has no relation to the matter
in hand.'

Soph. El. 11. 171ᵇ34–172ᵃ7

'The eristic disputant stands somewhat in the same relation to the
dialectician as the pseudographer to the geometer; for in his paralogisms he starts from the same principles as dialectic uses, just as the
pseudographer apes the geometer. But the pseudographer is not
eristic, because he deduces his fallacies from the principles and conclusions which fall under the particular art (geometry); the other,
who uses the principles coming under dialectic, will clearly be eristic
with reference to other subjects. Thus, for example, the squaring
of the circle by means of lunules is not eristic, but the quadrature
of Bryson is eristic; the reasoning used in the former cannot be
applied to any subject other than geometry alone, whereas Bryson's
argument is directed to the mass of people who do not know what
is possible and what impossible in each department, for it will fit
any. And the same is true of Antiphon's quadrature' (ἢ ὡς 'Αντιφῶν
ἐτετραγώνιζεν).

The last words, relating to Antiphon, 'or as Antiphon squared (the circle)'—ἢ ὡς 'Αντιφῶν ἐτετραγώνιζεν—are a little vague, but they appear to imply that Antiphon is on the same footing as Bryson because he used an assumption the scope of which is not confined to geometry. This is slightly different from the implication in *Phys.* I. 2. 185ᵃ16, where Aristotle says that the geometer is only concerned to refute false deductions from admitted geometrical principles (such as 'the quadrature of the circle by means of segments'), but is not called upon to refute the attempt of Antiphon. The implication there is, as Simplicius says, that Antiphon started from other than geometrical principles (μὴ ἀπὸ γεωμετρικῶν ἀρχῶν ὡρμῆσθαι) or principles which do not hold in geometry, not principles which cover other things besides geometry.[1]

The question of Bryson's attempted quadrature of the circle is one of the most baffling in the history of Greek geometry for the reason that Aristotle's own allusions to it are very vague, only amounting to statements that Bryson's solution made use of assumptions which were not confined to the subject-matter of geometry but were equally applicable to other subjects and that his argument was therefore 'eristic'. The commentators give little assistance towards a reconstruction.

The comment by the Pseudo-Alexander (? Michael Ephesius) on *Soph. El.* c. 11[2] is scarcely worth consideration. According to this, Bryson inscribed a square in a circle and circumscribed another about it, while he also took a square intermediate between them (the commentator does not say how constructed); then he argued that, as the intermediate square is less than the outer square and greater than the inner, while the circle is also less than the outer and greater than the inner square, and, as *things which are greater and less than the same things respectively are equal*, it follows that the circle is equal to the intermediate square. Upon this the commentator observes that not only is the assumed axiom applicable to other things as well as geometrical magnitudes, but it is also false, because, for instance, 8 and 9 are both less than 10 and greater than 7 and yet they are not equal. Evidently the commentator was completely at sea.

According to Philoponus, however,[3] Alexander made a better suggestion, namely, that the circle is greater than *every* inscribed rectilinear figure and less than *every* circumscribed figure; again, a *rectilinear* figure drawn between the inscribed and circumscribed figures is less than the latter and greater than the former; but things greater and less than the same thing are equal to one another;

---

[1] Cf. pp. 94-7, below.   [2] p. 90. 10-21 Wallies, 306ᵇ24 ff. Brandis.
[3] On *An. Post.* I. 9. 75ᵇ37; Philop. 111. 20-31 Wallies.

therefore the circle is equal to the intermediate rectilinear figure. Themistius, too, observes that Bryson said that the circle is greater than *all* inscribed rectilinear figures and less than *all* circumscribed figures.[1] This suggests a probable explanation of what would otherwise seem to be an absurd argument. Bryson may have increased the number of sides in both the inscribed and circumscribed regular figures by continual doubling; he may then have argued that, if we continue this process long enough, we shall have an inscribed and a circumscribed figure differing so little in area that, *if* we could describe between the two another polygon, which would therefore be intermediate in area between the inscribed and the circumscribed polygon, then the circle, which is also intermediate in area between them, must be equal to the intermediate polygon. If this is the true explanation, Bryson's name by no means deserves to be banished from histories of Greek mathematics; on the contrary, in his method of approaching the area of the circle both from above and below, by circumscribing as well as inscribing polygons, he went a step beyond Antiphon, and the importance of this step is proved by the fact that this is the regular practice of Archimedes in using the 'method of exhaustion'; that is, he makes both inscribed and circumscribed figures approach the area to be measured, thereby *compressing*, as it were, a circumscribed and an inscribed figure into one so that they *coincide* both with one another and with the curvilinear figure in question.

It is natural therefore to ask whether Bryson and the Greeks before Eudoxus and Euclid had any idea of such a thing as a continuous series of magnitudes divided into two parts by what mathematicians know as a 'Dedekind-Schnitt'?[2]

According to Philoponus, Proclus objected to the suggestion of Alexander (and Themistius) on the ground that it would make Bryson's quadrature identical with that of Antiphon, because the

---

[1] Themistius on *An. Post.* p. 19. 6–20 Wallies.

[2] This is argued by O. Becker, who examines our passages in detail in the second of two 'Eudoxos-Studien' (*Quellen und Studien zur Geschichte der Mathematik*, B. Studien, vol. ii, p. 369 f.). The assumption of Bryson, says Becker, would amount to saying that 'Alles was dieselbe Einteilung (denselben Dedekindschen "Schnitt") in einer linear geordneten Menge von Grössen hervorbringt, einander gleich ist'; in other words, what is assumed is the *uniqueness*, not the *existence*, of the magnitude constituting the 'Schnitt'. Becker finds an approach to an assumption of *existence* in the same passage of Proclus (ap. Philop.) where he says, 'The circle is greater than every inscribed rectilinear figure and less than every circumscribed rectilinear figure, *and where, in relation to a thing, there exists a greater and a less, there exists also an equal to it*', the conclusion being that there *exists* a rectilinear figure equal to the circle, though Bryson did not attempt to construct it.

intermediate figure between those inscribed and circumscribed would coincide with the circumference of the circle. This, however, is not necessary; it is only necessary that there should be drawn (anyhow) *some* rectilinear figure intermediate between the inscribed and the circumscribed, which intermediate figure would then have the same area as the circle.

It is clear that there was some difference between Antiphon's and Bryson's methods, for Aristotle's criticisms of them are different. He blames Antiphon for starting from non-geometrical principles; he blames Bryson for using premisses which do not belong specially to the subject-matter of geometry but apply to other subjects as well. Antiphon had argued that, if you continue far enough the process of doubling the number of sides in the inscribed polygon, you will *some time* have a polygon the sides of which will, owing to their smallness, *coincide* with the circumference of the circle. According to Simplicius, Alexander held that the geometrical principle infringed by Antiphon was the truth that a straight line touches a circle at one point only (although, as Simplicius points out, this is not a principle but a theorem proved by Euclid in his Book III); Eudemus, the better authority, considered that the principle infringed was the truth that magnitudes are divisible without limit; this principle shows that the process described by Antiphon would *never* result in using up the whole area of the circle or in making the sides of the polygon coincide with the circumference.[1]

As we have seen, however, Aristotle himself seems to object, not to Bryson's principle in itself (whatever it was), but only to its use in the particular case because it is not specifically geometrical but is of wider application. But it is difficult to see why it is less legitimate to use it (if true) in a particular application than it is to use, in like circumstances, the axiom that 'things which are equal to the same thing are equal to one another', the 'common axiom' which Aristotle is constantly citing. It seems, on the whole, that we are not really in possession of sufficient information about Bryson's procedure to enable us to judge how far Aristotle's objection was sound.

(f) *First principles of mathematics*

An. Post. I. 10. 76ª31–77ª4

'By first principles in each genus I mean those the truth of which it is not possible to prove. What is *denoted* by the first (terms) and those derived from them is assumed; but, as regards their *existence*, this must be assumed for the principles but proved for the rest. Thus

[1] Simpl. in *Phys.* I. 55. 12–24, Diels.

what a unit is, what the straight (line) is, or what a triangle is (must be assumed); and the existence of the unit and of magnitude must also be assumed, but the rest must be proved. Now of the premisses used in demonstrative sciences some are peculiar to each science and others common (to all), the latter being common by analogy, for of course they are actually useful in so far as they are applied to the subject-matter included under the particular science. Instances of first principles peculiar to a science are the assumptions that a line is of such-and-such a character, and similarly for the straight (line); whereas it is a common principle, for instance, that, if equals be subtracted from equals, the remainders are equal. But it is enough that each of the common principles is true so far as regards the particular genus (subject-matter); for (in geometry) the effect will be the same even if the common principle be assumed to be true, not of everything, but only of magnitudes, and, in arithmetic, of numbers.

'Now the things peculiar to the science, the existence of which must be assumed, are the things with reference to which the science investigates the essential attributes, e.g. arithmetic with reference to units, and geometry with reference to points and lines. With these things it is assumed that they exist and that they are of such-and-such a nature. But, with regard to their essential properties, what is assumed is only the meaning of each term employed: thus arithmetic assumes the answer to the question what is (meant by) "odd" or "even", "a square" or "a cube", and geometry to the question what is (meant by) "the irrational" or "deflection" or (the so-called) "verging" (to a point); but that there are such things is proved by means of the common principles and of what has already been demonstrated. Similarly with astronomy. For every demonstrative science has to do with three things, (1) the things which are assumed to exist, namely the genus (subject-matter) in each case, the essential properties of which the science investigates, (2) the common axioms so-called, which are the primary source of demonstration, and (3) the properties with regard to which all that is assumed is the meaning of the respective terms used. There is, however, no reason why some sciences should not omit to speak of one or other of these things. Thus there need not be any supposition as to the existence of the genus, if it is manifest that it exists (for it is not equally clear that number exists and that cold and hot exist); and, with regard to the properties, there need be no assumption as to the meaning of terms if it is clear: just as in the common (axioms) there is no assumption as to what is the meaning of subtracting equals from equals, because it is well known. But none the less is it true that there are three things naturally distinct, the subject-matter of the proof, the things proved, and the (axioms) from which (the proof starts).

'Now that which is *per se* necessarily true, and must necessarily be thought so, is not an hypothesis nor yet a postulate. For demonstration has not to do with reasoning from outside but with the reason dwelling in the soul, just as is the case with the syllogism. It is always possible to raise objection to reasoning from outside, but to contradict the reason within us is not always possible. Now anything that the teacher assumes, though it is matter of proof, without proving it himself, is an hypothesis if the thing assumed is believed by the learner, and it is moreover an hypothesis, not absolutely, but relatively to the particular pupil; but, if the same thing is assumed when the learner either has no opinion on the subject or is of a contrary opinion, it is a postulate. This is the difference between an hypothesis and a postulate; for a postulate is that which is rather contrary than otherwise to the opinion of the learner, or whatever is assumed and used without being proved, although matter for demonstration. Now définitions are not hypotheses, for they do not assert the existence or non-existence of anything, while hypotheses are among propositions. Definitions only require to be understood: a definition is therefore not an hypothesis, unless indeed it be asserted that any audible speech is an hypothesis. An hypothesis is that from the truth of which, if assumed, a conclusion can be established. Nor are the geometer's hypotheses false, as some have said: I mean those who say that "you should not make use of what is false, and yet the geometer falsely calls the line which he has drawn a foot long when it is not, or straight when it is not straight". The geometer bases no conclusion on the particular line which he has drawn being that which he has described, but (he refers to) what is *illustrated* by the figures. Further, the postulate and every hypothesis are either universal or particular statements; definitions are neither' (because the subject is of equal extent with what is predicated of it).

This passage contains perhaps the best and most complete statement of Aristotle's views about the 'principles' (ἀρχαί), 'necessary principles' ($74^{b}5$), or 'immediate premisses' ($72^{a}7$) on which the demonstrative sciences in general and the science of mathematics in particular are based. An 'immediate premiss' or 'proposition' (πρότασις ἄμεσος) is one which has no other proposition prior to it ($72^{a}8$). Knowledge is not all demonstration: the 'immediate premisses' are indemonstrable; 'seeing that it is necessary to know the things which are prior and from which demonstration starts, and that immediate premisses must stop somewhere, they must necessarily be indemonstrable' ($72^{b}19-22$).

Another passage, however, dealing with *definition, thesis, hypothesis,* and *axiom* should be quoted:

An. Post. I. 2. 72ᵃ14–24

'Among immediate syllogistic principles I call that a *thesis* which
it is neither possible to prove nor absolutely essential for any one to
hold who is to learn anything; but that which it is necessary for
any one to hold who is to learn anything whatever is an *axiom*; for
there are some principles of this kind, and axiom is the most usual
name by which we speak of them. But, of *theses*, one kind is that
which assumes one or other side of a statement, as, for instance, that
something exists or does not exist, and this is an *hypothesis*; the
other kind, which makes no such assumption, is a *definition*. For
a definition is a *thesis*; thus the arithmetician posits (τίθεται) that
a "unit" is that which is indivisible in respect of quantity; but this is
not an *hypothesis*, since what is meant by a unit and the fact that
a unit exists are different things.'

What interests the historian of mathematics in the passages cited
is the picture that they afford of the terminology in use in Aristotle's
time for the elementary principles of mathematics as compared with
that set out and fixed for all time in Euclid's *Elements*, beginning
with the *Definitions* (in each Book), the *Postulates*, and the *Common
Notions* or *Axioms*. In recapitulating the main points it is necessary
to take account of some recent researches such as those of H. P. D.
Lee[1] and B. Einarson.[2]

Every demonstrative science, says Aristotle, must start from
indemonstrable principles; otherwise the steps of demonstration
would be endless. Of these indemonstrable principles some are (*a*)
common to all sciences, others are (*b*) particular, or peculiar to the
particular science.

(*a*) The principles common to all the sciences are *axioms*, most
commonly exemplified by 'if equals be subtracted from equals, the
remainders are equal' or 'of two contradictories one must be true'.
Aristotle has other alternative names for axioms, 'common (things)',
τὰ κοινά,[3] or 'common opinions', κοιναὶ δόξαι.[4] The word 'axiom' is
said to be the term used by mathematicians ('the so-called axioms in
mathematics').[5] It corresponds to Euclid's *Common Notions*; Euclid
does not use the word 'axiom', as is clear from the fact that Aristotle's
favourite illustration ('if equals be subtracted from equals, the
remainders are equal') is the third of the three Euclidean *Common
Notions* accepted as genuine by Heron and others.

[1] 'Geometrical Method and Aristotle's Account of First Principles' (*Classical
Quarterly*, xxix, pp. 113–24).

[2] 'On Certain Mathematical Terms in Aristotle's Logic' (*American Journal of
Philology*, lvii. 1, pp. 33–54).

[3] *An. Post.* I. 11. 77ᵃ30.   [4] *Metaph. B.* 2. 996ᵇ28.

[5] *Metaph. Γ.* 3. 1005ᵃ20.

Though the axioms are truths common to all sciences, the particular sciences need to use them only so far as regards their own subject-matter respectively:[1] thus, 'that, when equals are subtracted from equals, the remainders are equal is a common (principle) in the case of all quantities; but mathematics takes a separate department (ἀπολαβοῦσα) and directs its investigation to some portion of its subject-matter, as, e.g., lines or angles, numbers or any of the other quantities'.[2]

The indemonstrable character of the axioms is emphasized in the *Metaphysics*. It is impossible that there should be demonstration of everything, as there would be an infinite series of demonstrations: if the axioms were the subject of a demonstrative science, there would have to be, here too, as in other demonstrative sciences, a subject-genus, its attributes, and corresponding axioms;[3] thus there would be axioms behind axioms, and so on continually. The axiom is the most firmly established of all principles.[4] It is ignorance alone that could lead any one to try to prove the axioms;[5] the supposed proof would be a *petitio principii*.[6] If any one thought to prove the axioms, he could at once be refuted; if he did not attempt to say anything, it would be ridiculous to argue with him; he would be no better than a vegetable.[7]

When we come to (b), the principles peculiar to a particular science, we have, first, the *genus* or subject-matter, the *existence* of which has to be assumed, e.g. magnitude in the case of geometry, or the unit in the case of arithmetic. Under this we must assume *definitions* of manifestations, forms, or attributes of the genus, e.g. in geometry, straight lines, triangles, 'deflections', etc. But in geometry, in addition to the genus, we have to assume the *existence* of a few *primary* things which are defined, namely, points and lines only: the existence of everything else, e.g. the various figures made up of these, as triangles, squares, tangents, and their properties, e.g. incommensurability, etc., has to be *proved*. In arithmetic we assume the *existence* of the unit only: as regards the rest, only the definitions, e.g. those of odd, even, square, and cube, are assumed, and *existence* has to be proved.

'Definitions', then, (ὅροι) and 'axioms' (ἀξιώματα) were the recognized terms in Aristotle's time for what they signified, with the qualification that 'common opinions' or 'common notions' might alternatively be used for the latter. But what, if any, was the recognized technical term for the third kind of assumption, equally necessary at the beginning of any science, namely, that of the genus

---

[1] *An. Post.* I. 10. 76ᵃ39–42.   [2] *Metaph.* K. 4. 1061ᵇ20–4.
[3] Ib. *B.* 2. 997ᵃ5–8.   [4] Ib. *Γ.* 3. 1005ᵇ11–18.   [5] Ib. 1006ᵃ5–8.
[6] Ib. 1006ᵃ17.   [7] Ib. 1006ᵃ11–15.

or subject-matter in general, or of specific parts of it? In 72ᵃ20 the assumption of existence or non-existence is distinctly called an *hypothesis*, which is stated to be a subdivision of *thesis*. A *thesis* (literally 'positing' or 'laying-down') is an assumption that cannot be proved, says Aristotle: if the thesis posits the existence or non-existence of a thing, it is an *hypothesis*; if it says nothing of existence or non-existence, it is a *definition* (ὁρισμός). Aristotle's use of the word 'hypothesis' here recalls the similar use of ὑποθέμενοι and ὑπόθεσις in the famous passage of the *Republic* (510 C), where Plato speaks of the hypotheses of mathematics: 'I think you know that those who treat of geometries and calculations (arithmetic) and such things take for granted (ὑποθέμενοι) odd and even, figures, angles of three kinds, and other things akin to these in each, implying that they know these things, and, though using them as hypotheses, do not condescend to give any account of them, either to themselves or others. . . .' I agree with Cornford[1] that Plato means here to restrict 'hypotheses' to assumptions of *existence*, and not to include definitions in the term; therefore Aristotle's use of it in our passage corresponds to Plato's. But, in view of the very limited scope of 'hypothesis' in this sense, I think that Aristotle can only have used the term here for want of a better, seeing that he uses the word elsewhere in a variety of senses; I do not believe that it can have been the practice of mathematicians in his time to make it a technical term with this particular sense only; they probably ignored the necessity of making a separate class of assumption merely affirming the existence of mathematical entities. I agree with Mr. Lee that Aristotle used the classification 'definitions, hypotheses, axioms' where Euclid has 'definitions, postulates, common notions' respectively. But I do not believe that the senses in which Aristotle uses the word 'hypothesis' in other passages are 'subsidiary' senses as suggested by Mr. Lee.[2] On the contrary, the senses in which ὑπόθεσις is used in the other passages are generally more natural than the supposed technical sense. I agree with Cornford[3] that, even in the passage of the *Republic* where Plato seems to restrict ὑπόθεσις to an assumption of existence, he also seems to have in mind the original meaning of ὑποτίθεσθαι and thinks of the mathematician's assumptions as put to the learner for acceptance in the course of instruction. The same is true of Aristotle in the passage where he says that the teacher who assumes something without proof, though it is matter for proof, states an *hypothesis* (ὑποτίθεται), which is not an hypothesis in an absolute sense, but an hypothesis relatively to the pupil. Then there is the place (76ᵇ40) in our passage referring to the geometer who ὑποτίθεται that a line which he has

---

[1] *Mind*, vol. xli, p. 41.　　　　[2] loc. cit., p. 116 n.　　　　[3] loc. cit.

drawn is straight, or is a foot long, when it is not. I need not multiply references to other uses of ὑπόθεσις in Aristotle;[1] but cf. the regular use of ἐξ ὑποθέσεως, *hypothetically*, the passage in *De caelo* 299ᵃ2–6 where it is remarked that the idea of constructing bodies out of planes is inconsistent with the 'hypotheses' of mathematics (which must there surely include *definitions*, such as those of straight line and plane), and *Metaph. E.* 1. 1025ᵇ11, 'some sciences assuming the *definition* (τί ἐστιν) as an *hypothesis*'. It would seem, therefore, that Aristotle, when giving the restricted meaning to ὑπόθεσις, was not so much looking to the common terminology used by geometers as himself appropriating the term to a particular kind of assumption which they had not found it necessary to distinguish. Nor is ὑποτίθεσθαι the only word used even in our passage for the sense of assuming the existence of points and lines. In 76ᵇ2–6 the geometer's points and lines and the arithmetician's units are ἃ λαμβάνεται εἶναι, 'things which are *taken* to exist'. Λαμβανόμενα would, in fact, have been a possible word to describe the 'technical' hypotheses; but in itself λαμβάνειν, like ὑποτίθεσθαι, has a much wider signification, and it may have been the use of ὑποθέμενοι by Plato in the passage of the *Republic* which led Aristotle to prefer the word 'hypothesis'. He decided definitely against the word αἴτημα, 'postulate', for the assumption of existence, probably because αἴτημα was associated in his mind with αἰτεῖν τὸ ἐξ ἀρχῆς, *petitio principii*. Comparing Euclid's terminology with Aristotle's, we notice, first of all, that the first three of Euclid's postulates introduced by ᾐτήσθω assume the possibility of drawing a straight line from one point to another, producing a straight line to any extent, and describing a circle with any centre and radius. These are equivalent to assumptions of existence and therefore correspond to Aristotle's 'hypotheses'. But Euclid's postulates include two more which are quite different in kind, namely (4) that all right angles are equal, (5) the Parallel Postulate. It was of these that I was thinking when I wrote[2] that Aristotle's description of an αἴτημα as an assumption, without proof, of something which is a proper subject of demonstration, 'when the learner either has no opinion on the subject or has a contrary opinion', would fit Euclid's postulates fairly well; I did not wish to imply (if I did imply) that Aristotle recognized αἴτημα as the proper technical term for such assumptions. On the contrary, it is probable, as Mr. Lee says, that Euclid was the first to appropriate the term 'postulate' to a class of assumptions which he found necessary in addition to Definitions and Common Notions. Even Archimedes has various names for the same class of assumptions made at the beginning of his treatises. In *On the Sphere and Cylinder* he has

[1] See *Ind. Ar.* 796ᵇ59–797ᵃ15.   [2] *Euclid*, I, p. 120.

'Axioms and assumptions' (ἀξιώματα καὶ λαμβανόμενα); some of these are practically definitions, others correspond to what are generally called postulates, e.g. the so-called 'Axiom of Archimedes' to the effect that 'Of unequal lines, unequal surfaces, and unequal solids, the greater exceeds the less by such a magnitude as when added to itself (continually) can be made to exceed any assigned magnitude among those which are comparable with [it and with] one another'. In the treatise *On Spirals* and in the *Quadrature of a Parabola* the same assumption for lines and areas is called a 'Lemma'. Similar assumptions at the beginning of the work *On Plane Equilibriums* are called 'postulates' (αἰτούμενα); in *On Floating Bodies*, 'hypotheses' (ὑποκείσθω). It is clear therefore that the terminology was not altogether fixed even in the time of Archimedes (287–212 B.C.).

(g) '*Ungeometrical*' questions

An. Post. I. 12. 77ᵇ16–33

'Seeing then that there are geometrical questions, is there such a thing as ungeometrical questions? And in each science, say geometry, what sort of ignorance is it that (while vitiating questions) leaves them within geometry? Is the syllogism resting on ignorance (1) the syllogism constructed from premisses opposite to the true ones, or (2) the paralogism which is (wrong, but) based on geometrical principles? Or shall we say (3) that the "ignorant" syllogism is that which draws its premisses from another art, as, for instance, a musical question is ungeometrical when the subject is geometry; whereas the idea that parallels meet is in a sense geometrical but in another way ungeometrical, since "ungeometrical" has two meanings like "unrhythmical", one thing being ungeometrical because it has no geometry in it at all as the unrhythmical (has no rhythm), and another because the geometry in it is unsound. The latter kind of ignorance, namely that which argues from principles of this kind (within the science but wrong) is contrary (to science).

'In mathematics the paralogism is not so possible, because it is always the middle term which is ambiguous, since the major is predicated of the whole of it, while it is predicated of the whole of the minor—the predicate of course never has "all" prefixed to it. The terms in mathematics you may *see*, as it were, with the mind's eye; but in dialectic their meaning may escape you. Is every circle a figure? If you draw it, this is clear. But again, are epics circles? It is manifest that they are not (the diagram shows it).'

This passage is, I think, mostly self-explanatory, though differences of reading, among other things, caused Zabarella and Pacius to write at length upon it. These commentators are both insistent that, with what I have called (3), 'Or shall we say . . .', begins Aristotle's own answer to the preceding questions, the ἤ before ἐξ ἄλλης τέχνης being Aristotle's common way of introducing his own views. Waitz is careful to point out that it is the ἤ before ἐξ ἄλλης τέχνης, and *not* the ἤ before ὁ παραλογισμός, which corresponds to the πότερον before ὁ κατὰ τὴν ἄγνοιαν συλλογισμός. This latter remark is true, in so far as it makes it clear that what I have marked (1) and (2) in the above translation both refer to the 'ignorant' man who nevertheless keeps within the domain of geometry, whereas (3) refers to the man who introduces arguments from some other science altogether which has no connexion with geometry. Aristotle's first illustration, then, the musical question which is ungeometrical περὶ γεωμετρίας, i.e. when we are discussing geometry, is an illustration of (3). The next illustrations are of what I have marked (1) and (2); the idea a man may have that parallels meet is in a sense geometrical, while in another way it is not. Aristotle goes on to explain that the word 'ungeometrical' may be used in two senses, (a) of that which has no geometry in it at all, (b) of that which is bad geometry, being within the science but based on wrong principles, principles opposite to the true ones. It is the ignorance shown in (b) which is contrary to science, in this case geometry. Aristotle adds that mathematics has, from the point of view of avoiding paralogisms, the advantage that its terms are all defined, so that there is little or no room for misunderstanding.

'Are epic poems a circle?' Philoponus says that this refers to epigrams so framed that they end as they began, or so that the order of the lines may be varied. The reference, however, is more probably to the poems which were called κυκλικά, the cycle of post-Homeric poems supplementing Homer, poems 'which some attribute to others than Homer, and some to Homer himself' (Philop.). We cannot mistake a cycle of poems for a circle because we have the definition of a circle always before us, visible to our mind's eye, as it were.

(h) 'Applied' mathematics

In *An. Post.* I. 13 Aristotle distinguishes between what he calls 'the syllogism of the fact' (ὅτι) and the syllogism of the cause (διότι) in any science, showing that the one is obtained from the other by interchanging the middle and major terms. He illustrates by two examples: (1) the planets are non-twinkling stars because they are near; (2) the moon shows its phases because it is spherical in shape.

He continues as follows:

An. Post. I. 13. 78ᵇ32–79ᵃ13

'Thus in one and the same science it is in respect of the position of the middle terms that there are these differences between the syllogisms of the fact and of the cause respectively. But there is another way in which the cause may differ from the fact: the investigation of the two things may belong to different sciences. This is the case where the subjects are so related that one falls under the other, in the way that optics is related to geometry, harmonics to arithmetic, and phenomena [observational astronomy] to astronomy. Some of these sciences are in practice called by the same name, e.g. mathematical and nautical astronomy, mathematical and acoustical harmonics. Here knowledge of the fact is the business of sense-perception, that of the cause is the business of mathematicians; for it is the mathematicians who are in possession of the demonstrations of the causes, and often they do not even know the fact, just as those who investigate the universal are often, owing to inadvertence, unaware of some of the particulars. The subjects of which I am speaking [the subjects of the subordinate sciences] are such as, though constituting a separate class in respect of their substance, yet manifest forms. Now mathematics is concerned with forms; mathematical properties are not predicated of any substratum; for, even though geometrical facts are predicated of some substratum, they are not predicated of it as *such*. Again, as optics is related to geometry, so may another subject be related to it, e.g. the theory of the rainbow; in this case it is the business of the physicist to know the fact, but to know the cause is the business of the student of optics either as such or *qua* its mathematical side.'

The dependence of optics on geometry is seen in all books on optics from Euclid's *Optics* onwards. Philoponus illustrates by the proposition: 'Things seen from afar appear smaller, things seen near at hand appear larger' (Euclid's *Optics*, Prop. 5).

Suppose an object *CD* seen by an eye at *A*, so that *AC*, *AD* are the extreme 'visual rays' (ὄψεις), as the Greeks called them. The object is therefore seen in the angle *CAD*.

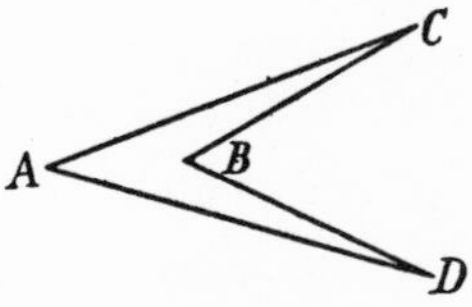

Now suppose the eye moved nearer to the object, say to *B*: *BC* and *BD* are then the extreme 'visual rays'.

Fig. 16

As *B* is within the triangle *ACD*, *CB* and *DB* are straight lines drawn from the ends of the base of a triangle to a point within the triangle.

Hence (Eucl. I. 21) the straight lines *CB*, *BD* are together less than the straight lines *CA*, *AD*, but include a greater angle.

Therefore the angle *CBD* is greater than the angle *CAD*.

But (Eucl. *Optics*, Def. 4) 'Things seen under a greater angle appear greater and under a lesser angle less'.

Therefore from *B* the object *CD* appears greater than it does from *A*.

On 'mathematical and acoustical harmonics' Philoponus observes that the Pythagorean music judges harmony by (numerical) ratio not by sense-perception, pursuant to Pythagoras' discovery of the dependence of the musical intervals on the ratios of lengths of string at the same tension, whereas common or popular music judges the harmonious or discordant by the ear. The 'ordinary listener' knows only the fact; mathematics gives, in the numerical ratios, the cause.

Themistius, to illustrate how the mathematician who demonstrates the causes is frequently unaware of particular cases, says that he himself, though he knows from mathematics why the 'highest' tone harmonizes with the 'middle', cannot perceive the harmony because of his want of practice in the subject!

The subjects of the subordinate sciences, 'though constituting a separate kind in respect of their substance' (79ᵃ6–7) yet manifest forms, i.e. they embody the pure mathematical forms (points, straight lines, planes, etc.) and so admit of mathematical theorems being applied to them. As Themistius says, 'Geometry uses only the form of the straight line, which form has no existence in itself but is always found in some substance. The "straight" may be in air, in stone, in wood, or any other material. The geometer inquires into it, not *qua* present in any of these things, but in itself; the student of optics assumes the straight line in a ruler, or straight lines in the air.'

When Aristotle mentions the theorem of the rainbow (79ᵃ10) as an illustration of another science related to optics, in the same way as optics is related to geometry, he need not be taken quite literally. According to Philoponus, Proclus thought that Aristotle referred to κατοπτρική, the theory of mirrors, as the other science in question; this can hardly be right, for Proclus in his own commentary on Eucl. I gives Geminus' classification of the sciences and their branches, and Catoptric there appears as a branch of optics, the others being optics proper and scene-painting respectively; and Aristotle himself goes on to say that it is for the *physicist* to know the fact as regards the rainbow, but for the student of optics to know the 'why'. Themistius paraphrases thus: 'The student of optics is in many cases placed in the same relation to the physicist as that in which the geometer stands to him (the student of optics), as, for example, in the matter of the rainbow; for that the rainbow is the refraction of the visual ray from such-and-such a cloud to the sun is what the physicist tells us, but *why* it is such as it is in figure and colour is for the student of optics to explain.'

We shall come in due course to the important passage about the rainbow in Aristotle's *Meteor.* III, c. 5 with its very interesting geometry.[1]

(i) *Universal proof versus 'particular'*

As the specific case used as an illustration in the following passages is that of the proof of the theorem that the angles of a triangle are together equal to two right angles, the passages should be read in connexion with *An. Post.* I. 5. 74^{a}16–^{b}4.[2]

An. Post. I. 23. 84^{b}6–9

'For example, the property that their angles are together equal to two right angles belongs to the isosceles and to the scalene triangle in virtue of something common (to both), namely because they are both a certain figure [a triangle], not because they are the different figures respectively [scalene and isosceles triangles].'

Ib. I. 24. 85^{a}20–31

(Which is the better proof, the universal or the particular?)

'The following considerations might lead some persons to think that the particular is the better. That is the better which gives us greater knowledge—the excellence of demonstration consists in this —and we know an individual thing better when we know it in itself than when we know it in virtue of something else; thus we know the musician Coriscus better when we know that Coriscus is musical than when we know that man is musical, and similarly in other cases. But what the universal proves is another result, not the particular one required. Thus it shows that the isosceles triangle has a certain property, not because it is isosceles but because it is a triangle, whereas the particular demonstration shows that the particular triangle itself has it. Seeing then that the demonstration that a thing *as such* has the property is the better, and it is the particular demonstration rather than the universal that has this result, the particular demonstration must be the better.'

This is the first of two arguments supposed to be put forward by some critic who wishes to show that the particular demonstration (being nearer to the point in question) is preferable to the universal. The argument is put in the most uncompromising form accordingly. The universal does not prove what we actually want to know about a particular figure (the isosceles triangle): it proves something different. Aristotle's answer is as follows:

[1] See pp. 181–90, below.   [2] pp. 41–4, above.

An. Post. I. 24. 85^{b}4–15

'May we not reply that the first argument [the above] applies no more to the universal demonstration than it does to the particular? For if the two-right-angles property belongs to the isosceles triangle not *qua* isosceles but *qua* triangle, the man who knows that it belongs to the isosceles triangle knows it to belong to the subject to which *per se* it belongs to a less degree than he who knows it to inhere *qua* triangle. To sum up: if the property does not inhere *qua* triangle, and you try to prove it, there can be no demonstration; but, if it does so inhere, the rule applies that he who knows any property as belonging to the subject in which *per se* it inheres has the greater knowledge. Seeing then that triangle is the wider term, and its definition is one and the same—the term not being equivocal—and since the two-right-angles property belongs to every triangle, it is not the triangle *qua* isosceles that has the property but the isosceles *qua* triangle. Hence he who knows the universal demonstration has greater knowledge of the property *qua* inhering than he who knows the particular. Therefore the universal demonstration is better than the particular.'

An. Post. I. 24. 86^{a}22–30

'What makes it most clear that the universal demonstration is more authoritative is the fact that, when we are in possession of the prior proposition, we know in a sense the posterior as well, that is, we are in possession of it potentially. For example, if we know that any triangle has its angles together equal to two right angles, we know in a sense, i.e. potentially, that the isosceles also has, even though we do not know that the isosceles is a triangle; but he who is in possession of the posterior proposition (that "isosceles" has the two-right-angles property) by no means knows the universal proposition, either potentially or actually. Moreover, the universal demonstration is *intelligible* (νοητή, a matter of intellectual grasp), while the particular ends in sense-perception.'

(j) Exterior angles of rectilinear figures

An. Post. I. 24. 85^{b}37–86^{a}3

'The fullest knowledge is attained when we come to a property which no longer inheres in a thing because it is something else. When, therefore, we recognize that the exterior angles (of a figure) are equal to four right angles because it is isosceles, it still remains to inquire why the isosceles has the property, the answer being "because it is a triangle", and again, as regards the triangle, "because it is a rectilinear figure". If the rectilinear figure no longer has the property because it is something else, it is at this point that our knowledge is most complete. We know it then universally; the universal demonstration is therefore better.'

We have here an allusion to a famous theorem which was discovered by the Pythagoreans, no doubt as an inference from the theorem that the sum of the three angles of a triangle is equal to two right angles, which was also discovered and proved by the Pythagoreans. The latter proposition is, of course, that of Eucl. I. 32, but the corollary to it referred to by Aristotle, though obviously well known to him, was not included by Euclid in the *Elements*; it was in due course added as a corollary to I. 32, along with another upon which it follows, by Robert Simson. Simson's first corollary is to the effect that 'All the interior angles of any rectilinear figure, together with four right angles, are equal to twice as many right angles as the figure has sides'; in other words, if n be the number of the sides in any rectilinear figure and R denotes a right angle, the sum of the interior angles of the figure is equal to $(2n-4)R$.

The truth of this is easily seen. For the rectilinear figure can be divided into as many triangles as the figure has sides by joining every one of the angles A, B, C, ... to any one point O within the figure. Then all the angles of the n triangles added together must be equal to $2nR$, because the angles of any one of the triangles, as AOB, are together equal to $2R$.

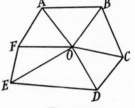

FIG. 17

Now the sum of all the angles of all the triangles is equal to the sum of all the interior angles A, B, C, ... of the figure together with the sum of all the angles at O, as AOB, BOC, ...

But, by another famous theorem, also due to the Pythagoreans, all the angles about O added together make up four right angles, or $4R$.

Therefore the sum of the interior angles A, B, C... of the figure *plus* $4R$ is equal to $2nR$.

Subtracting $4R$ from both, we see that the sum of the interior angles of the figure is equal to $(2n-4)R$.

It is now easy to deduce the theorem cited by Aristotle (Simson's Cor. 2).

Produce each of the sides of the figure, as shown in the diagram, making 'exterior' angles at A, B, C, ...

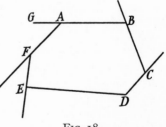

FIG. 18

(An 'exterior' angle of a figure is that obtained by producing one of the sides forming an angle. Thus, if BA be produced to G, the angle GAF is an 'exterior' angle at A.)

Then at each angular point, as at A, we have an exterior angle and an interior angle, the sum of which is equal to two right angles (Eucl. I. 13).

Therefore the sum of all the interior and all the exterior angles is equal to $2nR$.

But, by 'Cor. 1' (above), the sum of all the interior angles is equal to $(2n-4)R$.

Therefore, by subtraction, the sum of all the exterior angles is equal to the difference between $2nR$ and $(2n-4)R$, that is, $4R$.

Aristotle's point is that, if we only know the property to be true of an isosceles triangle, we do not know it fully: it is only true of an isosceles triangle because it is a triangle, and of a triangle again because it is true of any rectilinear figure with any number of sides. Only of this latter figure is it true *primarily*, that is to say, in the sense that no more general figure can be found of which it is true.

(k) 'Exactness', priority, τὰ ἐξ ἀφαιρέσεως, τὰ ἐκ προσθέσεως

An. Post. I. 27. 87ª31–7

'That science which, being one and the same, deals with both the fact and its cause, and is not science of the fact separately from the science of the cause, is more exact and prior. Secondly, the science dealing with properties not inhering in a substratum is more exact than that dealing with properties which do so inhere, e.g. arithmetic is more exact than harmonics; and, thirdly, the science which is based on fewer (elements or principles) is more exact than that which involves additional (elements), e.g. arithmetic is more exact than geometry. What I mean by involving additional (elements) is this: a unit, say, is substance without position, while a point is substance with position; the latter, I say, involves an additional (element).'

ἀλλὰ μὴ χωρὶς τοῦ ὅτι τῆς τοῦ διότι (87ª32). The order of words should, as Philoponus says, rather be ἀλλὰ μὴ τοῦ ὅτι χωρὶς τῆς τοῦ διότι. Themistius, in his paraphrase, omits τῆς and speaks of the more exact science as that which 'proves the fact from the cause', in contrast to the science which only proves 'the fact apart from the cause'.

The second contrast, as Philoponus says, is between things intellectual and immaterial on the one hand and things sensible and material on the other. Thus arithmetic is more exact than harmonics because arithmetic considers arithmetical ratios in themselves, whereas harmonics considers them as applied to lengths of strings at the same tension.

The third contrast is between the simpler (containing fewer elements or principles) and the more composite or more *conditioned*. τὰ ἐκ προσθέσεως (things based on or involving additional elements) is the opposite of τὰ ἐξ ἀφαιρέσεως, by which Aristotle commonly denotes mathematical entities, the notions of which are obtained from physical or material objects by abstraction (ἀφαίρεσις). The following passages from other treatises are the most important in this connexion.

Metaph. K. 3. 1061ᵃ28–ᵇ3

'The mathematician's investigations are about things reached by abstraction (ἐξ ἀφαιρέσεως); for he investigates things after first eliminating all sensible qualities, such as weight, lightness, hardness and its contrary, also heat and cold and the other sensible contrarieties, leaving only the quantitative and continuous—the latter being continuous one way, two ways, or three ways, as the case may be—and the properties of these things *qua* quantitative and continuous; and he investigates them in relation to nothing else, considering in some cases their relative positions and the facts consequent on these, in other cases their commensurabilities and incommensurabilities, in other cases again their ratios; but nevertheless we lay it down that it is one and the same science which deals with all these things, namely geometry.'

Physics B. 2. 193ᵇ31–5, 194ᵃ1–7

'The mathematician, too, studies these [the shapes of the sun, moon, and earth, etc.] but not *qua* limits in each case of a natural body. Nor does he investigate their attributes *qua* attributes of natural bodies. This is why he separates (the mathematical objects), since they can be separated in thought from motion and this makes no difference; nor does any falsity arise through the separation. . . . This will become clear if we try to give, for both kinds of object [the mathematical and the physical], the definitions of the things themselves and of their attributes. For odd and even, straight and curved, as well as number, line, and figure, are independent of movement, whereas flesh, bone, and man are not so, but these latter terms are analogous to "snub nose" and are not like what we mean by "curved".'

De an. III. 7. 431ᵇ12–16

'But the so-called abstractions of mathematics (τὰ ἐν ἀφαιρέσει λεγόμενα) the mind thinks as it might conceive the snub-nosed; *qua* snub-nosed, it would not be conceived apart from flesh, whereas *qua* hollow, if anyone ever had actually so conceived it, he would have conceived it without the flesh in which the hollowness resides. So, too, when we think of mathematical objects, we conceive them, though not in fact separate from matter, as being separate.'

The distinction between τὰ ἐξ ἀφαιρέσεως (things reached as the result of *abstraction*) and τὰ ἐκ προσθέσεως (things involving *additional* elements or conditions) is well illustrated in the first of the above passages by the contrast between a unit and a point (87ᵃ35–7), the former being a 'substance without position' (οὐσία ἄθετος) and the latter a 'substance having position' (οὐσία θετός). The reference is to the Pythagorean definition of a point as a 'unit having position' (μονὰς θέσιν ἔχουσα, *De an.* I. 4. 409ᵃ6) or as 'unit with position *added*' (μονὰς προσλαβοῦσα θέσιν, Proclus *in Eucl.* I, p. 95. 22); here is a case of the *added* condition. Conversely, the Pythagoreans called the unit a 'point without position' (στιγμὴ ἄθετος, *Metaph.* M. 8. 1084ᵇ26); this illustrates a stage in *abstraction*.

Themistius further illustrates by the contrast between solid geometry and astronomy: 'Solid geometry is more "exact" than astronomy because solid geometry deals with body simply, whereas astronomy treats of moving bodies'. Philoponus observes that Theodosius' *Sphaerica* represents a science more 'exact' than the work of Autolycus, *On the Moving Sphere*, and the latter again, being purely theoretical, a subject more 'exact' than astronomy.

The four passages together set out quite clearly Aristotle's view of *mathematica*, mathematical objects. These subsist in natural bodies, but we can consider them in themselves, as if they were apart from matter, by an effort of the mind, by dint of abstraction (ἐξ ἀφαιρέσεως), i.e. by taking away from them in thought all material and sensible qualities such as weight and lightness, hardness and softness, heat and cold, and the like, and leaving only quantity and continuity, the continuous being continuous in one way or direction, in two ways, or in three ways, respectively, i.e. being in one, two, or three *dimensions*, respectively. We thus get mathematical lines (pure length without breadth), planes and plane areas, solids and solid content. These are not separable from the bodies in which they inhere; but the mathematician considers their attributes as 'not belonging to body of a given sort', but as being reached by *abstraction* (*De an.* I. 1. 403ᵇ14, *An. Post.* I. 13. 79ᵃ7–10). Contrast these things with 'snub-nosed' (σιμόν), a favourite example with Aristotle. 'Snub' has no meaning except in relation to 'nose'; its definition must include the matter as well as the form; it is not a term like 'curved' (καμπύλον, *Phys.* B. 2. 194ᵃ6) or 'hollow' (κοῖλον, *De an.* III. 7. 431ᵇ15). Cf. *Metaph.* Z. 5. 1030ᵇ30: 'it is impossible to speak of snub without the thing of which it is an essential property: for snubness is hollowness *in the nose*', and many other passages.

Notwithstanding the above distinction between mathematical objects in themselves and as embodied in matter (the straight line, for example, contrasted with its embodiment in the ruler), Aristotle explains elsewhere that there is a sense in which mathematical objects have, in fact, matter as well as form, but the matter is of a different kind, 'intelligible matter' (ὕλη νοητή) as distinct from 'sensible matter' (ὕλη αἰσθητή).[1] In the *De an.* III. 4. 429ᵇ18–19, we are told that, 'when we come to the abstractions of mathematics, the straight answers to the quality "snub-nosed", being never found apart from the *continuous* (μετὰ συνεχοῦς γάρ)'. Even the straight line, τὸ εὐθύ, may be analysed into its matter, continuity (more precisely continuity in space, extension, or length), and its form. 'Though the geometer's line is length without breadth or thickness, and therefore abstract, yet extension is a sort of geometrical matter which enables the conceptions of mathematics to be after all concrete.'[2]

(*l*) *No knowledge through sense alone*

An. Post. I. 31. 87ᵇ35–88ᵃ5

'It is clear that, even if it had been possible to perceive, by sense, that the triangle has its angles equal to two right angles, we should nevertheless have looked for a demonstration, and we should not have possessed knowledge of the fact as some assert; for what we perceive by sense is necessarily a particular, whereas science comes by recognition of the universal. Hence even if we had been on the moon and had seen the earth obstructing the sun's light, we should not have known the *cause* of the eclipse. We should have perceived the fact of the eclipse, but not the cause by any means; for, as we said, sense-perception is not of the universal. Not but what, from observing that the phenomenon was of frequent occurrence, we should have sought out the universal and so have obtained the demonstration; for it is from a multiplication of particulars that the universal is revealed.'

Ib. 88ᵃ11–17

'There are, however, some points in problems which are referable to a failure of sense-perception. Some things, if we could have seen them, we should not have investigated further, on the ground not that we know by seeing, but that from seeing we become possessed of the universal. For example, if we had seen perforations

[1] See Ross's note on *Metaph. Z.* 10. 1036ᵃ9–10, vol. ii, pp. 199–200.

[2] Hicks, *De an.*, p. 491.

in the burning-glass and the light going through, it would also have been clear why ignition took place: seeing this separately in each instance, we should at the same time have conceived that the same thing happens in all.'

Sense could only tell us (if at all) that the angles of a particular triangle are together equal to two right angles; it could not show that every triangle has the property; knowledge of this fact could only be acquired by demonstration.

In the case of the eclipse of the moon Aristotle says that sense-perception can only show us the fact, *not* the cause applying universally. Philoponus takes him as saying that we should have known the *why* (διότι) in the particular case (νῦν) but not generally. The former seems to be the literal interpretation. But we should compare the following passage:

An. Post. II. 2. 90ª24–30

'That the object is always to find the middle term is made obvious by the cases in which the middle term is perceptible by sense. It is when we have not perceived it that we have to inquire whether there is or is not a middle term to give the cause of an eclipse. If we had been on the moon we should not have had to inquire either as to the fact or as to the cause: they would both have been simultaneously clear. For sense-perception would have enabled us to arrive at knowledge of the universal. Sense-perception tells us that there is at the present moment an obstruction of the sun's light, since it is clear that an eclipse is now taking place; and from this fact we should have inferred the universal.'

The difference of interpretation at 88ª2 seems to depend on the meaning we attach to ὅλως in καὶ οὐ διότι ὅλως. I have translated it '(not) by any means' or 'at all': but it might mean 'altogether' and imply that the particular case reveals the cause 'in some sort'.

(m) Definition and demonstration

Ib. II. 3. 90ª36–ᵇ17

'Let us now explain how the essential nature of a thing [the "what it is"] is shown, in what way it can be resolved into a demonstration, what a definition is, and what things can be defined. But first let us dispose of some difficulties involved in these questions. The doubt may well arise whether it is possible to know the same thing in the same aspect both by definition and by demonstration, or this is impossible. For definition is thought to be definition of the essential nature, and essential nature is, in every case, universal and affirmative. Of syllogisms, on the other hand, some are negative, and some are not universal; thus those in the second figure are all negative, and those in the third not universal. Further, not even all those which are in the first figure and affirmative are susceptible of definition, e.g. that every triangle has its angles together equal to two right angles. The explanation of this is that to have scientific knowledge of that which is matter for demonstration is to possess the demonstration, so that, if there is a demonstration of such things, there clearly cannot also be a definition of them; if there could be, one might have knowledge of them in virtue of the definition also, without possessing the demonstration, for there is nothing to prevent our having one of them without the other. We may be sufficiently convinced of this by induction: never yet by defining a thing—whether essential attribute or incident—did we get to know it. Again, if the definition is recognition of a substance, it is manifest that attributes and incidents are not substances.'

Ib. II. 3. 90^{b}28–91^{a}6

'But, if there cannot be a definition and a demonstration of the same thing in all cases, can there be in any particular case? Or is this impossible, since there can be no demonstration of that which is defined? For a definition is a statement of the essential nature (the "what it is") and substance of a thing, whereas demonstrations all appear to presuppose and assume the essential nature: mathematical demonstrations, for example, take for granted what a "unit" is, and what is the meaning of "odd", and so with all other demonstrations. Further, every demonstration proves some predicate with reference to some subject, either as present or not present; but in a definition no one thing is predicated of another, e.g. animal is not predicated of two-footed or two-footed of animal, and figure is not predicated of plane, for a plane is not a figure, nor is a figure a plane. Again, to show what a thing is and to show that it exists are different things. The definition shows the essential nature (the "what"), the proof shows that such-and-such a thing can or cannot be predicated of such-and-such a subject. Different things require different demonstrations, save in the case where one is related to the other as part to whole. I mean that it has been proved that the two-right-angles property is true of an isosceles triangle if it is true of every triangle; for the one (isosceles) is part and the other (triangle) is a whole. But the fact that a thing exists and the definition of what it is are not related to one another in this way. Neither is a part of the other.'

These generalities connect themselves with the long passage on first principles, definitions, hypotheses, etc., quoted above from ib. I. 10.[1]

---

[1] pp. 50–2, above.

With these passages should be read the following:

An. Post. II. 7. 92^{b}12–25

'Further we say that it is by demonstration that we prove the existence of everything, save it were being itself. But being is not substance for anything; that which is, or being, is not a genus. Therefore that a thing exists is matter for demonstration; and this is the actual practice in the sciences. What a triangle is, the geometer assumes, but that it exists he proves. What then is there for one who defines the essential nature to prove? Triangle? If so, a person knowing by definition the essential nature of a triangle will yet not know that it exists. But this is impossible.

'It is manifest even from the character of the definitions now in use that they who define do not prove that the thing defined exists. Suppose even that there exists something which extends equally from the centre (in all directions); why is it the thing defined? And why is that a circle? One might equally well call it the definition of mountain copper. The fact is that definitions do not include any proof that the thing defined may exist or that it is the thing of which they claim that it is the definition. It is always open to anyone to ask, Why?'

'The geometer', says Aristotle, 'assumes *what* a triangle is, but that it exists he has to prove.' This agrees with the dictum in ib. I. 10. 76^{b}5 f. that geometry assumes the *existence* of points and lines only, but has to *prove* the existence of everything else that belongs to geometry, triangle, and what not. So also in ib. I. 71^{a}11–16 'we must assume of a triangle that *it means a certain thing* whereas of a unit we must know both, namely what it means and that it exists'. A definition only needs to be understood. The inference is that the existence of such a figure as a triangle has to be proved, by construction or otherwise; in Greek geometry the usual method is actual construction.

I have noted elsewhere[1] that light is thrown on Aristotle's views by the old distinction between the so-called *nominal* and *real* definitions. Gerolamo Saccheri[2] distinguished between what he calls *definitiones quid nominis* and *definitiones quid rei* or *reales*; the former are, he says, only intended to explain the meaning that is to be attributed to a given term, whereas the latter, besides declaring the meaning of a word, affirm at the same time the existence of the thing defined or, in geometry, the possibility of constructing it. The *definitio quid nominis* becomes a *definitio quid rei* 'by means of a *postulate*, or when we come to the question whether the thing exists and it is answered affirmatively'. *Definitiones quid nominis*

---

[1] *Euclid*, i, pp. 144–5.   [2] *Logica Demonstrativa* (1697).

are in themselves quite arbitrary and neither require nor are capable
of proof; they are provisional and are only intended to be turned as
quickly as possible into *definitiones quid rei*, either (1) by means of
a postulate in which it is asserted or conceded that what is defined
exists or can be constructed, for example, in the case of *straight lines*
and *circles*, the drawing of which is postulated in Euclid's *Posts.* 1–3,
or (2) by means of a demonstration reducing the construction of a
figure to the successive carrying out of a certain number of those
elementary constructions which are postulated.

Confusion between the *nominal* and the *real* definition, as thus
described, i.e. the use of the former before it has been turned into
the latter by the necessary proof that the thing defined exists, is,
according to Saccheri, one of the most fruitful sources of illusory
demonstration.

To like effect are the remarks of Leibniz : 'If we give any definition,
and it is not clear from it that the idea which we ascribe to the
thing is possible, we cannot rely upon the demonstrations which we
have derived from that definition, because, if that idea by chance
involves a contradiction, it is possible that even contradictories may
be true of it at one and the same time, and thus our demonstrations
will be useless. Whence it is clear that definitions are not arbitrary.
And this is a secret which is hardly sufficiently known.'

Euclid's practice is consistent with Aristotle's views. He does not
use straight lines at right angles to one another before he has constructed a perpendicular to a straight line (I. 11, 12), nor the figure
which he describes as a *square* in I, Def. 22 before he has constructed
one (I. 46), and so on.

(*n*) *Angle in a semicircle*

Ib. 11. 94ª24–35

'You cannot have a truth from which a given fact can be inferred
as a necessary consequence if you assume one premiss only : there
must be two such at the least, and the two suffice whenever they
have one middle term. When we have got this middle term, the
conclusion necessarily follows. This will be clear from the following
example. Why is the angle in a semicircle a right angle? From what
fact does it follow that the said angle is right? Let *A* be a right
angle, *B* the half of two right angles, and *C* the angle in a semicircle.
Now *B* is the cause of *A*, the right angle, being an attribute of *C*, the
angle in the semicircle : for *B* is equal to *A*, and *C* is equal to *B*,
since *C* is the half of two right angles. Therefore it is in virtue of *B*
being half of the two right angles that *A* is an attribute of *C*, or, what
is the same thing, that the angle in a semicircle is a right angle. And

B is identical with the essential nature or quiddity of *A*, because it is what the definition of *A* signifies.'

This passage is of interest because it hints at the particular method in use in Aristotle's time for proving that the angle in a semicircle is a right angle. To understand it, it is useful to compare Euclid's method (in III. 31). I have set out this proof above.[1] If *BAC* be an angle in the semicircle *ABC*, Euclid produces *BA* to *F* and then proves that the angles *BAC*, *FAC* are equal. Hence, he says, each of them is a right angle (by I, Def. 10).

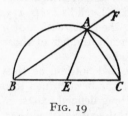

FIG. 19

Euclid has no occasion to say that the angle *BAC* is equal to the half of two right angles. This step is unnecessary because I, Def. 10 is to the effect that 'when a straight line set up on a straight line makes the adjacent angles equal to one another, each of the equal angles is a right angle'. In Euclid's proof, therefore, the angle in a semicircle is not a right angle because it is half of two right angles, but because, by the definition, it *is* a right angle.

Aristotle's interposition of the step that the angle *BAC* is half of two right angles shows that the proof which he had in mind was one in which the angle *BAC* was proved to be equal to half the sum of certain angles in the figure, which turned out to be equal to two right angles. The most natural proof satisfying this condition would be one like the alternative proof interpolated in the text of Euclid after III. 31. In this proof we argue thus:

Since the exterior angle *AEC* of the triangle *ABE* is equal to the sum of the interior angles *EAB*, *ABE* (Eucl. I. 32), and, because *EA* = *EB*, the angles *EAB*, *ABE* are equal, the exterior angle *AEC* is double the angle *EAB*.

For the same reason, the angle *AEB*, being the exterior angle of the triangle *AEC*, is equal to double the angle *EAC*.

By addition, the sum of the two angles *AEB*, *AEC* is double the whole angle *BAC*.

But the angles *AEB*, *AEC* are together equal to two right angles (Eucl. I. 13); therefore the angle in the semicircle *BAC* is equal to the *half of two right angles*, and is therefore a right angle.

It would seem therefore almost certain that *this* is the proof which Aristotle had in mind.

It is true that the passage of the *Metaphysics* already referred to[2] seems to indicate, though in a different connexion, a proof which took a different course. I dealt with this passage in my note on Eucl. III. 31.[1] I then translated the text as it appears in Christ's edition; but Ross has since discussed the text exhaustively, and I have no hesitation in following the reading which he adopts. The passage comes immediately after some words referring to the proof of the proposition that the angles of a triangle are together equal to two right angles, the truth of which (as Aristotle says) is instantaneously seen as soon as we have drawn a parallel to one side (through an angular point)—this would apply equally to the Pythagorean way of drawing the parallel or to Euclid's.[2]

Aristotle goes on:

Metaph. Θ. 9. 1051ᵃ26–9

'Why is the angle in a semicircle a right angle universally? If there be three equal straight lines two of which form the base, and the third is the straight line erected (at right angles) from the middle (point) of the base, the fact is clear by simple inspection to anyone who knows the aforesaid theorem [that the angles of a triangle are together equal to two right angles].'

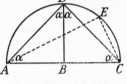

FIG. 20

Let *AB*, *BC*, equal straight lines, be placed so as to form one straight line ('the base'), and let *BD* be erected from *B* at right angles to *AC*. Draw the semicircle *ADC* with *B* as centre and *AC* as diameter. Then *ADC* is an 'angle in a semicircle'.

Now anyone knowing that the angles of a triangle are together equal to two right angles, and looking at the obviously isosceles triangles *BAD*, *BCD*, would see that in each of them (the angles at *B* being right angles) the equal angles which I have marked *α* must all be equal to half a right angle. The angle *ADC* contains two angles *α*, and is therefore a right angle.

The only difficulty is that the argument proves only that the one particular angle *ADC* is a right angle, namely, that formed at *D*, the middle point of the circumference, whereas, according to our text, Aristotle says, 'Why is the angle in a semicircle a right angle *universally*?' To arrive at this conclusion we have to use, in addition, the theorem of Eucl. III. 21 that angles in the same segment of a circle are equal, from which it follows that, if the angle *ADC* is right, so is any other angle, as *AEC*, in the semicircle. Alexander, in his commentary, writes as though his text read διὰ τί ἐν ἡμικυκλίῳ ὀρθή ἐστι, καὶ καθόλου διὰ τί; which, as he observes, seems to indicate

---

[1] Vol. ii, pp. 63–4.   [2] For both of these see p. 29, above.

two questions: (1) why is an angle in a semicircle right? and (2) why is it *universally* a right angle?

(*o*) Alternando *in proportion*

An. Post. II. 17. 99ª1–23

'Can one and the same effect have a cause which is not the same in every instance but different? Or is this impossible? May we not say that, if the effect has been proved as inhering essentially and not by way of a sign or an incident, it is not possible—for then the definition of the major term is the middle term—otherwise it is possible. It is possible to consider the effect and the subject in which it is found as an accidental association; but we do not regard this as constituting a scientific problem. If we do so regard it, the middle term will correspond to the major and minor terms; if they are equivocal, the middle term will be equivocal; if they represent one genus, the middle term will do so likewise. For example, why are four terms in proportion proportional alternately? The cause is different with lines and with numbers respectively, and yet it is the same; in so far as lines are lines and not numbers, it is different, but so far as such-and-such a definite increment is involved it is the same; and so in all cases. But the cause of colour being similar to colour is different from the cause of figure being similar to figure, because "similarity" is here equivocal; in the one case it means, shall we say, having the sides proportional and the angles equal respectively; but with colours it means producing one and the same sensation or something of that kind. And, where things are the same by analogy, the middle terms will also be analogous. The cause, the effect, and the subject correspond to one another in the following way. If we take the species separately, the effect is more extensive than the subject: thus, for example, the property that the exterior angles are together equal to four right angles extends beyond triangle or square, but, when the species are all taken together, it is coextensive: thus if we take *all* the figures which have their exterior angles together equal to four right angles, the middle term also corresponds. The middle term is the definition of the major term: this is the reason why all sciences come into being through definition.'

The example of the proof of the *alternando* theorem in proportion, which applies equally to all sorts of things, numbers, lines, areas, solids, times, etc., has been dealt with above.[1] As we said, if Aristotle had been asked to give a name to the genus which would be held to cover all these subjects, it would no doubt have been ποσόν,

[1] pp. 43–4.

quantity, for all the subjects in question are *quanta*; here he describes them as things 'susceptible of increase of a certain sort', which, of course, is true of *quanta*.

In his short definition of similar figures Aristotle uses the vague word ἴσως, 'perhaps', or 'let us say'; but it corresponds exactly to Euclid's definition (VI, Def. 1) of similar rectilinear figures: 'Similar rectilinear figures', says Euclid, 'are such as have their angles equal severally, and the sides about the equal angles proportional.' It should be understood that the sides and angles are taken in corresponding order.

The last illustration, that of the property of all rectilinear figures (having the sum of all their exterior angles equal to four right angles), has also been dealt with.[1]

[1] pp. 62–4.

V

TOPICS

(a) Pseudographemata

'Again, besides all the syllogisms referred to,[1] there are the paralogisms which start from premisses peculiar to certain sciences, paralogisms such as we have met with in geometry and the sciences akin to it. This type of reasoning seems to differ from the syllogisms aforesaid; for the pseudographer does not reason from things which are true and primary, nor from things generally accepted. He does not fall within the definition, because what he assumes are not things which commend themselves to all, or to most people, or to philosophers—still less to all of these or the most of them or the most esteemed—but he constructs his argument out of assumptions which, though appropriate to the science, are not true. He may effect his paralogism either by circumscribing the semicircles in the way they should not be circumscribed, or by drawing certain lines in the way they ought not to be drawn.'

I have translated ὁ ψευδογραφῶν (101ᵃ10) by 'pseudographer' because it means, I think, more than a person who draws an incorrect figure: the 'pseudographer' also covers a person who puts forward a proof or argument which is false (whether based on an incorrect figure or not), in accordance with the special use of the word γράφειν itself, which not infrequently means to *prove* and not merely to *draw*, just as διάγραμμα often means, not merely a diagram, but a proposition or theorem.

We shall come across the words ψευδογράφος, ψευδογραφεῖν, and ψευδογράφημα in later passages of the *Topics* and *Soph. El.* Cf. 132ᵃ31, where we are told that 'it is not true to say of the geometer that he is incapable of being deceived by an argument, for the geometer may be deceived when a false argument is put before him (ἐν τῷ ψευδογραφεῖσθαι)'. In 157ᵃ1 Aristotle mentions, among the various ways in which one may be prevented from seeing the flaw in an argument, 'the device of lengthening it out and introducing considerations which have nothing to do with the argument, as is done by the pseudographer'. Again (160ᵇ34), 'the man who knows that it is on such-and-such a point that the argument depends knows

---

[1] The 'syllogisms referred to' are (a) true demonstrations based on premisses that are true and primary, (b) 'dialectical' reasonings, (c) 'contentious' or 'eristic' reasonings.

the solution. This applies when you are dealing with false geometrical proofs (ἐπὶ τῶν ψευδογραφουμένων); it is not enough to object, even if the proposition demolished is false, but you must also show *why* it is false.' In *Soph. El.*, c. 11, Aristotle says (171ᵇ34) that the 'eristic' or 'contentious' disputant stands, in some sort, in the same relation to the dialectician as the pseudographer does to the geometer; 'for his mis-reasoning starts from the same premisses as the dialectical argument does, and similarly the pseudographer [apes] the geometer. But the pseudographer is not eristic, since his false arguments are based upon the principles and conclusions falling under the art of geometry.' Similarly, Aristotle has said just before (171ᵇ12–16) that 'false geometrical arguments (ψευδογραφήματα) are not "eristic" (for the paralogisms which they contain are within the scope of the art of geometry), still less is any false argument in support of a truth "eristic"—I mean an argument like that of Hippocrates or the squaring by means of the lunules '.[1]

The commentator on *Soph. El.* (p. 76. 22–4) observes (on *Soph. El.* 170ᵃ30) that ψευδογραφήματα include not only false arguments which do not start from the true principles of the science, but also those which do start from those principles but go wrong in some particular point, such as the *Pseudographemata* of Euclid. Now the work of Euclid here referred to can hardly be anything other than what we know as the *Pseudaria*, which Proclus[2] describes in the following passage:

'Inasmuch as many things, while appearing to rest on truth and to follow from scientific principles, really tend to lead one astray from the principles and deceive the more superficial minds, he (Euclid) has handed down methods for the discriminative understanding of these things as well, by the use of which methods we shall be able to give beginners in this study practice in the discovery of paralogisms, and to avoid being misled. This treatise by which he puts this machinery in our hands, he entitled (the Book) of *Pseudaria*, enumerating in order their various kinds, exercising our intelligence in each case by Theorems of all sorts, setting the true side by side with the false and combining the refutation of error with practical illustration. This book, then, is by way of cathartic and exercise, while the *Elements* contain the irrefragable and complete guide to the actual scientific investigation of the subjects of geometry.'

Now it would seem inconsistent with this description to say that the pseudographer's mistakes were merely due to drawing diagrams incorrectly and basing wrong conclusions on the incorrect diagrams, though no doubt some of them may have been due to this cause, as witness Aristotle's own illustration of mistakes made 'either through

---

[1] Cf. pp. 33–6, above. [2] Proclus *in Eucl.* I, p. 70. 1–18.

circumscribing the semicircles in the wrong way or through drawing
straight lines as they should not be drawn'.

The Greek commentators attempt to explain a possible case of
circumscribing semicircles in the wrong way. The idea is that of
a pseudographer who might purport to prove by means of a wrong
figure that two sides of a triangle are together equal to, or less than,
the third, instead of greater. On straight lines AB, BC, which are
in a straight line, semicircles are supposed to be drawn with centres
D, E, the middle points of AB, BC, respectively. These semicircles
would, of course, touch at B, but they are wrongly drawn so as to
make them appear to *intersect*, not only at B, but at a point F
outside AC as well. Then, if we join F to each of the centres D, E,
the sum of DF, FE will be equal to DE, so that two sides DF, FE
of the triangle DFE would appear to be together *equal* to, instead
of greater than, the third side DE.

I am more inclined to see in Aristotle's words an allusion to the
second of two attempted 'quadratures by means of lunes' which,
according to Simplicius, *In Phys.*,[1] were given by Alexander. I have
referred above[2] to this fallacious attempt to square the circle. From
the figure[3] it will be seen that semicircles were described on the sides
of a regular hexagon inscribed in a circle, forming, with the arcs of
the circumference of that circle, six lunes. The fallacy consisted in
the assumption by the author of the construction that these particular lunes had been squared, whereas they had not, and are not
susceptible of being squared. This case fits fairly well Aristotle's
phrase about 'circumscribing the semicircles in the way they should
not be circumscribed' (101ᵃ15–16).

(b) 'Indivisible lines'

Topics IV. 1. 121ᵇ15–23

'We should see whether the said genus fails, or might be thought
to fail, to include any one of a number of things not differing in
species, or, if you are constructing an argument, whether it does
include some one of them; for all things which do not differ in species
belong to the same genus. If then it is shown that the genus includes
one, it includes all, and, if it does not include one, it clearly does not
include any. For instance, suppose that a person who assumes
indivisible lines should assert that "the indivisible" is their genus.
Now the said genus does not include lines which admit of division,
but such lines do not differ as regards their species from the indivisible lines; for straight lines are all indistinguishable from one
another as regards their species.'

[1] pp. 56–7 Diels.   [2] pp. 33–6.   [3] p. 36.

Blancanus assumes that Leucippus and Democritus were bound, as part of their atomistic theory, to hold that lines are made up of indivisible lines. This has been disputed so far as Democritus is concerned, mainly on two grounds. The first is that Democritus was too good a mathematician to uphold any such doctrine. In support of this Apelt[1] refers to Democritus' famous dilemma about the equality or inequality of successive parallel circular sections of a cone. The second argument is based on a passage of Simplicius, on *Phys.* 185ᵇ5,[2] referring to an assumption that '$αὐτή$' (understood by Apelt as meaning each of the Democritean atoms) is continuous and divisible *ad infinitum*. This does not seem so clear when Simplicius' note is considered as a whole. Aristotle remarks, with reference to Parmenides' view of Being ($τὸ ὄν$) as One, that 'being one' may mean different things, namely, (1) being continuous, (2) being indivisible ($ἀδιαίρετον$), (3) being one in *notion*. If Being is continuous, it must be divisible and therefore 'many', as well as 'one'; if it is indivisible, it cannot be a quantity or a quality at all. Simplicius observes: 'If Being is one in the sense of indivisible, (we must bear in mind) that "indivisible" itself may mean different things: it may be (1) that which has not yet been divided but is capable of being divided, like everything that is continuous, (2) that which by its own nature cannot be divided, either because it has no parts into which it can be divided, like a point or a unit, or because, though having parts and size, it cannot be acted on (it is $ἀπαθές$) because of hardness and solidity like the atoms of Democritus. Now, if Being is one as being continuous, it will once more be many; but if it is one like the atom ($ὡς ἡ ἄτομος$), it is, to begin with, absurd and incongruous to call the universe ($τὰ πάντα$) "one atom" and then to say that it too ($καὶ αὐτή$) is continuous and divisible *ad infinitum* and is in consequence potentially many.' To infer from this last sentence that Democritus held that his atoms were mathematically divisible *ad infinitum* certainly seems unsafe. The opposite view is strongly maintained by S. Luria.[3] Luria holds that Democritus did indeed distinguish between the physical atom and the mathematically indivisible magnitude ($ἄτομον μέγεθος$ or $ἐλάχιστον μέγεθος$), but asserted indivisibility in both cases. Cf. *De caelo* III. 4. 303ᵃ4: '(Leucippus and Democritus) say that $τὰ πρῶτα μεγέθη$ are infinite in number but indivisible in magnitude'; Simpl. *In Phys.* VI. 1 (925. 13 D.): 'Leucippus and Democritus think that not only may resistance ($ἀπάθεια$) be a cause of the indivisible,

---

[1] *Beiträge zur Geschichte der griechischen Philosophie*, 1891, p. 265.

[2] p. 82. 5 Diels.

[3] See his long article 'Die Infinitesimaltheorie der antiken Atomisten' in *Quellen und Studien zur Gesch. der Mathematik*, B (Studien), ii. 106–83.

but smallness and τὸ ἀμερές as well'; Aët. I. 16. 2 = Stob. Ecl. I. 14. 2: 'Democritus held that division stops at τὰ ἀμερῆ'. Further, Aristotle and Simplicius consistently say that Democritus' views conflict with mathematical principles.

Luria observes that it is not enough to reply that Democritus was too good a mathematician to hold the doctrine of indivisible lines; this sort of argument has been used of others. Philoponus says[1] that Plato was not so ἀγεωμέτρητος as to think that a body could be resolved into planes; Simplicius says of Xenocrates:[2] 'Seeing that Xenocrates was a clever man, how came he to assume indivisible lines?'

Plato himself seems to have been attracted to the idea of indivisible lines. According to Aristotle,[3] Plato objected to the genus 'point' as a geometrical fiction, calling a point the 'beginning of a line' and often positing 'indivisible lines' in the same sense. But the idea took shape in the Platonic school, and with Xenocrates became a definite doctrine. In this connexion Democritus and the Platonists including Xenocrates are always associated.[4]

(c) Definition of 'same ratio'

Topics VIII. 3. 158ᵇ29–159ᵃ1

'In mathematics, too, some things would seem to be not easily proved for want of a definition, e.g. that the straight line, parallel to the side, which cuts a plane [a parallelogram] divides similarly both the line and the area. But, once the definition is stated, the said property is immediately manifest; for the (operation of) reciprocal subtraction applicable to both the areas and the lines is the same (or gives the same result); and this is the definition of the same ratio. And generally, given the definitions, for example, of the nature of a line and a circle, the first elementary propositions are very easy to prove, although there are not many arguments that can be attempted with regard to them because there are not many intermediate terms; but if the definitions of the principles are not laid down, it is difficult, and may be quite impossible, to apply them.'

The word for 'to be proved' (158ᵇ30) is γράφεσθαι, which cannot merely mean the drawing of a figure, but must mean 'to be proved', as it frequently does in Archimedes.

We are to suppose a parallelogram, as *ABDC*, and a straight line

---

[1] On Arist. *De gen. et corr.* II. 1. 329ᵃ21.
[2] *In Phys.*, p. 142. 16 D. [3] *Metaph. A.* 9. 992ᵃ20.
[4] Cf. Simplicius on *De caelo* III. 7. 306ᵃ26 (p. 648 Heib.).

EF drawn parallel to *AB* or *CD*, and cutting *AC*, *BD* in *E*, *F* respectively. Then, as proved in Eucl. VI. 1, the straight line *AC* and the area *AD* are divided similarly, i.e. in the same ratio, by the straight line *EF*. To understand this we need a definition of the 'same ratio', and Aristotle indicates what must have been a current definition in his time, such as 'Things are in the same ratio to one another which have the same ἀνταναίρεσις'. Alexander in his commentary[1] uses the word ἀνθυφαίρεσις. 'The definition of proportionals which the ancients used is this: "Magnitudes are proportional to one another which have the same ἀνθυφαίρεσις",' observing that Aristotle describes ἀνθυφαίρεσις as ἀνταναίρεσις. To get at the im-

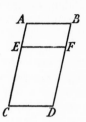

FIG. 21

plication, consider the etymology of the words. ὑφαιρέω means to 'take away', to 'filch', ἀναιρέω to 'take away' or 'abolish'; and the prefix ἀντι- indicates that the 'taking away' or 'subtraction' from one magnitude answers to, or alternates with, a 'taking away' or 'subtraction' from another. So far therefore as the etymology goes, the words ἀνθυφαίρεσις or ἀνταναίρεσις might reasonably be used of the taking away of corresponding *fractions*, which would fit the old and imperfect (because solely arithmetical) theory of proportions due to the Pythagoreans: cf. Euclid's Book VII, Def. 20: 'Numbers are proportional when the first is the same multiple, or the same part, or the same parts, of the second that the third is of the fourth.' ['Part' means here a submultiple, a fraction with unity for numerator, as $\frac{1}{2}$, $\frac{1}{3}$; 'parts' means any proper fraction, such as $\frac{2}{3}$.]

This has been the view generally taken. Pacius observes that, according to Aristotle, to be 'similarly divided' means, in the case supposed, that 'linea et spatium habent eandem subtractionem', and, drawing a figure, he illustrates by supposing that the transversal *EF* cuts off (towards *A*, say) a certain proportion such as $\frac{1}{2}$ or $\frac{1}{3}$ from the line *AC*, in which case it cuts off the same proportion from the area *AD*. Blancanus translates 'nam eandem ablationem habent loca et linea, sive latus planae figurae, est autem definitio eiusdem proportionis haec'. Waitz interprets similarly; having the same ratio means that 'quot partes ab uno demantur, totidem simul etiam demantur ab altero'. The Oxford translation has 'the areas have the same fraction subtracted from them as have the sides; and this is the definition of "the same ratio" '.

But a much more interesting suggestion has been made recently by O. Becker.[2] He points out that, while the substantive ἀνθυφαίρεσις

---

[1] 545. 12–17.

[2] 'Eudoxus-Studien I. Eine voreuklidische Proportionslehre und ihre Spuren

is not found anywhere in Euclid, Euclid does in two places (in Books VII and X respectively) use parts of the verb ἀνθυφαιρεῖν in the same connexion, namely, in his descriptions of the operation of finding the greatest common measure, first in VII. 2 between any two integral numbers and secondly in X. 3 between any two magnitudes of the same kind. In VII. 1 Euclid says: 'Two unequal numbers being set out, and the less being continually subtracted in turn from the greater (ἀνθυφαιρουμένου δὲ ἀεὶ τοῦ ἐλάσσονος ἀπὸ τοῦ μείζονος), if the number which is left never measures the one before it until a unit is left, the original numbers will be prime to one another.' VII. 2 uses the same language in describing the operation of finding the greatest common measure of two numbers which are *not* prime to one another. The same phrase is used of the same process in regard to unequal magnitudes in X. 2, 3, the first of which shows that, if no remainder ever measures the magnitude before it, i.e. the process never comes to an end, the two magnitudes are incommensurable. Where the magnitudes are commensurable, X. 3 shows how to find their greatest common measure.

Now this special use by Euclid of the word ἀνθυφαιρεῖν in describing the method of finding the greatest common measure of two quantities suggests that ἀνθυφαίρεσις may, before his time, have been a recognized technical term for the operation itself. The essence of the operation is that it gives a series of quotients, which are integral numbers, whether the original quantities the greatest common measure of which has to be found are numbers or magnitudes generally. Suppose now that, in order to test the equality or inequality of two ratios between quantities, we take the terms of the first ratio and apply the process of finding their greatest common measure; this gives a series of quotients, a, b, c, ..., say. If now the same method is applied to the terms of the second ratio, and the series of quotients is precisely the same a, b, c, ... and in the same order throughout, we may properly say that the two ratios have the same ἀνθυφαίρεσις; and, if the series of quotients is throughout identical, it is a fact that the two ratios must be equal. Hence, on this interpretation of ἀνθυφαίρεσις, it would be quite a proper definition of equal ratios to say that two ratios are equal when they have the same ἀνθυφαίρεσις.

The interesting thing about this 'old' definition as thus interpreted is that it applies to all magnitudes whether commensurable or incommensurable. This leads Becker to suppose that there existed a *general* theory of proportion based upon this definition before Eudoxus created *his* general theory which Euclid reproduces

bei Aristoteles und Euklid' in *Quellen und Studien zur Geschichte der Mathematik*, B (Studien), ii, 1933, pp. 311–33.

in his Book V, and, after a careful analysis and classification of all the propositions of Book V, Becker attempts to reconstruct such a pre-Eudoxian theory in a regular series of formal propositions, taking advantage, for the sake of clearness, of modern algebraical notation. The difficulty is that in none of our possible sources of information, namely Euclid himself, Proclus, Aristotle, and the commentators upon him, is there any real evidence of the actual existence of such a theory. I for one, therefore, can ɔ ˙ ˙ regard Becker's article as a highly interesting speculation.

(d) Definitions

An. Post. II. 13. 96ᵃ24–ᵇ1

'Of the attributes which always belong to a particular subject some have a wider application, without, however, extending beyond the genus. By attributes having a wider application I mean all such as are universal attributes of each separate subject but nevertheless are attributes of others also. There may, for instance, be an attribute which belongs to every triad, but also belongs to what is not a triad, as "being" belongs to the triad but also belongs to what is not even a number. On the other hand, the attribute "odd" belongs to every triad and has a wider application, for it belongs to the pentad also; but it does not extend beyond the genus (of triad), for the pentad is a number and nothing outside number can be "odd". We must therefore take attributes of this kind until the point at which we have for the first time obtained a number of them such that each by itself has a wider application but the sum of them taken together has not; this sum will necessarily constitute the substance of the thing. For example, every triad has the attributes of number—odd, and prime in both senses of the word, i.e. as not being measured by any number, and as not being made up of numbers (added together). At this point we can say this is what a triad is, namely, a number, odd and prime in such-and-such a way. For these several attributes belong, some [the first two] to all odd numbers as well, and the last to the dyad also, but the sum of them taken together belongs to nothing else.'

The expression 'prime in both senses' should be noted. The first sense, that of 'a number which is not measured by any number', corresponds to the usual definition given by other authors, which is, no doubt, Pythagorean. We should generally say 'by any number except unity'; but a unit is here excluded from the meaning of number. According to Aristotle, the unit is not a number: cf. *Metaph. N.* 1. 1088ᵃ4–8: 'The term "one" means that it is a measure of some multitude, and "number" that it is a measured multitude, or a multitude of measures. It is only reasonable therefore that "one" is not a number, for neither is a measure measures, but the measure and the one are the beginning', i.e. the unit is the beginning of number but not a number. This was the view of the early Pythagoreans. It appears in Nicomachus where he is beginning his explanation of *figured* numbers, in which numbers are shown as a number of points so arranged as to imitate geometrical figures. This system was early Pythagorean, as we know from Aristotle.[1] Nicomachus goes on to say[2] 'unity then, having the relation and place of a point, will thus be the beginning of distances and numbers, but not yet a distance or a number, as a point is the beginning of a line or a distance but is not yet a line or a distance'. But in another connexion, speaking of prime numbers, Nicomachus seems to incline to the opposite view, for he says:[3] 'It (the prime number) has received the name "prime and incomposite" because it can be measured by the number common to all, the very first (number), the unit, alone, and by no other, and also because it is produced from no other number continually added to itself, except the unit alone, 5 from adding it to itself five times, 7 seven times, and the rest according to their quantity.'

Euclid defines a prime number as that which is measured by a unit alone.[4] Theon of Smyrna's definition[5] is a sort of combination of Aristotle's and Euclid's 'a number measured by no number but by a unit only'.

Nicomachus and Iamblichus regard prime numbers as a subdivision, not of numbers, but of *odd* numbers. They therefore exclude 2 from the class of prime numbers, whereas Aristotle expressly includes it, for he says[6] that 'the dyad is the only even number which is prime'. 2 also satisfies Euclid's definition, but Theon of Smyrna excludes 2 from the class of prime numbers; he says that even numbers are not measured by the unit alone, except 2, which is therefore[7] odd-*like* without being prime. In the *Theologumena arithmetices* the dyad, like the monad, is excluded from number and considered to be (along with 1) only number-forming or potential number; the first actual number is 3.

The second sense in which, according to Aristotle, we may think of prime numbers, that of 'not being the sum of numbers', applies only to 2 and 3, which are the sum respectively of two units and of one unit and 2, so that (a unit not being a number) the sum is in neither case a sum of two numbers. We do not find this distinction in Nicomachus.

---

[1] *Metaph. N.* 5. 1092^{b}10–13. [2] *Arithm.* II. 6. 3. [3] Ib. I. 11. 3.
[4] VII, Def. 11. [5] p. 23. 9. [6] *Topics* VIII. 2. 157^{a}39. [7] p. 24. 7.

Topics VI. 4. 141ᵃ24–142ᵃ9

'Whether [in a definition] a man has stated and defined the essence or quiddity, or has failed to do so, we must judge from the following considerations. See first whether he has failed to frame his definition by means of terms which are prior and better known. For, since a definition is given in order that we may know the thing described, and we acquire knowledge not from things taken at random but from things prior and better known, as we do in scientific demonstrations—for this is the condition of all teaching and learning—it is manifest that a man who has not defined by means of such terms has not defined at all. Otherwise there will be more than one definition of the same thing. For it is clear that in any case the man who has defined by means of the prior and better known has also given a definition and a better one, so that both definitions will be definitions of the same thing. But such an idea is not thought to be correct; for, with each particular thing that exists, to be what it is is *one thing*, so that if there are to be more than one definition of the same thing, then, for the thing defined, to be what is set forth in both definitions must be the same thing. But they are not the same thing, since the definitions are different. It is clear therefore that one who has not defined by means of the prior and better known has not defined at all.

'The statement that the definition has not been expressed by means of terms better known may be understood in two ways: (it applies) if the definition has been constructed either from things less known in the absolute sense or from things less known *to us*— both meanings are possible. In the absolute sense the prior is better known than the posterior, e.g. a point than a line, a line than a plane (surface), a plane than a solid, just as a unit is better known than a number. Similarly also a letter is better known than a syllable. But, relatively to us, the reverse is often the case; the solid comes within the scope of sense-perception most of all, more than the plane, the plane more than the line, the line more than the point. In fact most people acquire knowledge of the former before the latter; for the former can be grasped by any ordinary intelligence, the latter by accurate and exceptional understanding only.

'Absolutely then it is better to try to acquire knowledge of the later by means of the prior; for such a method is more scientific. Not but what, when we have to deal with persons who have not the ability to acquire knowledge by means of the prior terms, it may no doubt be found necessary to give the explanation through terms better known to them. Among definitions of this kind are those of the point, the line, and the plane. All these definitions explain the prior by means of the posterior, for they say that a point is an extremity of a line, a line of a plane, and a plane of a solid. It must, however, not be forgotten that it is not possible for those who define in this way to show the essential nature of the thing defined unless it happens that what is better known to us and what is better known in the absolute sense are in the particular case one and the same, assuming that he who defines correctly must define by means of the genus and the differentiae, and that these belong to the class of things absolutely better known than, and prior to, the species. For the destruction of the genus and the differentiae destroys the species, so that they are prior to the species. They are also better known; for when the species is known, the genus and the species must be known too: for example, he who knows "man" knows also "animal" and "walking", whereas, if the genus or the differentia be known, it does not follow that the species is also known; hence the species is the less known. Again, those who assert that such definitions are really and truly definitions—I mean such as start from terms better known to the individual—will have to admit that there are many definitions of the same thing; for, as a matter of fact, different things are better known to different persons, and not the same things to all, so that a different definition would have to be given to each individual if we must frame our definitions from what is better known to each individual. Moreover, even to the same people different things are more known at different times: at first the objects of sense-perception are better known, but, when they are trained to greater accuracy, the reverse is true, so that those who say that the definition should be expressed by means of terms better known to the individual will not always have to give the same definition to the same person. It is clear, therefore, that we ought not to define by means of terms of that kind [i.e. better known to the individual], but by means of terms better known in the absolute sense; for only so can you have a definition which is always one and the same.'

(e) Definitions: failure to define by prior terms and need to specify genus

Topics VI. 4. 142ª22–ᵇ19

'Of failure to define by means of terms which are prior there are three kinds.

'1. The first arises where an opposite has been defined by means of its opposite, e.g. good by means of bad; for opposites are by nature simultaneous. But we must not forget that some things are probably not capable of definition in any other way, e.g. the double apart from the half, and all such terms as are essentially relative, for with all such things their being is identical with having some relation to something, so that it is impossible to know one without the other, and, consequently, in the definition of one of them, the other too must necessarily be comprehended. . . .

'2. Another case occurs where the definer has made use of the very thing defined. This may not be noticed when he does not use the actual name of the thing defined, e.g. if he has defined the sun as a star appearing by day; for he who makes use of "day" makes use of the sun. To probe such cases you should substitute for the word the definition of it, e.g. "day is the transit of the sun over the earth"; it is clear that one who has spoken of the transit of the sun over the earth has mentioned the sun, so that he who has made use of "day" has made use of "sun".

'3. Thirdly, see if he has defined one of two contrasted members of a bipartite division by the other, e.g. "odd number" as "that which is greater by one than an 'even number' ". For two contrasted things taken from the same genus are by nature simultaneous, and "odd" and "even" are so contrasted, since they are both differentiae of number.

'Similarly, too, see if he has defined the superior by means of terms that are subordinate, e.g. an "even" number as "that which can be halved", or "good" as a "state of virtue". For halving is derived[1] from 2, which 2 is an even number; and virtue is a kind of good; hence the said terms ["halving" and "virtue"] are subordinate to the others ["even" and "good" respectively]. Moreover, he who uses the subordinate to a term necessarily uses the term itself also. He who uses the term virtue uses "good" also, because virtue is a certain kind of good; and similarly one who uses "in half" uses "even", because to be divided "in half" means to be divided "into two", and two is "even".'

Ib. 5. 142^{b}22–9

'A second commonplace rule is to see whether, when the thing is in a genus, it has not been placed in a genus. This kind of error occurs in all cases in which the essence of the thing does not stand first in the description, e.g. in the definition of a body as "that which has three dimensions", or supposing anyone should think to define a man as "that which knows how to count". For it is not stated *what* it is that has three dimensions, or *what* it is that knows how to count. But it is the genus which indicates the "what" (or the substance), and this is the first thing to specify among the constituents of the definition.'

---

[1] This is more obvious in Greek owing to the words used. To 'halve' is δίχα διαιρεῖν 'to divide into two (equal) parts', δίχα being obviously related to δίς and δύο.

(f) Definition of 'line'

Topics VI. 6. 143ᵇ11–144ᵃ4

'Again there is the case where one divides the genus by negation, as those do who define a line as "breadthless length". This signifies nothing except that it has not any breadth. The effect in this case will be that the genus will partake of the species; for every length is either breadthless or possessed of breadth, because either an affirmation or the corresponding negation is true of anything whatever, and hence the genus of a line, being length, will be either breadthless or possessed of breadth. Now "breadthless length" is the definition of a species, and so is "length possessed of breadth"; for "breadthless" and "possessed of breadth" are differentiae, and the definition of the species is made up of the differentia and the genus, so that the genus would admit of the definition of the species. Similarly, it would admit of the definition of the differentia, since one or other of the said differentiae is necessarily predicable of the genus. This commonplace rule is of service in arguing with those who assume the existence of "Forms". For, if absolute length exists, how can it be predicated of the genus that it is "possessed of breadth" or is "breadthless"? For one or other of these attributes must be true of every length, if it is to be true of the genus. But this is not the case, for there are breadthless lengths and lengths possessed of breadth. Hence the rule is useful as an argument against those only who assert that the genus is numerically one. This is what is done by those who assume the "Forms"; for they assert that absolute-length and absolute-animal are the genus.

'But perhaps in some cases it is actually necessary for one who defines to use a negation as well, e.g. in defining a privation; "blind", for instance, means a thing which is not possessed of sight when it is its nature to have it. There is no difference between dividing the genus by negation and dividing it by an affirmation such as must necessarily be contrasted with the corresponding negation, e.g. if one has defined something as "length possessed of breadth"; for what is contrasted with that which has breadth is that which is not possessed of breadth, and nothing else; so that the genus is once more divided by negation.'

The difficulties connected with the definitions of the most elementary things in geometry, the point and the line, could hardly be more lucidly put than they are in the long passages just quoted. Definitions should, in the first place, be in terms of things absolutely prior, or prior in the order of thought, to the things defined. There being nothing in geometry prior in the absolute sense to a point, a point must be defined, if at all, either by means of a posterior term or by negation. The first method is illustrated by the definition of a point as an extremity of a line, the second by Euclid's definition of a point as 'that which has no part'. The latter definition or its equivalent appears frequently in Aristotle: cf. *Metaph. Δ.* 6. 1016^b24-6, where we are told that that which is indivisible every way in respect of magnitude and has not position is a unit (μονάς), while that which is similarly indivisible but has position is a point; *De an.* iii. 6. 430^b20-1, 'The point and every division [e.g. in a length or in a period of time], and that which is indivisible in this sense, are exhibited as privation (δηλοῦται ὥσπερ ἡ στέρησις).' Simplicius, quoted by an-Nairīzī, the Arabic commentator on Euclid, observes that Euclid defined a point negatively for the reason that it is arrived at by first detaching surface from body, then line from surface, and finally point from line. Since then body has three dimensions, it follows that a point (arrived at after successively eliminating all three dimensions) has none of the dimensions and has no part. The difficulty in Euclid's definition is the very one pointed out by Aristotle in 142^b25; the words 'that which' in 'that which has no part' almost invite the question, *what* is it that you mean by 'that'? As Aristotle says, when you define a body as 'that which has three dimensions', you do not say *what* it is that has three dimensions; you do not state a *genus* as you ought to do. But what would the genus be in this case? Aristotle does not say. Perhaps 'figure' might be suggested; but there is no proper definition of 'figure', and we are no better off. Aristotle indeed says that 'figure' is 'a sort of magnitude' (*De an.* III. 1. 425^a18), and that 'angle', 'straight', and 'circular' are kinds of figure (*Phys.* I. 5. 188^a25), but he regards it as useless to attempt a definition of 'figure' (*De an.* II. 3. 414^b19): 'From this it is clear that there is one definition of soul in the same way as there is one definition of "figure", for in the one case there is no figure except the triangle, the quadrilateral, and so on, nor in the other case is there any soul other than those above mentioned. . . . Hence it is absurd, here as elsewhere, to seek a definition which will not properly be a definition of anything in existence.' Even Euclid can give no better definition of 'figure' than 'that which is contained by any boundary or boundaries'. Plato in the *Meno* (76 A), after observing that 'roundness' or the 'round' is a 'figure', and so is the 'straight', and so on, says with reference to any figure, 'I say that that in which the solid terminates is a figure or, to put it shortly, a figure is an extremity of a solid'. Posidonius, too, regarded 'figure' as a 'confining extremity' or 'limit' (πέρας συγκλεῖον).

The Pythagorean definition of a point as a 'unit having position', the first definition of a point in positive terms, tells us nothing of its nature.

The view of a point as an extremity of a line, and of a line as an extremity of a surface, appear in Euclid, who adds to his definitions of a point and a line (as Def. 3) 'The extremities of a line are points', and to the definition of a surface (as Def. 6) 'The extremities of a surface are lines'. This was evidently a concession to tradition; he thought it worth while to include these old definitions as *obiter dicta* supplementing his definitions proper.

Aristotle is perfectly clear as to the relation between the point and the line. A point being indivisible, points cannot make up anything continuous like a line: 'point cannot be contiguous with point',[1] and 'a line is not made up of points'.[2] A point is like the *now* in time; now is indivisible and is not a part of time, it is only a beginning or end, or a division, of time; and, similarly, a point may be an extremity, a beginning, or a division of a line, but is not a *part* of it or of magnitude.[3] It is only by motion that a point can generate a line[4] and thus be the origin of magnitude.

Proclus observes[5] that, whereas the definition of a point is purely negative, the line introduces one dimension (length) so that its definition is to that extent positive, while it has a negative element which denies to it the other two dimensions (διαστάσεις). He alludes to a definition of a line which calls it 'a magnitude in one dimension' or 'a magnitude extended one way' (μέγεθος ἐφ' ἕν διαστατόν). Aristotle gives a similar definition: a line is a magnitude 'divisible one way only'[6] or 'continuous one way' or 'in one direction',[7] as compared with magnitudes which are divisible, or continuous, two ways or three ways, i.e. surfaces and solids. In the latter of the two passages he says that a magnitude continuous one way or in one direction is length, a magnitude continuous two ways is breadth, and continuous three ways is depth respectively, but explains that length means a line, breadth a surface, and depth a body.

The definition of a line as 'breadthless length' (which is Euclid's definition) was pre-Euclidean and seems to be attributable to the Platonic school if not to Plato himself. Aristotle probably took no serious objection to it as a definition of a line; he uses it here only for the purpose of making a point against those who postulate 'Ideas' or 'Forms', and among such 'Forms' αὐτὸ μῆκος 'length in itself'. If, he says, there is an 'idea' of length and it is *one*, and if there are breadthless lengths and lengths having breadth, the idea

---

[1] οὐ γάρ ἐστιν ἐχόμενον σημεῖον σημείου ἢ στιγμὴ στιγμῆς, *De gen. et corr.* I. 2. 317ᵃ11.

[2] οὐ σύγκειται ἐκ στιγμῶν, *Phys.* IV. 8. 215ᵇ19.

[3] Cf. *De caelo* III. 1. 300ᵃ14; *Phys.* IV. 11. 220ᵃ4, VI. 1. 231ᵇ6 f.

[4] *De an.* I. 4. 409ᵃ4.   [5] *Comm. in Eucl. I*, pp. 96-7 F.

[6] *Metaph.* Δ. 6. 1016ᵇ25-7.   [7] *Metaph.* Δ. 13. 1020ᵃ11.

or genus is self-contradictory. But, as Alexander saw, the argument is decidedly sophistical, because αὐτὸ μῆκος, in fact, *excludes* breadth; a length which has breadth is not a line but a surface.

The definition of an odd number as 'exceeding by one an even number' is objected to by Aristotle as unscientific because odd and even are co-ordinates, both being differentiae of number, so that one should not be defined by means of the other. This faulty definition, evidently pre-Euclidean, was so far traditional that Euclid did not think it right to ignore it, for he says:[1] 'An odd number is that which is not divisible into two equal parts, or [that which] differs by a unit from an even number.'

Another definition of an 'odd number' is criticized in the following passage.

Topics VI. 12. 149ᵃ29–36

'If he has given the definition of the differentia, see whether the definition given is common to it and to something else as well; for example, whenever he speaks of an odd number as "a number having a middle", you must further define in what way it has a middle; for the word number is common to both descriptions [presumably that of "number" and that of "odd number"] and it is for the word "odd" that the phrase ("having a middle") has been substituted. But both a line and a body have a middle, though they are not odd, so that "having a middle" cannot be a definition of "odd". If then "that which has a middle" has several meanings, we must define in what way "odd" is a thing which has a middle.'

The allusion is clearly to a definition of 'odd' which was current at the time:[2] e.g. the odd is a number which has a middle. The same idea, with the necessary distinction as to the kind of middle that is meant, is found in Nicomachus' definition of 'even' and 'odd':[3] 'That is *even* which is capable of being divided into two equal parts without a unit falling in the middle, and that is *odd* which cannot be divided into two equal parts because of the aforesaid intervention of the unit' (that is, the middle in question is a single unit). Nicomachus adds that this definition is based 'on the popular conception', but that the Pythagorean doctrine is that 'an even number is that which admits of being divided by one and the same operation into the greatest and least (parts), greatest in size (πηλικότητι) and least in quantity (ποσότητι) . . . while an odd number is that which cannot be so treated, but is divided into two *unequal* parts'. That is, the *parts* of an even number are the greatest possible (being half of the number), but the *number* of parts is the least possible, in fact, 2. The 'parts' are, of course, aliquot parts.

[1] VII, Def. 7.　　[2] Cf. *Soph. El.* 13. 173ᵇ8.　　[3] *Arithm.* I. 7. 3.

(g) Definition of 'straight line'

Topics VI. 11. 148ᵇ23–32

'If we are given a definition of something complex, we must see
whether, when we take away the definition of one of the elements in
the complex, the remainder of the definition corresponds to the
remainder of the complex, for, if it does not, it is clear that neither
is the whole definition the definition of the whole complex. Suppose,
for example, that some one has defined a limited straight line as
"the limit of a limited plane, the middle of which (limit) covers the
ends", then, if the definition of a limited line is "the limit of a limited
plane", the rest, namely "the middle of which covers the ends",
must be the definition of "straight". But an unlimited straight line
has neither middle nor end, and yet is straight, so that this remainder
is not a definition of the remainder (of the thing to be defined).'

The definition of 'straight' as 'that the middle of which covers the
ends' is given by Plato:[1] 'straight is whatever has its middle in
front of (ἐπίπροσθεν) both its extremities'. The words used by
Aristotle, οὗ τὸ μέσον ἐπιπροσθεῖ τοῖς πέρασιν, are equivalent. ἐπιπροσ-
θεῖν means 'to stand in front of' so as to obscure the view of something: ἐπιπρόσθησις is used in *De caelo* II. 14 of the earth passing in
front of the moon during a lunar eclipse. The idea is that you are
to look at a straight line *end-on*, as it were, in which case you would
only see the extremity nearest to you (assuming that you could see
a point at all), the straight line being behind it and hidden; hence
it would seem more natural to say that the ends cover the middle
rather than the reverse. Aristotle's point is again rather sophistical;
the definition refers to a limited straight line, a line which *has*
extremities; an infinite straight line has no extremities, and therefore the definition does not apply to it, but only to a segment of it.

The defect of the definition is that it implies an appeal to sight,
and amounts to the postulate that we *see straight*. Euclid's definition,[2] 'a straight line is a line which lies evenly with the points on
itself', is also unsatisfactory, and even its interpretation has given
rise to endless discussion. For a detailed examination of the whole
subject I would refer to *The Thirteen Books of Euclid's Elements*,
vol. i, pp. 165–9. I still think that the simplest explanation of Euclid's
definition is to suppose that Euclid saw that the Platonic definition
(with which he must have been familiar) was open to the objection
that it appealed to the sense of sight, and tried to express the same
thing in terms eliminating that appeal. He was unsuccessful from
the nature of the case, since his definition would hardly help anyone

---

[1] *Parmenides* 137 E.   [2] I, Def. 4.

to understand the nature of a straight line who had not some idea of it already.

Other ancient definitions may be mentioned, though they all import quasi-physical considerations.

   1. 'A line stretched to the utmost' (Heron, Def. 4), i.e. like a stretched string. Cf. Archimedes' *postulate* that a straight line is the shortest distance between two points ('Of all lines which have the same extremities the straight line is the least', *On the Sphere and Cylinder*, i, *init.*).

   2. 'A line such that all parts of it fit on (coincide with) all other parts alike or in all ways.' To this definition Heron adds the words 'when it is, as it were, turned round in the same plane' and 'about the same ends keeping always the same position'. This sort of definition has often been put forward in modern times. Cf. Gauss: 'The line in which lie all points that, during the revolution of a body (or part of space) about two fixed points, maintain their position unchanged is called a straight line.'

(h) Utility of arguments: multiplication table

Ib. VIII. 14. 163ᵇ17–28

'We should know by heart arguments useful in answer to those questions which are of most frequent occurrence and especially (those) about the primary assumptions; for it is here that those who are questioned often give up in despair. Again, we must have a good supply of definitions, and have ready to hand those of things familiar and of things primary; for it is by means of these that syllogisms are framed. We should try also to have a firm grasp of the points to which other arguments most frequently reduce. Just as in geometry it is an advantage to have had practice in the elements, and in arithmetic to be ready with the multiplication table up to ten, which is a great help towards recognizing the products of other numbers as well, so it is of service in arguments to be ready with the principles, and to have the premisses at the tip of one's tongue.'

At 163ᵇ25 we have what seems to be a solitary reference to a multiplication table. Alexander explains that by κεφαλισμοί are meant all numbers up to 10 multiplied by one another, and he illustrates the remark that the table helps towards multiplying bigger numbers by the fact that from the product of 2 and 2 we know at once the product of 2 and 20, of 20 times 20, of 200 times 20, and so on.

VI

PHYSICS

(a) Quadrature of the circle: Hippocrates, Bryson, Antiphon

Soph. El. 11. 171ᵇ12–18; 171ᵇ34–172ᵃ7

Phys. I. 2. 185ᵃ14–17

The translation of the first two passages has been given above.[1] Both fall to be considered in connexion with the passage from the *Physics*, which has also been mentioned.[2]

The first passage says that the so-called geometrical *Fallacies* are not 'eristic' because they come within the art of geometry, 'much less any such fallacy as relates to a true proposition, as e.g. that of Hippocrates or the squaring by means of lunes'. But the method of Bryson is sophistical because it uses principles which are not confined to geometry, but of wider application.

The second passage repeats that 'the quadrature of the circle by means of lunes' is not eristic, whereas Bryson's method is sophistical or eristic 'because it is addressed to the mass of people, who do not know what is possible and what impossible in each science, for it will fit any; *and the same thing is true of Antiphon's quadrature*' (ἢ ὡς Ἀντιφῶν ἐτετραγώνιζεν).

Phys. I. 2. 185ᵃ14–17

'The exponent of any science is not called upon to solve every kind of difficulty that may be raised, but only such as arise through false deductions from the principles of the science: with others than these he need not concern himself. For example, it is for the geometer to expose the quadrature by means of segments, but it is not the business of the geometeʳ to refute the argument of Antiphon.'

We have first to consider the allusion to Hippocrates[3] οὐδέ γ' εἴ τί ἐστι ψευδογράφημα περὶ ἀληθές, οἷον τὸ Ἱπποκράτους ἢ ὁ τετραγωνισμὸς ὁ διὰ τῶν μηνίσκων. The word understood with τό must be ψευδογράφημα, 'the false argument of Hippocrates or the quadrature by means of lunes'. It was a false argument 'relating to something true', by which we must presumably understand an argument which, though supposedly fallacious, aimed at establishing a true proposition, in this case a real solution of the quadrature-problem.

Two questions arise here. When Aristotle speaks of 'the fallacy of Hippocrates or the quadrature by means of lunes', does he refer

[1] p. 47.   [2] pp. 34, 48.   [3] *Soph. El.* 171ᵇ14–16.

to one and the same fallacy, or to two different ones? And what is 'the quadrature by means of segments'? Is it the same as 'the quadrature by means of lunes'? On this Simplicius[1] writes shrewdly as follows: 'As regards "the squaring of the circle by means of segments" which Aristotle reflected on as containing a fallacy, there are three possibilities, (1) that it hints at the quadrature by means of *lunes* (Alexander was right in expressing the doubt implied by his words "if it is the same as the quadrature by means of lunes"), (2) that it refers, not to the proofs of Hippocrates, but to some others, one of which Alexander actually reproduced, or (3) that it is intended to reflect on the squaring by Hippocrates of the circle *plus* the lune, which Hippocrates did in fact prove by means of segments, namely the three ⟨in the greater circle and the six⟩ in the lesser circle. Perhaps this proof might more properly be called "The proof by means of segments" than "the (proof) by means of lunes". . . . On this third hypothesis the fallacy would lie in the fact that the sum of the circle and the lune is squared and not the circle alone.'

Now the remarkable fact is that the genuine quadratures of lunes by Hippocrates contain no fallacies whatever. There are only five types of lunes such as those of Hippocrates which can be squared by 'plane' methods in geometry, i.e. by the use of the straight line and circle only; Hippocrates discovered three of the five and squared them: a very brilliant achievement. The squaring of the other two was left for Martin Johan Wallenius of Åbo (1766) and the great Euler (1772) respectively.

Equally clever was the squaring of the sum of a circle and a lune by Hippocrates.[2]

Since the 'quadrature by means of segments' was such that, in the opinion of Aristotle, the geometer need not even consider it, it cannot have been the last-mentioned case. It must therefore have been some quadrature by means of lunes which contained a fallacy, probably the fallacious quadrature given by Alexander.[3] The explanation is no doubt that Aristotle, as well as Alexander, was not well informed on the subject of the quadratures of lunes that were genuinely attributable to Hippocrates.

We are more fortunate in that we have authentic information on the subject. We owe this to the admirable Simplicius, who gives in his commentary on the passage of the *Physics* a long extract from the *History of Geometry* by Eudemus, the pupil of Aristotle, which is lost except for extracts preserved by Simplicius, Proclus, and others. The particular extract by Simplicius is one of the most precious documents that we possess about the history of geometry before Euclid's time.

[1] In *Phys.* 68. 34–69. 11 Diels.   [2] See pp. 33–6, above.   [3] See pp. 35–6, above.

Simplicius, after reproducing Alexander's version of the quadratures of lunes, observes that, so far as Hippocrates is concerned, we
must allow that Eudemus was in a better position to know the facts
since he was nearer the times, being a pupil of Aristotle. Simplicius
says accordingly that he will quote Eudemus word for word (κατὰ
λέξιν) except for a few additions referring to Euclid's *Elements*
which are necessitated by the summary ('memorandum-like') style
of Eudemus. The separation of Eudemus' text from Simplicius'
additions can be made with fair certainty.[1]

Antiphon

The objection taken by Aristotle to Antiphon's attempted quadrature of the circle was clearly that it was based on other than geometrical principles,[2] i.e. on something which conflicted with the
admitted principles of geometry. Simplicius gives us the tradition
about Antiphon's procedure. He began with an equilateral triangle
or a square inscribed in a circle; then in each of the segments of the
circle cut off by the sides of the triangle or square, he inscribed an
isosceles triangle, thereby obtaining an inscribed regular polygon
with double the number of sides. Continuing this process with that
polygon, and so on, he thought 'that in this way the area of the circle
would be used up, and we should some time have a polygon the sides
of which, owing to their smallness, would coincide with the circumference of the circle. And, as we can construct a square equal to
any polygon . . . we shall be able to make a square equal to a circle.'[3]

No doubt Eudemus was right in supposing that the geometrical
principle infringed by Antiphon was the truth that geometrical
magnitudes are divisible without limit, so that Antiphon's process
would *never* end, and he could never arrive at a regular polygon
which is *equal* in area to the circle.[4] Antiphon was, in fact, confronted
with the precise difficulty which Zeno and Democritus had stated
with such force. But Antiphon deserves an honourable place in the
history of geometry for having originated the idea of *exhausting*
the area of a circle by means of inscribed regular polygons with
a continually increasing number of sides, an idea upon which
Eudoxus based his great and fruitful 'method of exhaustion' for
finding the areas and volumes of curvilinear figures. Even Eudoxus
did not *solve* the difficulty raised by Zeno (which does not seem even to-
day to be finally disposed of) ; but he circumvented it in such a way as
to enable geometry to advance without hindrance by showing that it
is sufficient for the purpose to prove, for example, in the case of the

---

[1] See *Greek Mathematics*, i, pp. 187–99 for the complete story.
[2] μὴ ἀπὸ γεωμετρικῶν ἀρχῶν, Simpl. *in Phys.* 54. 15 D.
[3] Simpl. *in Phys.* 55. 6–11 D.   [4] Cf. p. 50, above.

circle that, if Antiphon's procedure be continued far enough, the sum of the small segments left over between the sides of the inscribed polygon and the circumference of the circle can be made less than any assigned area.[1] Eudoxus did not, of course, any more than Antiphon, actually 'square the circle', i.e. construct, or show how to construct, a square equal in area to a given circle; for this is beyond the power of 'plane' geometry. But, by his method, one area or solid content involving π, the ratio of the circumference of a circle to its diameter, can be found in terms of another area or solid content also involving π. Thus Eudoxus proved by his method that circles are to one another as the squares on their diameters, spheres are to one another as the cubes on their diameters, and a cone is equal to one-third of the cylinder on the same base and of equal height; and he found the actual content of any pyramid by proving that it is one-third of that of a prism on the same base and of equal height. These propositions duly appear in Euclid.[2]

(b) Things known to us and things prior in the order of nature. Definition of circle

Physics I. 1. 184ª10–b12

'In all studies in which there are principles or causes or elements, it is from an acquaintance with these that knowledge, that is, scientific knowledge, is acquired. For we consider that we know a thing when we are acquainted with the first causes and the first principles down to the elements. Obviously therefore, in the science of Nature too, we must first try to determine what belongs to the principles. The natural course leads from what is better known and clearer *to us* to what is clearer and better known in the order of nature; for it is not the same things that are known to us and known in the absolute sense respectively. Hence it is necessary to advance in this way from what is less clear in the order of nature but clearer to us to what is clearer and better known in the order of nature. Now the things which are at first obvious and clear to us are more of the nature of confused aggregates; it is only afterwards that, as we analyse them, the elements and the principles become known to us. Hence we must proceed from the universal [here, the concrete whole] to the particular [the components]; for it is the whole that is better known so far as sense-perception is concerned, and the universal is a sort of whole, since it embraces a multitude of parts, as it were. Names too stand, in a sense, in the same relation to definitions; for the name denotes a certain whole without distinction

[1] Cf. Eucl. X. 1 and XII. 2.   [2] XII. 2, 18, 10, 7.

[of parts or properties], e.g. a circle, whereas the definition of a circle analyses it into its particular components.'

On the interpretation of this passage as a whole I need only refer to Ross's remarks.[1]

On the contrast between things prior and better known *to us* and things prior in the order of nature, and the necessity of basing definitions on the latter rather than the former, cf. *Topics* VI. 4. 141ᵃ24 and pp. 85–6, above.

The definition of a circle is not given by Aristotle in so many words, but if he had given one, it would hardly have been substantially different from Euclid's: 'a circle is a plane figure contained by one line such that all the straight lines falling upon it from one point among those lying within the figure are equal to one another; and the point is called the centre of the circle.' Aristotle actually has the expression 'the circular figure bounded by one line';[2] he also speaks of 'the plane equal (i.e. extending equally all ways) from the middle', meaning a circle,[3] and he contrasts with the circle 'any other figure which has not the lines from the middle equal, as, for example, an egg-shaped figure'.[4] Cf. Plato, *Parmenides* 137 E: 'Round ⟨i.e. circular⟩ is, I take it, that the extremes of which are every way equally distant from the middle.'

(c) *Mathematics and Physics*

Phys. II. 2. 193ᵇ22–194ᵃ15

'Since we have determined in how many senses we speak of Nature, we must next consider wherein the mathematician differs from the physicist or the philosopher of Nature. For physical bodies contain planes, solids, lengths, and points, which are what the mathematician investigates. Again, astronomy is either different from, or a branch of, physics; for it is absurd to suppose that it is the business of the physicist to know what the sun and moon are, but not to know any of their essential attributes, especially as we find that physicists do in fact discuss the shape of the moon and sun, and the question whether the earth and the universe are spherical or not.

'The mathematician too studies these ⟨shapes⟩ but not *qua* limits, in each case, of a natural body. Nor does he investigate their attributes *qua* attributes of such bodies. This is why he separates the mathematical objects; for they can be separated in thought from all motion, and they are not affected thereby, nor does the separation involve any error. . . . This will become clear if we try to give definitions of both mathematical and physical bodies, the

---

[1] pp. 456–8.　　　　　　　　[2] *De caelo* ii. 4. 286ᵇ13–16.
[3] *Rhetoric*, iii. 6. 1407ᵇ27.　　　[4] *De caelo* ii. 4. 287ᵃ19.

things themselves and their properties. For odd and even, straight and curved, as well as number, line, and figure, are independent of motion, whereas flesh, bone, man are not, but the latter terms are analogous to "snub-nose".

'The distinction is further made clear by the more physical branches of mathematics like optics, harmonics, and astronomy; these stand in a sort of inverse relation to geometry; for geometry considers a physical line [a line subsisting in a natural body] but not *qua* physical, whereas optics considers a mathematical line, not however *qua* mathematical but *qua* physical.

'And since nature means two things, form and matter, we should study it just in the same way as we should consider, say, the definition of "snubness"; that is to say, we must consider them neither independently of matter nor, on the other hand, exclusively with reference to matter.'

The second paragraph of the above extract has been given and commented upon above.[1] The relation of the 'pure' mathematical subjects (geometry and arithmetic) to the 'applied' mathematical subjects (optics, harmonics, mechanics, astronomy) has also been described.[2] It remains to consider the relation of astronomy to physics. Astronomy is here said to be (1) one of the more physical branches of mathematics, 194[a]7–8, and (2) either different from, or a part of, physics. We should naturally expect the physicist to consider the matter or substance of the heavenly bodies and the properties appertaining to them as material bodies; he has to consider what the sun and moon are; but, says Aristotle, he is not debarred from inquiring into their essential attributes, and does, in fact, discuss the shapes of the sun and moon, the earth and the universe. According to Simplicius, the astronomer considers the properties of physical bodies, but not *qua* physical, and deals with the heavenly bodies merely as moving bodies having certain shapes. The astronomer does not even attempt to show that such forms, sizes, and motions are appropriate to the physical constitution of the heavenly bodies. Take the case of the spherical shape of the universe. The physicist, says Simplicius,[3] argues that the universe is spherical, because the sphere is a 'primary, simple, perfect, and uniform' figure, and in this respect is alone among solid figures— rectilinear solid bodies being all bounded by several surfaces or 'faces' and not by *one* surface as is the sphere—and hence the shape of the sphere is appropriate to the first of all bodies, the universe. The astronomer, on the other hand, would, in arguing that the universe is spherical, base himself on the mathematical ground that

[1] pp. 65-7.   [2] pp. 58-61.   [3] *In Phys.* 291 D.

of all solid figures having a surface of equal area the sphere is the largest, and therefore holds more. Simplicius goes on to quote Alexander's word-for-word reproduction of a long passage taken from Geminus' summary of the *Meteorologica* of Posidonius, which was, according to Simplicius (or Alexander), based on Aristotle. I have quoted this passage in full and commented upon it elsewhere.[1] It must suffice here to give a short summary.

It is the business of the physicist to consider the substance of the heaven and the stars, their force and quality, their coming-to-be and passing-away; he may even be able to prove facts about their size, shape, and arrangement; but it is the astronomer who, starting from the assumption that the universe is a real κόσμος, deals with shapes, sizes, and distances, and tells us about eclipses and conjunctions and the quality and extent of the movements of the heavenly bodies. These things, involving the investigation of quantity, size, shape, and arrangement, require the use of arithmetic and geometry, and the astronomer gives us only what these enable him to prove. If the physicist and the astronomer set out to prove one and the same point, e.g. that the sun is of great size or that the earth is spherical, they do not take the same road. The physicist proves each fact by consideration of substance, of force, of change, and the like; the astronomer uses the properties of figures or magnitudes, the amount of the movements, and the times they occupy. To explain facts, the physicist will often look for the cause of them in creative force; the astronomer does not trouble about the cause; having observed the phenomena, e.g. the occurrence of eclipses or the irregular motions of the planets, he will invent something by way of hypothesis to account for them, and will state particular expedients by the assumption of which the phenomena 'will be saved', e.g. the hypotheses of eccentric circles or epicycles, or even the heliocentric hypothesis (Aristarchus of Samos); and of different hypotheses he will choose that which in his view best corresponds to the visible phenomena. But he goes to the physicist for his first principles, namely, that the motions of the stars are simple, ordered, and uniform.

(d) Necessity in mathematics

Physics II. 9. 200ᵃ15–19

'There is a certain similarity between the necessity that rules in mathematics and the necessity governing things which come about by natural processes. For, given that the "straight" has such-and-

---

[1] *Arstiarchus of Samos*, pp. 275–6 ff.

such a character, it is a necessary consequence that the angles of a triangle are together equal to two right angles; but it does not follow that, given the latter (theorem), the former [our conception of the nature of a straight line] is necessarily true; we can only say that, if the triangle has *not* the property in question, the "straight", as we understand it, does not exist.'

We gather from *Metaph.* 1051ᵃ24–6 that the proof of the proposition about the angles of the triangle which was familiar to Aristotle was that of Eucl. I. 32. This depends on the properties of parallels given in I. 29, and these cannot be proved except by means of Euclid's Postulate 5 or some equivalent assumption. Aristotle's meaning here is that, if the theorem of Eucl. I. 32 is not true, the original assumptions on which the whole of Euclidean geometry is based must be revised, including the definition, or the generally accepted notion, of a straight line. It is as if he had had a sort of prophetic idea of some geometry based on other than Euclidean principles, such as the modern 'non-Euclidean' geometries. Thus on Riemann's hypothesis the angles of a triangle are greater than two right angles, a straight line is a 'closed series' returning on itself, any two straight lines intersect in two points (all straight lines being, as it were, great circles on a sphere indefinitely large), and there is no such thing as parallel lines. It is not possible that Aristotle could consciously have conceived such an idea as Riemann's; but we can imagine him asking himself the question, 'If the angles of a triangle were together *not* equal to two right angles, what sort of thing would a straight line have to be?'

(e) *The gnomons*

Phys. III. 4. 203ᵃ10–15

'The Pythagoreans identify the infinite with the even. For this, they say, when cut off and limited by the odd, gives to things their unlimited character. An indication of this is what happens with numbers. For, if the gnomons be placed round ⟨in two ways, namely⟩, first round the 1, and secondly so as to exclude ⟨the 1⟩, the resulting figure is in the one case ⟨the latter⟩ always different, in the other ⟨the former⟩ always one and the same.'

Ross[1] has given a very full account of the different explanations that have been offered of this passage. The main difficulty is in the words καὶ χωρίς following 'gnomons placed round the 1'. They clearly indicate that the second case is a 'separate' one of 'placing gnomons round'; and there is, in my opinion, no doubt that what

---

[1] *Physics*, pp. 542–5.

is meant is the putting of *even* gnomons (as opposed to *odd*) round 2 (thereby leaving out the 1 altogether), which is contrasted with the putting of odd gnomons, the successive odd numbers, round 1. The first figure shows the successive odd numbers 3, 5, 7,... placed as

FIG. 22

gnomons round 1, and producing always square numbers, 4, 9, 16,..., that is to say, figures of the same form always (squares). The second figure shows that the addition of the successive *even* gnomons 4, 6, 8,... to 2 produces the so-called *oblong* numbers (ἑτερομήκεις) 6, 12, 20,..., which represent rectangles with sides always differing by 1, namely, (2. 3), (3. 4), (4. 5),..., their shapes being always different, since the ratios 2 : 3, 3 : 4, 4 : 5,... are always different.

This interpretation exactly suits the distinction which Aristotle draws between the gnomons which make the figures always the same and the gnomons which make them always different. It is also that suggested by Stobaeus,[1] purporting to come from Moderatus, a Pythagorean: 'Further, when the odd gnomons are placed about 1 the resulting figure is a square; when the even ⟨gnomons⟩ are similarly put round, the resulting numbers are all oblong and unequal, and none equal-times-equal.'

It is true that it is not here stated that the gnomons for oblong numbers are placed round 2, and not 1. But Iamblichus, in a long passage on the subject,[2] makes this quite clear. He says[3] that the class of oblong numbers 'has no need of unity in its formation', and again[4] he says that, if in the construction of oblong numbers you proceed by the method of putting gnomons round, 'it is the dyad only which will be found to admit of and sustain the process of "putting round" '.

(f) *Infinity*

I shall here, generally speaking, give only such extracts as appear to have mathematical significance.

Phys. III. 4. 203^{b}15–30

'If we think of it, belief in the existence of something infinite or unlimited would seem to arise out of five considerations:

(1) that of *time*: for it is infinite;

[1] *Ecl.* i. 1. 10.   [2] *In Nicom.* 73. 15 ff. Pistelli.   [3] p. 73. 23–4.   [4] At p. 77. 4–8.

(2) that of the division of magnitudes: for mathematicians also use the notion of the infinite;

(3) if coming to be and passing away do not give out, this can only be true on the assumption that the source from which things come to be is infinite;

(4) the limited must always come up to some limit, whence it follows that there can be *no* limit if one thing must always come up to some other thing as its limit;

(5) above all and most decisive—there is what constitutes the difficulty that all alike feel, namely that number and mathematical magnitudes and what is outside the universe appear to be infinite because they never give out in *thought*.

'Assuming then that what is outside the universe is infinite, we are led to believe that infinite body exists and an infinite number of worlds; for why should there be body in one part of the void rather than in another? If therefore mass is in any one place, it must be everywhere. Again, if void exists and place is infinite, it follows that there must be infinite body too; for in things eternal there is no distinction between what is possible and what is.'

In going through the five considerations leading to the belief in the existence of the infinite, Simplicius[1] puts first the dilemma about *time*. If time is not infinite, 'there was (a moment or point) when there was no time and there will be (another) when there will be no time' [the Greek idiom enables Simplicius to leave out words such as those bracketed: he can say ἦν ὅτε and ἔσται ὅτε simply]; 'but "was" and "will be" are again parts of time so that, when there is ⟨supposed to be⟩ *no* time, there is time ⟨even so⟩; hence time exists always; therefore time is infinite'.

On the second point, the infinite divisibility of mathematical magnitudes, Simplicius gives two illustrations: (1) If, when we draw a chord in a circle, it can never coincide with the circle, it is clear that the plane area bounded by the chord and the arc can be further divided *ad infinitum*; for if the division were to stop the chord would coincide with the circumference.

(2) If we have an isosceles triangle ABC, right-angled at A, the sum of the two equal sides BA, AC is greater than BC. Take away from their sum a length equal to BC by cutting off from BA a length BE equal to BD (where D is the middle point of BC) and from CA a length CF equal to CD. Join EF. Then AEF is another right-angled triangle similar to ABC. Similarly from the triangle AEF we can

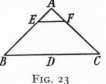

FIG. 23

[1] *In Phys.* 466. 13 f.

cut off towards A another similar triangle still smaller, bearing the same ratio to AEF as AEF does to ABC; and we can continue this process *ad infinitum* without exhausting the area of the original triangle.

The fact that increase never gives out in *our thought* is illustrated first by the case of numbers. There is no number that can be named to which we cannot conceive an addition being made of 1 or a higher number; and so it is with mathematical magnitudes in general.

As for 'what is outside the heaven' (^{b}25) Simplicius[1] quotes from Eudemus the story that Archytas put the question in this way: 'If I were, say, at the extreme limit of the heaven of the fixed stars, could I stretch my hand or my stick outwards or not? To suppose that I could not is absurd; but if I do stretch it out, that which is outside must be either body or place, and it will make no difference, as we shall see. Similarly we can go on to what is from time to time the limit and ask the same question; and if there is always something else to which the stick can point, that something must clearly be infinite. If it is body, the proposition is proved; but if it is place, and place is that in which body is or could be, while with things eternal we must regard what potentially is as being (in fact), it follows equally that infinite body and place will exist.'

Phys. III. 4. 204^{a}2–7

'We must first distinguish in how many senses we use the term infinite. In one sense it is (1) that which cannot be gone through because it is not its nature to be gone through—this is like the sense in which voice is invisible. In another sense it is (2) what admits of being gone through but is such that going through it is either (*a*) endless or (*b*) hardly possible. Or (3) it is that which is of a nature to be gone through but does not actually admit of being gone through or does not actually reach a limit.

'Again, everything that is infinite is infinite in one of three ways, by way of addition, of division, or of both.'

The commentators observe that instances of the things which cannot be gone through because it is not their nature to be gone through are the *point* and anything that is not a magnitude. The things (2) which, though their nature admits of it, cannot be gone through, or hardly, are illustrated by labyrinths and the pit at Sparta into which condemned criminals were thrown, where, of course, it was not the length of the passage through, but the difficulty of finding the exit, that was the obstacle. Aristomenes, the Messenian

[1] *In Phys.* 467. 26 f.

hero, found his way out of the pit thanks to the guidance of a fox. The thing (3) which, though of a nature to admit of passage through, has not a passage-*through*, or a *limit*—the emphasis is on the word 'through' and the meaning is that this thing cannot be *cleared* or got out of—is illustrated by a circular *ring*: you can go along it endlessly, but it is not *infinite* because you are not, during the journey, always coming on something new that has not been traversed; after going once round you repeat the *same* journey over and over again.

There remains the distinction (204ᵃ6–7) between the three ways in which a thing may be infinite. As Ross says, Aristotle's view is that number is infinite by way of addition, space by way of division, and time in both ways.

Ib. III. 5. 204ᵃ34–ᵇ4

'No doubt it is a more general question whether the infinite can exist also in things mathematical and in those which have no magnitude. But we are here considering sensible objects and those which are the subject of our inquiry as physicists, and we have to inquire whether among these there is or is not a body which is infinite in the direction of increase.'

Aristotle goes on in c. 5 to prove first by dialectic and then by general arguments that infinite body is an impossibility. He continues (c. 6) as follows:

Ib. III. 6. 206ᵃ9–ᵇ27

'On the other hand it is clear that, if an infinite does not exist at all, many impossibilities arise: time will have some beginning and end, magnitudes will not be divisible into magnitudes, and number will not be infinite. If therefore, when the case has been set out as above, neither view appears to be admissible, we need an arbitrator; clearly there is a sense in which the infinite exists and another sense in which it does not.

'Being means either being potentially, or being actually, and the infinite is possible by way of addition as well as by way of division (reading διαιρέσει). Now, as we have explained, magnitude is never actually infinite, but it is infinite by way of division—for it is not difficult to refute the theory of indivisible lines—the alternative that remains, therefore, is that the infinite exists potentially. But in what sense does it exist potentially? You may say, for example, that a given piece of material is potentially a statue, because it will (sometime) be a statue. Not so with something potentially infinite: you must not suppose that it will be actually infinite. Being has many meanings, and we say that the infinite "is" in the same sense as we say "it *is* day" or "the games *are* on", namely in virtue of

one thing continually succeeding another. For the distinction between "potentially" and "actually" applies to these things too:
there *are* Olympian games both in the sense that the contests may
take place and that they do take place.

'It is clear that the infinite takes different forms, as in time, in
generations of men, and in the division of magnitudes. For, generally speaking, the infinite is so in the sense that it is again and again
taking on something more, this something being always finite, but
different every time. In the case of magnitudes, however, what is
taken on during the process stays there; whereas in the case of time
and generations of men it passes away, but so that the source of
supply never gives out.

'The infinite by way of addition is in a manner the same as the
infinite by way of division. Within a finite magnitude the infinite
by way of addition is realized in an inverse way (to that by way of
division); for, as we see the magnitude being divided *ad infinitum*,
so, in the same way, the sum of the successive fractions when added
to one another (continually) will be found to tend towards a determinate limit. For if, in a finite magnitude, you take a determinate
fraction of it and then add to that fraction in the same ratio, and
so on [i.e. so that each part has to the preceding part the same ratio
as the part first taken has to the whole], but *not* each time including
(in the part taken) one and the same amount of the original whole,
you will not traverse (i.e. exhaust) the finite magnitude. But if you
increase the ratio so that it always includes one and the same
magnitude, whatever it is, you will traverse it, because any finite
magnitude can be exhausted by taking away from it continually any
definite magnitude however small. In no other sense, then, does the
infinite exist; but it does exist in this sense, namely potentially and
by way of diminution. In actuality it exists only in the sense
in which we say "it *is* day" or "the games *are* on", and potentially
it exists in the same way as matter, but not independently as the
finite does. Thus we may even have a potentially infinite by way of
addition of the kind we described, which, as we say, is in a certain
way the same as the infinite by way of division; it can always take
on something outside (the total for the time being), but the total
will never exceed every determinate magnitude (of the same kind)
in the way that, in the direction of division, it passes every determinate magnitude in smallness, and becomes continually smaller
and smaller. But in the sense of exceeding every (magnitude) by
way of addition, the infinite cannot exist even potentially, unless
there exists something actually infinite, but only incidentally so,
infinite, that is, in the sense in which natural philosophers declare
the body outside the universe to be infinite, whether its substance

be air or anything else of the kind. But if it is not possible that there can be a sensible body actually infinite in this sense, it is manifest that neither can there be such a body which is even potentially infinite by way of addition, save in the sense which we have described as the reverse of the infinite by way of division.'

Phys. III. 6. 206ᵇ33–207ᵃ2

'It turns out that what is infinite is the opposite of what people call infinite. What is infinite is not that which has nothing outside it, but that which always has some part of it outside ⟨its amount for the time being⟩.'

Aristotle's statement of his views on the infinite is of great interest from a mathematical point of view, with reference, especially, to the puzzles of Zeno (and Democritus), the 'Axiom of Archimedes', and Eudoxus' method of exhaustion; and I make no apology for including extracts of such length.

The doctrine of *Indivisible Lines* (206ᵃ17) is attributed to Plato and Xenocrates and recently (by S. Luria) to Democritus. The subject is to some extent dealt with by Aristotle elsewhere.[1]

The tract *On Indivisible Lines* included in the Aristotelian corpus is not by Aristotle. It may be by Theophrastus or some other pupil of Aristotle. We can imagine Aristotle stopping at some point in his lectures where indivisible lines were mentioned, apologizing for not going farther into the matter, and suggesting to some pupil that he might take up the subject and write a thesis upon it. The actual tract is directed against Xenocrates. Simplicius and Philoponus say that it was attributed to Theophrastus, and this is confirmed by a list of his works given by Diogenes Laërtius. But, as Professor Joachim says, the tract may not be by a pupil of Aristotle at all, but by Strato or some person otherwise unknown. We shall hope to comment on the work itself in the proper place.

The distinction between potentiality in the case of material for a statue (206ᵃ18–21) and in the case of the infinite is well brought out by Themistius. In the case of the material for a statue, which is potentially a statue, there comes a point at which the statue is finished and it becomes a complete whole. At that point the potentiality ceases or is destroyed, and actuality takes its place. Not so with the infinite. Its potentiality is never at an end; you can always go on adding to it or subtracting from it. If we could suppose the potentiality terminated and the thing become an actual thing, a complete whole, this would imply something fixed, some shape or form; to suppose it actual in this sense would be nothing less than

---

[1] v. *Phys.* VI, cc. 1, 2 and *Metaph. A.* 9. 992ᵃ22.

trying to give it boundaries or limits, and this would destroy its infinite character. In short, if the 'potentiality' in the infinite came to an end, it would cease to be infinite. Similarly with the infinitely divisible. The division is carried farther and farther, but *never* comes to an end; the potentiality of farther division never ceases; it can never give place to actuality.

In the case of day, time, or the games, their very existence consists in becoming, in a continual succession of instants or events; if the becoming came to an end, they would cease to *be*. You cannot conceive of their ever constituting, as it were, a totality, a complete whole. This is developed in the sentence bracketed by Ross at 206ᵃ29–34 as, according to Philoponus, not being in the best texts: 'Being has many meanings, and you must take the infinite to be, not "this individual thing" such as a man or a house, but comparable to what we mean by "day" or "the games", the being of which is not like that of a substance which has come to be, but consists always in a process either of coming to be or of passing away, so that, while at a given moment they are finite, they are continually changing into something else.'

The lines from 206ᵇ3 to ᵇ12 are difficult to translate in a way which shall keep closely to the Greek and yet give the correct mathematical sense. I am clear that the words πρὸς τὸ ὡρισμένον (ᵇ6) mean that the sum of the added terms tends 'to a definite or determinate *limit*'. The Oxford translation is, I think, wrong in its rendering, 'we see addition being made to *what is already* marked off', if this means, as I presume it does, the first fraction taken, and so on; if this had been the meaning, Aristotle would surely have said πρὸς τὸ ληφθέν. ὡρισμένον means 'definite' or 'determinate', in this case the limit to which the sum of a never-ending series of terms diminishing in geometric ratio tends. The Greek idiom always favours the definite article with the word denoting an assigned magnitude, where we use the indefinite article. Cf. Archimedes[1] τὰν δοθεῖσαν σφαῖραν ἐπιπέδῳ τεμεῖν ὥστε τὰ τμήματα αὐτᾶς ποτ᾽ ἄλλαλα τὸν ταχθέντα λόγον ἔχειν, where we translate: 'To cut *a* sphere by a plane so that the segments of it have to one another *a* given ratio.'

We can illustrate Aristotle's remark by the simplest case. Suppose we have a magnitude *a* and we first take away its half, then the half of that, and so on continually. We then have the terms

$$\frac{1}{2}a, \ \frac{1}{4}a, \ \frac{1}{8}a, \ \frac{1}{16}a, \ \ldots \ \frac{1}{2^n}a.$$

It is thus that we see the magnitude *a* being divided *ad infinitum*.

---

[1] *De Lin. Spir.* 4. 13 (Heiberg).

By ταύτῃ προστιθέμενον Aristotle means the sum of the terms, or

$$\frac{1}{2}a + \frac{1}{4}a + \frac{1}{8}a + \ldots + \frac{1}{2^n}a.$$

If n is infinitely great, or the series goes on without limit, algebra tells us that the sum of such a series 'to infinity' is the first term (here $\frac{1}{2}a$) divided by $1-r$, where r is the common ratio, in this case $\frac{1}{2}$; in other words, the definite or 'determinate' magnitude to which the sum of the terms 'to infinity' tends is

$$\frac{1}{2}a/(1-\frac{1}{2}) = \frac{1}{2}a/\frac{1}{2} = a.$$

In like manner, if we had begun by taking away $\frac{1}{3}$, instead of $\frac{1}{2}$, of the original magnitude a, the sum to infinity of the series

$$\frac{1}{3}a + \frac{1}{9}a + \frac{1}{27}a + \ldots + \frac{1}{3^n}a$$

would be $$\frac{1}{3}a/(1-\frac{1}{3}) = \frac{1}{3}a/\frac{2}{3} = \frac{1}{2}a.$$

(When in the next sentence Aristotle says: 'If, in a finite magnitude we take a definite or "determinate" fraction (ὡρισμένον) and then take an additional fraction *in the same ratio*', he means that, if $1/r$ is the determinate fraction, we take a/r, then add to it $\frac{1}{r}\left(\frac{a}{r}\right)$ or $\frac{1}{r^2}a$, then $\frac{1}{r}$ of this or $\frac{1}{r^3}a$, and so on; he does not mean, as the Loeb translator makes him say, take a definite piece away and then go on to take away the same proportion of *what is left*, but the same proportion of the first piece taken.)

If the first fraction taken is $1/r$, where r is greater than 1, the successive terms 'do not contain or include one and the same fraction of a however small' (in Aristotle's words, 206^b8–9), because if they did and if a/p were such a fraction, p being any integral number whatever, then p times a/p would exhaust the magnitude a, so that if each of the terms $\frac{1}{r}a$, $\frac{1}{r^2}a$, $\frac{1}{r^3}a$, ... were not less than a/p, the sum of p terms (or a less number of terms) would exhaust a. The essence of the case is that the successive terms diminish without limit, and are not subject to a minimum limit as a/p or any other *determinate* fraction of a.

In 206^b9 Aristotle goes on to say: 'But if you increase the ratio so that the terms always include [i.e. are not less than] the same amount of the whole whatever it is [e.g. a/p], the magnitude will in time be exhausted.' Simplicius points out one way in which the ratio could be increased so as to produce this result. Suppose that the original magnitude is 6 finger-breadths. If you first deduct $\frac{1}{6}$th,

you leave 5. If now you increase the ratio from ⅙th to ⅕th and deduct
⅕th from the 5, you leave 4. Deduct ¼th from 4 and 3 remain,
⅓rd from 3 and 2 remain, ½ from 2 and 1 remains. It is true that, to
use up this 1, the fraction ½ has to be increased to the whole.

Phys. III. 7. 207ᵃ33–ᵇ34

'It is after all only reasonable that it should be thought that by
way of addition there is not an infinite such as to exceed every
magnitude but that by way of division there *is*. For the infinite,
like the matter ⟨of a thing⟩, is contained inside ⟨what contains it⟩
and what contains both is the form.

'Reasonable too it is that in number there is a limit in the direction
of the minimum, while in the direction of increase it may exceed
any number assigned from time to time, but that in the case of
magnitudes, on the contrary, it is possible to surpass any magnitude
in the direction of smallness, while in the direction of increase there
is no infinite magnitude. The reason is that the One is indivisible
whatever it may be that is one; for example, a man is one man and
not many; but a number is several "ones" or a certain quantity of
them. Hence number must stop at the indivisible; two and three
are derivative words, and so is every other number. But in the
direction of "more" we can always think of a greater number. The
possible bisections of a magnitude are infinite in number; this
infinite is potential, not actual, but you can always assume a number
⟨of such bisections⟩ exceeding any assigned number. But this number
is not separable from the process of bisection, and its infinity is not
a stationary one but it is in process of coming to be, like time and
the number of time.

'With magnitudes the contrary is the case; for the continuous
magnitude is divisible *ad infinitum*, but in the direction of increase
there is no infinite. Whatever its size potentially, that size it can be
actually; hence, since there is no sensible magnitude that is infinite, it
is not possible to have an excess over every determinate magnitude;
if it were, there would have to be something greater than the universe.

'Now the infinite is not the same thing in magnitude, movement,
and time respectively, in the sense of being a single nature, but its
posterior sense depends on its primary sense: thus movement is
called infinite because the magnitude over which movement—or
modification or increase—takes place ⟨is infinite⟩, and time because
of the movement. I use these terms provisionally. I shall try later
on to explain the meaning of each of them, and why every magnitude
is divisible into magnitudes.

'Neither does my argument rob mathematicians of their study
because it denies that the infinite can exist in such a way as to be

actually infinite in the direction of increase, meaning thereby something that cannot be gone through. For, even as things are, mathematicians do not need or make use of it; they only require that the
finite straight line shall be as long *as they please*, and that, given
a ratio in which the greatest magnitude is cut, another magnitude
of any size whatever can be cut in the same ratio. Hence my argument makes no difference to mathematicians for the purpose of
their demonstrations; nor does it matter to them whether the
infinite exists among existent magnitudes.'

What most interests the historian of mathematics in the above
is the statement that, 'even as things are, mathematicians do not
need the infinite or make use of it; they only require that the finite
straight line shall be as long *as they please*'. This shows that Aristotle
was already fully aware of the second great discovery by Eudoxus,
which put mathematics on its feet again, as it were, after the
unsettlement caused by the doubts raised (notably in Zeno's paradoxes, in Democritus' dilemma about parallel circular sections of
the right cone, and by the partisans of 'indivisible lines') as to the
assumed divisibility of mathematical magnitudes *ad infinitum*. For
the axiom or postulate on which Eudoxus founded his 'method of
exhaustion' for measuring the content of curvilinear plane and solid
figures was framed precisely in accordance with the principle
enunciated by Aristotle in this passage. Our authority for this is
Archimedes, in whose treatises the 'method of exhaustion' plays
a preponderant part. In the preface to his *Quadrature of the Parabola*
Archimedes says that he assumes the following lemma: 'The excess
by which the greater of two unequal areas exceeds the lesser can,
if it be continually added to itself, be made to exceed any assigned
finite area.' The same assumption is stated more generally for lines,
surfaces, and solids in Assumption 5 at the beginning of *On the
Sphere and Cylinder*, I. In the *Quadrature of the Parabola* Archimedes
justifies his use of the lemma in these words: 'The earlier geometers
too have used this lemma; for it is by this means that they have
proved (1) that circles have to one another the duplicate ratio of
their diameters, (2) that spheres have to one another the triplicate
ratio of their diameters, (3) that every pyramid is one-third part of
the prism which has the same base with the pyramid and equal height;
and further (4) that every cone is one-third part of the cylinder which
has the same base with the cone and equal height they proved by
assuming a lemma similar to that aforesaid.'

Now in the preface to *On the Sphere and Cylinder*, I, Archimedes
says that it was Eudoxus who first gave a scientific proof of propositions (3) and (4), (though Democritus was the first to enunciate

them); and it is a fair inference that Eudoxus was the first to formulate Archimedes' axiom, either in the same or an equivalent form.

It is true that the lemma used by Euclid to prove the propositions about the pyramid and the cone (Eucl. XII. 3–10) and about the areas of circles (XII. 2) and the volumes of spheres (XII. 18) is not the same as the assumption of Archimedes, but is a sort of converse to it dealing with the division of magnitudes *ad infinitum*. It is proved in Eucl. X. 1 and is as follows: 'Two unequal magnitudes being set out, if from the greater there be subtracted a magnitude greater than its half, and from that which is left a magnitude greater than its half, and if this process be repeated continually, there will be left some magnitude which will be less than the lesser magnitude set out. . . . And the theorem can be similarly proved even if the parts subtracted be halves.' This theorem is also frequently used by Archimedes. It is possible that it may be the 'lemma similar to that aforesaid' referred to by Archimedes in the passage quoted above. In any case Archimedes' lemma is in effect used by Euclid to prove his X. 1. For Euclid's Def. 5 of Book V, there used, is to the effect that 'Magnitudes are said to have a ratio to one another which are capable, when multiplied, of exceeding one another', and this is true even if one of the magnitudes is as small as we please.

In his argument that the actually infinite cannot exist Aristotle is speaking of *physical* magnitudes; but he is aware that similar questions arise about mathematical magnitudes. At 204ª34 he has said that it may be that a more general inquiry would be necessary to determine whether the existence of the infinite is possible in mathematical objects and in the objects of thought which have no magnitude.

In *Phys.* III, c. 8, Aristotle deals with certain arguments in favour of the view that the infinite exists, not only potentially, but as a separate thing. It is only necessary to mention one of these.

208ª14–22

'It is futile to rely on our *thought* ⟨on the subject⟩; for in that case excess and defect would not be in the thing but in the thought. One might think that any one of us is many times bigger than he is and increase his size *ad infinitum*. But a man is not bigger than the size we are because someone thinks he is but because he *is*; the thought is a mere accident. Time and movement, and thought too, are infinite, but so that any part that is taken does not persist ⟨but passes away⟩. But magnitude is not infinite in virtue either of its ⟨possible⟩ diminution (*ad infinitum*) or in virtue of its increase in thought.'

The definition of 'number' (207^{b}7) as 'several ones' or 'a certain quantity of them' is only one of several definitions to the like effect in Aristotle. Others are: 'limited multitude',[1] 'multitude', or 'combination, of units', 'multitude of indivisibles',[2] 'multitude measurable by one',[3] and so on. The Pythagoreans defined a number as a 'collection of units' (μονάδων σύστημα) or a 'defined multitude'. The former of these two is said to be Thales' statement of the Egyptian view; the latter is also attributed to Eudoxus. Euclid[4] defines a number as 'a multitude composed of units'.

(g) *Place*

Phys. IV. 1. 208^{a}27–209^{a}30

'The physicist must have the like knowledge about Place as about the Infinite—namely, whether it exists or not, in what manner it exists, and what it is. Now, all persons conceive that things which exist exist somewhere (that which is not is nowhere; for where, pray, is the goat-stag or the sphinx?); and that form of movement which is most common and chiefest is change of place, what we call "locomotion".

'But the question what is place is beset with many difficulties; for, when viewed from the standpoint of all the different facts, it does not always present the same appearance. Moreover, we do not even find handed down by other thinkers any discussion of difficulties, or any contribution to a solution.

'That place exists is thought to be clear from the fact of mutual replacement. Where water now is, there, when the water has gone out as from a vessel, air is found once more; and at times some other body may occupy this same place; place, then is, thought to be different from all the bodies which come to be in it as they replace one another. For in the place where air now is there was water before; it is therefore clear that the place and the room into which and out of which they removed is something different from both.

'Again, the locomotion of the simple natural bodies, like fire, earth, and the like, show not only that place is something but that it also has some power or force. For each of these elements moves to its own place if not hindered, the one up, the other down. These are divisions or kinds of place—up and down and the rest of the six dimensions. These distinctions of up and down, right and left, are not only relative to us. To us they are not always the same—they depend on our position, according to the way we turn; hence the same thing may often be at different times right and left, up and

---

[1] πλῆθος τὸ πεπερασμένον, *Metaph.* 1020^{a}13.
[2] Ib. 1039^{a}12, 1053^{a}30, 1085^{b}22.   [3] Ib. 1057^{a}3.   [4] VII, Def. 2.

down, before and behind. But in nature each is distinct and separate. For 'up' is not anything you please but where fire and light objects are carried to; similarly down is not what you please but where things which have weight or are of the nature of earth are carried: this indicates that 'up' and 'down' differ not only in position but in potency or force. The evidence of mathematical objects confirms this: for, though they are not in place, nevertheless according to their position relatively to us they have a right and a left, being so called because of their position, though they do not possess these attributes by nature.

'Further, those who hold the theory of the void imply the existence of place; for the void must be place destitute of body.

'From these arguments we naturally conclude that place is something apart from bodies, and that every sensible body is in place. Hesiod, too, would seem to have been right when in his poem he made chaos first. Anyhow, he says: "first of all things chaos came to be, then, after it, broad-breasted earth", implying that there must first have been room for things, because he thought, like most people, that everything must be somewhere and in place. If such is its nature, the power of place must be marvellous, and must be prior to everything else. For that without which nothing else exists, whereas it can exist without the others, must necessarily be first; place is not annihilated when the things in it pass away.

'Not but what, even if it exists, it is difficult to say *what* it is and whether it is some sort of solid body [mass of body or bodily mass], or some other natural entity; we must first investigate its genus.

'Now it has three dimensions, length, breadth, and depth, by which every body is bounded. But place cannot *be* body; for if it were, there would be two bodies in the same place.

'Again, if there exists place and room for body, there must also be place and room for surface and all other limits of body; for the same argument will apply; where there were plane surfaces of water before, there will now be plane surfaces of air. Further we cannot make any distinction between a point and the place of the point, so that, if the place of a point is not different from the point, neither will the place of any of the other things be different from it, and place will not be something apart from each individual thing.

'What, then, in the world could we venture to suppose place to be? For its nature being such as we have described, it cannot be either an element or composed of elements, whether corporeal or incorporeal; for it has magnitude, but not body, and on the one hand the elements of sensible bodies are bodies, while on the other no magnitude can be made up out of objects of thought.

'Again, of what in existing things can we suppose place to be the

cause? None of the four causes can be present in it. It does not
serve (1) as matter for existent things (nothing can be constructed
out of it), or (2) as form and definition of things, or (3) as end; nor
(4) does it move existing things.

'Again, if place is itself one of existing things, where will it be?
Zeno's difficulty calls for some explanation. For, if everything that
exists is in place, it is clear that place also must have a place, and
so on *ad infinitum*.

'Further, just as all body is in place, so in all place there is body.
What then shall we say about things which grow? For it follows
from these premisses that their place must grow along with them, if
the place of each particular thing is neither less nor greater than it is.

'By this reasoning we are compelled to raise the whole question
of place, not only what it is, but whether it exists at all.'[1]

(h) Void and motion

Phys. IV. 8. 215^{a}14–22

'Again, as it is, things *thrown* continue to move, though that
which impelled them is no longer in contact with them, either
because of "mutual replacement" (ἀντιπερίστασις), as some say, or
because the air which has been thrust forward thrusts them with
a movement quicker than the motion by which the object thrown is
⟨naturally⟩ carried to its proper place. But in the void none of these
conditions can be present, nor will it be possible for anything to be
moved except in the way that a thing is carried as in a vehicle.
Further no one could give any reason why, having been set in
motion, it should stop anywhere: for why here rather than there?
Hence either it will remain at rest, or it must continue to move
ad infinitum unless something stronger impedes it.'

The question of things *thrown* will be dealt with later in connexion
with *Phys.* VIII. 10. 266^{b}28 ff., and *Mechanica*, 32–4. 858^{a}13 ff.

But attention should be drawn to the last sentence in the above
passage, because the statement in it constitutes a fair anticipation
of Newton's First Law of Motion. This is enunciated at the beginning
of the *Principia* as follows: 'Corpus omne perseverare in statu suo
quiescendi vel movendi uniformiter in directum, nisi quatenus illud
a viribus impressis cogitur statum suum mutare.' There is a sentence
in Plutarch, *De facie in orbe lunae*, c. 6, which has been noted as
containing a similar anticipation of Newton's First Law: 'For everything is borne along in its own natural direction unless this is changed

[1] *Editor's note*: The above is Sir Thomas Heath's translation of the passage;
he wrote no commentary on it.

by some other force.' Aristotle's statement seems to me rather more complete.

Phys. IV. 8. 215ᵃ24–ᵇ10

'Further, what we are maintaining is manifest from the following considerations. We see the same weight moving faster owing to two causes, (1) that there is a difference in the medium through which it moves—e.g. it may be water or earth or air—or (2) that, other conditions remaining the same, there is a difference in the moving body due to excess of weight or lightness.

'Now the medium through which a thing moves causes a difference in speed because it impedes the moving thing, most of all if it [the medium] is moving in the opposite direction but to a certain extent also when it is at rest; the resistance is greater if the medium is not easily divided, that is to say, is more dense.

'Thus A will move through B in the time C, and through D, a thinner medium, in the time E, and if the length of B is equal to D, the times will be in the proportion of ⟨the resistance of⟩ the impeding body.

'Let B be water and D air; then, in proportion as air is thinner and more incorporeal than water, so much faster will A move through D than through B. Let then the speed be to the speed in the same ratio as that in which air differs from water ⟨in thinness⟩. Then, if, for example, air ⟨D⟩ is twice as thin ⟨as water, B⟩, A will traverse B in twice the time it takes to traverse D—that is, the time C will be twice the time E.'

This passage is made more difficult to follow because Aristotle, in his casual way, speaks at one moment of the ratio of the *speeds* and at the next of the ratio of the *times* taken, at one moment of greater or less *density*, at another of greater or less *thinness*. His contention is, shortly, that the times taken are proportional to the (positive) densities, but the speeds are *reciprocally* proportional to the densities, i.e.

(time taken in B) : (time taken in D)
= (density of B) : (density of D) ;

but (speed in B) : (speed in D) = (density of D) : (density of B).

Passing to the case of the void compared with other media, Aristotle speaks in terms of density; the density of a void is of course *nil*.

Ib. 215ᵇ12–22

'But there is *no* ratio in which the void is exceeded ⟨in density⟩ by body, just as *nothing* has no ratio to a number. For 4 exceeds 3 by 1, and 2 by more ⟨than 1⟩, and 1 by still more than it exceeds

2 ; but when we come to *nothing* [zero] there is *no* ratio by which
4 exceeds it—for the number which exceeds must be divided into
⟨two, namely⟩ the excess and the number that is exceeded, so that
4 must be the sum of the excess and o—this is the reason, too, why
a line does not exceed a point (in any ratio), unless it is made up
of points! Similarly the void cannot bear any ratio to the full;
neither therefore can motion through the one bear a ratio to motion
through the other; but if the thing moves through the thinnest
medium such-and-such a distance in such-and-such a time, its
motion through the void would exceed in speed any ratio whatever.'

The language here is not without interest to the mathematician.
The comparison with the case of a point in relation to a line is
placed a little awkwardly. Its proper place would be after 'just as
nothing has no ratio to a number' (215^b13), but the long numerical
illustration intervenes ($^b13$–18).

Aristotle is clear, here and always, that a line cannot be made
up of points. A point being indivisible, no accumulation of points,
however far carried, can give us anything divisible, whereas a line
is a divisible magnitude. Point cannot be continuous with point.[1]
A point is like the *now* in time; *now* is indivisible and is not a part
of time; it is only the beginning or end, or a division, of time;
similarly a point may be an extremity, beginning, or division of
a line, but is not part of it or of magnitude.[2] It is only by motion
that a point can generate a line[3] and thus become the origin of
magnitude.

The fact that zero (o) cannot have any ratio to a number, or vice
versa, follows from the principle laid down by Euclid in V, Def. 4:
'Magnitudes are said to have a ratio to one another which are capable,
when multiplied, of exceeding one another; for no multiple of zero
can exceed 1 or any number.'

Ib. $^b22$–216^a11

'For let F[4] be a void equal in size to B and to D. Then, if A
traverses and moves through F in a certain time G, being less than
the time E, the void will have this ratio [$G : E$] to the full. But, in
the same length of time G, A traverses a part of D, say H. And of
course ⟨in the same time G⟩ it will pass through any medium F
differing in thinness ⟨or rarity⟩ from air in the ratio which the time
E bears to the time G. For, if the body F be thinner than D in the

---

[1] *De gen. et corr.* I. 2. 317^a11.

[2] Cf. *De caelo* III. 1. 300^a14; *Phys.* IV. 11. 220^a1–21, VI. 1. 231^b6 f.

[3] *De an.* I. 4. 409^a4.

[4] I use for Aristotle's letters *ΑΒΓΔΕΖΗΘ* the letters *ABCDEFGH* respectively.

same ratio by which E exceeds G, then A, assuming it to move, will traverse F in a time inversely proportional to the speed, i.e. in a time equal to G. If then there be *no* body in F, A will traverse F still more quickly. But it was in the time G that A was supposed to traverse F when void. But this is impossible. It is manifest then that, if there is any time during which A is carried through any part whatever of the void, this impossibility will result: it will be found to traverse some distance in an equal time whether it is full or empty; for there will always be *some* body which is to another body as one time is to another.

'In short, the cause of what results is clear, namely that there is always a ratio between a movement and a movement (for they take place in time, and any time has a ratio to any other time, if both are finite), but no ratio is possible between void and full.'

As will be seen from the translation, Aristotle's statement of the argument is somewhat confused. The letter D is used both for a medium of a certain size and for the distance traversed in it (215^b27); so with F (Z) denoting the void. At $^b25$ the 'ratio of the void to the full' means the ratio of the *density* of the void (*nil*) to that of D. At $^b27$ H (Θ) is brought in as the distance that would be traversed in D in the time G; H is not mentioned again; it is only introduced in order to show that the *distances* have a finite ratio to one another just as E, G have. At $^b30$ Aristotle denotes another medium intermediate in density between the void and D by the same letter F (Z) as he had used for the void at $^b23$. Lastly ($^b30$–216^a2), having up to that point spoken of times occupied, he suddenly introduces the ratio between the *speeds*, which are inversely as the times.

We may state the argument thus:

Suppose that A traverses in D a distance d in time E, but in F (the void) traverses the same distance d in time G ($< E$), the density of the void to that of D will then be in the ratio of G to E, 215^b25–6.

Moreover, in time G, A will traverse in the medium D some distance d' ($< d$), $^b27$.

Let us assume another medium F' of density which is to the density of D as G is to E. [Aristotle calls F' a medium differing in *rarity* from D in the ratio of E to G ($^b27$–30), which is the same thing.]

Now (since the *time* occupied in traversing a given distance is in direct proportion to the densities) A will traverse in the medium F' a distance d in a time which is to E as G is to E, that is to say, in the time G ($= 215^b30$–216^a2); and if there is no body whatever in F', the time will be still less, 216^a2.

But G was the time in which A was originally assumed to traverse the distance d in the void F; therefore A is found to traverse the same distance d in an equal time G whether the medium is full (F') or empty (the void F): which is impossible.

Phys. IV. 8. 216ª11–21

'In so far therefore as the media through which the motion takes place are different the result is as stated; but according as one body exceeds another, the effect is as follows. We observe that things which have a greater bias of weight or lightness, if conditions are in other respects the same, move more quickly over an equal distance, and that in the ratio which the magnitudes have to one another. Accordingly the same will be the case if they move through the void. But *this* is impossible; for what cause has the one to move faster than the other? In "full" media there *must* be difference of speed; the greater body by its strength divides the medium more quickly, for it divides it either by its shape or by the bias possessed by that which is moved or let go. ⟨In the void⟩ therefore all bodies will have the same speed; which is impossible.'

As Wicksteed remarks, 'It is tantalizing to find Aristotle actually arriving at the fact, familiar in modern laboratories, that a feather and a guinea, to take the classical example, will fall at the same pace through a vacuum, but treating it as a *reductio ad absurdum.*'

This is one of the passages which has been taken to justify the statement that 'Aristotle said that a weight of 10 lb., for example, falls ten times as fast as a weight of 1 lb.' Alternatively one might think of certain passages in the *De caelo* touching the speeds with which heavy things move towards the centre of the earth as the centre of the universe, and light things, like fire, away from the centre; especially as our present passage may refer to bodies not necessarily *falling*, but merely moving through a resisting medium, though it is true that the bodies are spoken of as having a greater or less *bias* due to weight or lightness.

It would be interesting to know from what definite passages Galilei concluded that Aristotle says that 'an iron ball of one hundred pounds falling from a height of one hundred cubits reaches the ground before a one-pound ball has fallen a single cubit',[1] to which Galilei adds: 'I say that they arrive at the same time' (*sc.* after falling the same distance, say 100 ft.). In the dialogue Salviati says:[2] 'I greatly doubt that Aristotle ever tested by experiment whether it be true that two stones, one weighing ten times as much as the other, if allowed to fall, at the same instant, from a height of, say, 100 cubits, would so differ in speed that, when the heavier

---

[1] *Dialogues concerning Two New Sciences*, tr. H. Crew and A. de Salvio, 1914, p. 64.　　　　　　　　　　　[2] Ib., p. 62.

had reached the ground, the other would not have fallen more than
ten cubits': to which Simplicio replies: 'His language would seem to
indicate that he had tried the experiment, because he says *"We
see the heavier"* . . .; now the word *see* shows that he had made the
experiment.' This seems to afford a clue; for the words in the Greek
text of our passage are (216ᵃ13) ὁρῶμεν γὰρ τὰ μείζω ῥοπὴν ἔχοντα
ἢ βάρους ἢ κουφότητος: *'we see that* those which have greater bias . . .'.
It looks as though these were the very words that Simplicio had
before him, though he translates as if τὰ μείζω should be taken
together as 'the greater (weights)'. It may therefore be true that
this was the specific passage on which Galilei relied, the more so
as in the preceding paragraphs he was referring to Aristotle's proof
that a vacuum does not exist, which comes just before our passage
(215ᵇ22–216ᵃ11).

(i) The 'now' in time and the point in space

Phys. IV. 10. 218ᵃ6–8

'The present instant, the "now", is not part of time; for a part
of a thing measures it, and the whole must be made up of the parts;
but time is not regarded as made up of "nows".'

Ib. IV. 11. 219ᵇ11–15

'The "now" marks the time in respect of "before" and "after".
The "now" is in one sense the same, in another sense not the same;
so far as it is in a succession ⟨of times⟩ it is different (this constitutes
the essential nature of the "now"), but so far as it is a subject it
is the same' (reading ὁρίζει in ᵇ12 and τὸ νῦν ⟨εἶναι⟩ in ᵇ14).

Ib. 220ᵃ4–13, 18–21

'Time, then, is continuous in virtue of the "now", and is divided
at the "now"; this relation follows that between a movement and
the moving body [not, Aristotle explains, *qua* being any particular
moving body but *qua* moving, ᵃ6–9], for the latter ⟨at any moment⟩
marks the division between the earlier and the later movement.
This too in a manner corresponds to the *point*, for it is the point
which connects length and also delimits it, since it is the beginning
of one length and the end of another. But when we take it in this
way, using the one point as two, we necessarily pause, if the same
point is to be the beginning of one length and the end of another.
. . . It is manifest that the "now" is no part of time, nor is a division of
a motion part of the motion any more than points are parts of a line:
it is the two *lines* [connected by the dividing point] that are parts
of one line.'

The gist of Aristotle's comparison of the 'now' and the point is this. The point on a straight line *connects* the two parts of it, while it *divides* the line into the two parts. It is also the limit of a straight line, the end of one line and the beginning of another, or the beginning and end of the same line. Similarly the 'now' is a connexion and a division in time. It divides the time that is past from the time that is coming and connects the two. But, according to Aristotle, there is this difference between the two cases. The point is the end of one line and the beginning of another, and therefore, in so regarding it, we treat it as two. There is no difficulty in this because the point has position; it stays where it is; it separates the two parts of a straight line and (as Alexander, quoted by Simplicius, says) it actually becomes two if you separate the two parts, for it goes with each. On the other hand, you cannot treat the 'now' as two, or 'take it twice', in the words of Themistius and Simplicius. The 'now' and the moving body would, if this were possible, have to stand still for the purpose, and this is impossible because the movement is continuous; the 'now' is 'continually' changing; it cannot wait for the next 'now' (Philoponus). You can only have two 'nows' bounding a certain definite time which has elapsed between them, just as the extremities of one finite straight line are points. The 'now' divides time, it is true, but only potentially, not actually, says Alexander, in the way that a point, by having position and remaining where it is, *shows* (δεικνύναι) the parts of the straight line. Alexander explains the statement that the 'now' divides a time potentially and not actually as meaning that it divides it *in our thought* (τῷ ἐπινοεῖσθαι); for, in consequence of the (ceaseless) flow of time, the parts of the time cannot be shown as subsisting (ὑπομένοντα) separately from one another.

(*j*) *Some definitions: 'together', 'in contact', 'successive', 'contiguous', 'continuous'*

Ib. V. 3. 226ᵇ21–2

'I say that things are "together" in place when their immediate or primary place is one.'

Ib. ᵇ23

'Things are "in contact", or "touching", when their extremities are together.'

Ib. ᵇ34–227ᵃ7

'I call "successive" that which, coming after the beginning, and having been marked off either in position or in form or in some other respect, has nothing of the same class between it and that to which it is successive. Examples are a line or lines in succession to a line, a unit or units to a unit, or a house to a house. There is nothing to prevent something of a *different* kind coming between. What is successive is successive to something and is something posterior to it; thus one is not successive to two, nor the first day of the month to the second day, but the other way about.

'I call "contiguous" anything which, being successive to something, also touches it.'

Phys. V. 3. 227ᵃ10–32

'The "continuous" is in the class of "contiguous", but I apply the term "continuous" when the extremities of each of two things in which they touch become one and the same, and the two things are held together, as the name implies; and this is not possible if the extremities are two. This being the definition, it is manifest that continuity attaches to things which naturally become one in virtue of their being joined together. And, whatever be the way in which what holds them together is one, the whole will be one in the same way, whether the connexion is by a peg, or by glue, or by attachment, or by growing together.

'It is manifest that the successive comes first in order; for that which touches must be successive, but not everything that is successive is in contact; hence the successive is found in things which are prior in notion, e.g. in numbers, while contact is not. And if a thing is continuous, there must be contact, but if there is contact, this is not enough to secure continuity; for the extremities, though they may be together, are not necessarily one, but, if they are one, they must be together. Hence growing together is the last to come into being; for the extremities must necessarily touch if they are to grow together. Things which touch do not all grow together, while things which are not in contact clearly cannot grow together [i.e. become organically one]. Hence if a point and a unit have, as some say, a separate existence, a unit and a point cannot be the same thing; for touching is characteristic of the one (points), and succession of the other ⟨units⟩. In the one case they can have something between them—every straight line is between points—in the other they cannot; there is nothing between one and two.'

Aristotle has defined, in IV. 2. 209ᵃ31 f., what he means by the immediate or primary place of a thing—'you are in the "place" which contains nothing but you'. Simplicius quotes Alexander as saying that one place is that which is not divided but continuous, by virtue of the things which are said to be together in place being continuous, as if they were parts of a continuous body, for no two or more bodies can be in a place *numerically* one, when they are said

to be together, in the sense of pervading one another.[1] Simplicius
replies that to restrict things 'together in place' to continuous things
cannot be correct, because things which are 'together' are, according
to Aristotle, more separate from one another than things which
touch (ἁπτόμενα), and these again are more separate than those
which are continuous (συνεχῆ). The primary place of a thing being
that which immediately (προσεχῶς) contains it, Simplicius suggests
that we may call it the first undivided place which, being one and
the same, does not contain other solid bodies (though it may contain
air) besides the things in question, which, not being continuous or
even in contact with one another, may still properly be said to
be 'together'. Eudemus, he says, considered *mixtures* to be the best
example of this.

According to Simplicius, Alexander, in accordance with the strict
view he took of 'together' (ἅμα), said that if things are to *touch*, their
extremities, which are 'together', must fit on to one another
(ἐφαρμόζειν) in the way that the surfaces of two bodies may do so.
Simplicius replies that it is sufficient for 'contact' that the surfaces
of two bodies should be connected (συνῆφθαι) by bringing the two
bodies together so that, *where they meet*, the surfaces are in one place,
there being no *depth* separating them (διὰ τὸ ἀβαθές).

It is worthy of note that, with Euclid and the Greek geometers
generally, ἅπτεσθαι usually means to *meet*, not necessarily to *touch*
as a tangent touches a curve, the word for which is almost always
ἐφάπτεσθαι (or ἐπιψαύειν); it is only occasionally that ἅπτεσθαι is
used of a tangent. Two other meanings of ἅπτεσθαι are, however,
common in Greek mathematics. ἅπτεσθαι is used of a point *lying
on* a straight line; Aristotle has ἐφάπτεσθαι in this sense, *Meteor.*
III. 5. 376[a]5: 'the point M will lie on a given (circular) circumference' (δεδομένης περιφερείας ἐφάψεται τὸ M), i.e. the locus of M is
a certain circle. In Eucl. IV, Defs. 1, 3, the angles of a rectilinear
figure inscribed in another, or in a circle, are said to lie on (ἅπτεσθαι)
the sides, or the circumference, of the circumscribing figure. More
rarely ἅπτεσθαι is used in the inverse sense of *passing through* a point,
Eucl. IV, Defs. 2, 6; again, Aristotle uses ἐφάπτεσθαι in this sense,
Meteor. III. 5. 376[b]9: 'a certain circle will pass through all the angles'
(ἁπασῶν ἐφάψεται τῶν γωνιῶν).

Motion which is one and continuous: 'uniform' motion

Ib. 4. 228[b]1–5

'Hence motion which is absolutely continuous and one must be
(*a*) the same in species throughout; (*b*) it must be the motion of one
thing; (*c*) it must be in one time. The time must be one in order

[1] Cf. *Phys.* IV. 6. 213[b]20.

that there may be no interval of immobility, for, when there is a break in the time, there must be rest. And if there is an intervening period of rest, the motion is not one but several motions.'

Phys. V. 4. 228ᵇ15–25

'Again, a uniform motion is one in a different sense from those mentioned. For in a sense a motion which is not uniform is thought not to be one, this term being more appropriate to the uniform motion, as it is, say, to a straight line, since a non-uniform motion is divisible (into different parts). But the difference between uniform and non-uniform motions seems to be one of degree. Every motion has the character of being uniform or not; for change may proceed uniformly, and locomotion may take place on a uniform course, e.g. a circle or a straight line, and similarly with growth and decay. Non-uniformity or irregularity of motion sometimes means a difference in the path taken; for it is impossible that motion should be uniform if the magnitude it traverses is not uniform, as, for example, motion on a broken line or motion in a spiral, or any other magnitude which is not such that any part of it whatever will fit on any other part whatever.'

By the 'spiral' Aristotle probably means a spiral that converges to a centre, e.g. the convolution of a snail-shell or the convolutions in the ear.[1] Other 'spirals' mentioned by Aristotle are: (1) the 'spirals of the heaven'[2] which are no doubt the spirals into which, according to Plato, the independent circles described by the planets are 'twisted by the circle of the same';[3] (2) the word is naturally used to describe the convolutions in the intestines of animals.[4] (3) There is another 'spiral' (of a sort) in the Aristotelian writings, that in *Problems*,[5] where it is asked: 'Why, when a circular disk is thrown forward, does it first describe a straight line and then, as it comes to rest, a spiral, until it falls?' 'Spiral' obviously has no strict sense here; the writer has in mind the wobbling of the disk as it comes near to falling.

There is one kind of spiral (the cylindrical helix) which is 'uniform' in the strict sense, namely, such that any portion of it will fit on any other portion whatever, a property proved by Apollonius of Perga (fl. 200 B.C.).

(k) *Motion divisible* ad infinitum

Ib. VI. 1. 231ᵃ21–232ᵃ22

'If "continuous", "touching", and "successive" have the meanings distinguished above (things being "continuous" the extremities of

---

[1] Cf. *De an.* II. 8. 420ᵃ13. [2] *Metaph. A.* 2. 998ᵃ5. [3] *Timaeus* 39 A.
[4] *De part. an.* III. 14. 675ᵇ20, and *De gen. an.* I. 4. 717ᵃ28. [5] XVI. 11. 915ᵃ38.

which are one, "touching" or "in contact" when their extremities are "together", and "successive" when they have nothing of the same kind between them), it is impossible that anything continuous should be made up of indivisibles, e.g. a line cannot be made up of points, seeing that a line is a continuous thing, and a point is indivisible. For (1) the extremities of points are not one—an indivisible has not any extremity as distinct from any other part— nor (2) are the extremities together, for that which has no parts has no extremity, since an extremity must be distinct from that of which it is the extremity.

'Further, if anything continuous is made up of points, the points must either be continuous or must touch one another, and the same argument applies to all indivisibles. Now (1) they cannot be continuous for the reason aforesaid. But (2) in all cases of touching the contact must be that of whole with whole, or of part with part, or of part with whole. And since the indivisible has no parts, the contact must be that of whole with whole. But if they touch as whole with whole, they cannot be continuous, since the continuous has parts different from one another, and is divided into parts different in this way, namely, separated in place.

'Neither again can a point be "successive" to a point or a "now" to a "now" in such a way as to make up a length or a time. For things are successive only when they have nothing of the same kind between them, and what is between points is always a line, and what is between "nows" is a certain time.

'Again, assuming that a line and a time can be divided into the parts of which they are respectively made up, they could be divided into indivisibles. But we saw that nothing that is continuous is divisible into elements that have no parts. And the points and the "nows" cannot have anything of a different kind between them. If they have, it is clear that it will be either divisible or indivisible, and, if divisible, divisible into parts either indivisible or divisible *ad infinitum*; and it is the last-named class of thing that is continuous.

'It is manifest, too, that everything continuous is divisible into parts that are divisible *ad infinitum*, for if the continuous were divided into indivisibles, we should have an indivisible touching an indivisible since the extremities of continuous things are one and in contact. The same argument applies to magnitude, time, and motion; either they are all made up of indivisibles and are divisible into indivisibles, or none of them is.

'This is clear from the following considerations. If a magnitude is made up of indivisibles, then a motion over that magnitude will also be made up of indivisible motions. Thus, if *ABC* is made up of the indivisible parts A, B, C, the motion DEF effected by Z over the distance ABC has each of its parts $\langle D, E, F \rangle$ indivisible. Seeing then that, when motion is present, there must be something that is being moved, and when something is being moved motion must be present, the "being moved" must also be made up of indivisibles. Now Z moved the distance A, being moved with the motion D, the distance B with the motion E, and C with the motion F. But a thing which is being moved from one place to another cannot at the same time both be moving and *have completed* its motion to the place to which it was moving when it was moving; thus, for example, if a man is walking to Thebes, he cannot at the same time be walking to Thebes and have *finished* his walk to Thebes. But Z was being moved over the distance A, which has no parts, in so far as the motion D was present; hence if Z completed the passage through *after* it was in process of passing through, the motion must be divisible; for while it was passing through it was neither at rest nor in the position of having passed through, but was at an intermediate stage. If at the same moment it is passing through and *has* passed through, the walking man too while walking will have *finished* his walk and will be at his goal, that is to say, in the position of *having* moved to the place whither he was moving. If now a thing is being moved over the whole ABC, and the motion by which it is moved consists of the three parts D, E, F, while over the section A which has no parts it is not moving at all but has *completed* its motion, then the motion $\langle DEF \rangle$ will consist, not of $\langle$continuing$\rangle$ motions, but of completed motions [or arrivals], that is to say, will result from something *having* moved without moving; for on our assumption Z has passed over A without ever being in process of passing. Hence it will be possible to have completed a walk without walking; for the walker has walked such-and-such a distance without walking the distance. Seeing then that everything must be either at rest or in motion, and Z is at rest on each of the sections A, B, C, it will follow that you can have something which is continuously at rest and also in motion at the same time. For Z was in motion over the whole ABC, but was at rest on any one of the parts of it and consequently on the whole of it. Moreover, if the indivisible parts D, E, F are motions, it will be possible, while motion is present in a thing, that it should be, not in motion but at rest; and, on the other hand, if the parts are not motions, it is possible for motion to be made up of things other than motions.

'It will follow too that time will, precisely in the same way as length and motion, be indivisible or be composed of "nows" which are indivisible. For if every distance[1] is divisible, and if a thing

---

[1] *Note.* I have taken γραμμή (distance) to be the word understood with πᾶσα

moving at the same speed traverses a lesser distance in a lesser time, the time will also be divisible; and conversely, if the time in which a thing moves over *A* is divisible, *A* too will be divisible.'

In order to prove that a line cannot be *made up* of points (or a time of 'nows'), Aristotle uses the method of exhausting the possibilities; he proves of points that they cannot be (1) 'continuous' or (2) 'in contact' or even (3) 'successive'. One proof suffices for (1) and (2). Points cannot be either, because points cannot have extremities: extremities must necessarily be different from the things of which they are the extremities; the point, if it had extremities, would have to have in it something apart from the extremities, i.e. it would have to have parts: but a point has no parts. (3) Points could only be successive if they had nothing of the same kind between them. They may, however, have a line between them, and it is (tacitly) implied that lines and points *are* things of the same kind (this is clear because Aristotle proceeds at 231^{b}12 to say that neither can points have anything *different* in kind between them). But, on a line, you can have any number of points; therefore there will be any number of points between the points which are supposed to be successive. Therefore the points cannot be 'successive'. This is brought out by the paraphrase of Themistius, who observes that on any line connecting the two points you can take another point; hence the two points will not be successive.

The argument in 231^{b}21–232^{a}17 about the motion *DEF* (in three parts) over *ABC* consisting of three parts *A*, *B*, *C* each of which is indivisible, is almost exactly parallel to Zeno's argument about the Arrow, to which we shall come later (239^{b}5–7). If, said Zeno, everything is at rest when it occupies a space equal to itself, while the object moved occupies at an instant a space equal to itself, the moving arrow is unmoved. The argument is this. It is impossible that the arrow can move in the instant, supposed indivisible, for, if it changed its position, the instant would at once be divided. Now the moving body is, in the instant, either at rest or in motion; but as it is not in motion it must be at rest; hence, as by hypothesis time is composed of nothing but instants, the moving object is always at rest. Aristotle puts the matter thus. If as regards the motion over *A* supposed indivisible (the motion denoted by *D*), you can distinguish between the stages at which *Z was moving* over *A* and *had moved* over *A* respectively, the motion over *A* is thereby at

in 232^{a}20 in preference to κίνησις, because this is more consistent with the words following in ^{a}21, δίεισιν ἔλαττον, which must mean traverses a less *distance*. Prof. Cornford's conjecture πᾶσ' ἡ *A* seems hardly appropriate when the rest of the sentence to ὁ χρόνος is in general terms, and there would be no particular point in saying, 'if *A* is divisible *throughout*'.

once divided, and so is the distance A itself, which is contrary to the hypothesis. Hence the motion DEF consists of three *arrivals* at the ends of A, B, C respectively without any antecedent passing *over* any one of them. Since, then, there was rest on each section, there must have been rest over the whole three sections taken together. If we insist that motion represented by DEF has taken place in three parts, the motion must be made up of parts which are not motions but rests. According to Themistius Epicurus firmly maintained that Z does move over the whole ABC but, on each of the indivisible sections A, B, C, Z *does not* move but *has moved*.

Thus, while the arguments of Zeno and Aristotle are practically the same, they draw different conclusions, Zeno that motion is impossible, Aristotle only that lines and times are not made up of indivisibles but are divisible *ad infinitum*.

Phys. VI. 2. 232ª23–b20

'Since every magnitude is divisible into magnitudes (for it has been proved that it is impossible for anything continuous to be made up of indivisibles, and all magnitude is continuous), it follows that the quicker thing must move a greater distance in an equal time and in a lesser time an equal distance, and even a greater distance, in accordance with the definition of "quicker" given by some thinkers.

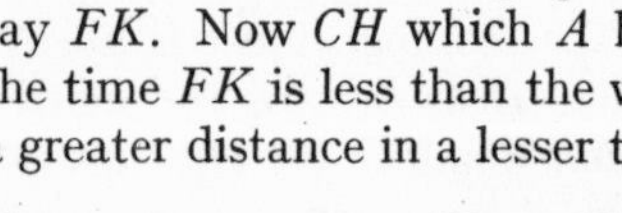

'Let A be quicker than B. Then, since that is quicker which changes earlier, if in the time FG, say, A has changed from C to D, B will not have reached D in that time but will be short of it, so that the quicker will in an equal time traverse a greater distance. But it will also traverse a greater distance in less time. For, in the time which A has taken to reach D, suppose B, the slower, to have reached E. Then, since A has reached D in the whole time FG, it will have reached H [a point between E and D] in a lesser time, say FK. Now CH which A has traversed is greater than CE, and the time FK is less than the whole time FG, so that A will traverse a greater distance in a lesser time. And from this it is also manifest that the quicker will traverse an *equal* distance in less time. For, since A traverses a greater distance in less time than the slower ⟨B⟩, while, taken by itself, it takes more time to traverse a greater than to traverse a lesser distance (LM, say, being the greater distance and LN

FIG. 24

FIG. 25

the lesser), the time *PR* in which it traverses *LM* will be greater than the time *PS* in which it traverses *LN*. Hence, if the time *PR* is less than the time *X* in which the slower ⟨*B*⟩ traverses *LN*, *PS* will also be less than *X*; for *PS* is less than *PR*, and that which is less than something which is less than a thing is also less than the thing ⟨itself⟩. Hence the quicker will traverse an equal distance in less time. Further, seeing that any one thing must move in an equal time or in less or more time ⟨in comparison with another⟩, while that which takes more time is slower, that which takes an equal time is of equal speed, and the quicker is neither of equal speed nor slower, it follows that the movement of the quicker cannot take an equal time or more time. It remains that it must take less time, whence it follows that the quicker traverses an equal distance in less time.'

Aristotle has made the argument in 232ᵃ23–ᵇ20 unnecessarily complicated by referring to two pairs of lines, with different lettering, when one would have been sufficient. Simplicius notes this, observing that he can only suppose that Aristotle wished to give the pupil or reader practice in following mathematical proofs!

The first part of the explanation is quite simple. If, in the time *FG*, *A* the quicker moves a distance *CD*, *B* the slower will in the same time move a lesser distance, say *CE*.

Now, since *E*, *D* are distinct points we can take a point, say *H*, between them so that *CH*>*CE*. But if *A* moves over *CD* in a time *FG* it will move over *CH* (<*CD*) in a lesser time *FK* determined by the proportion

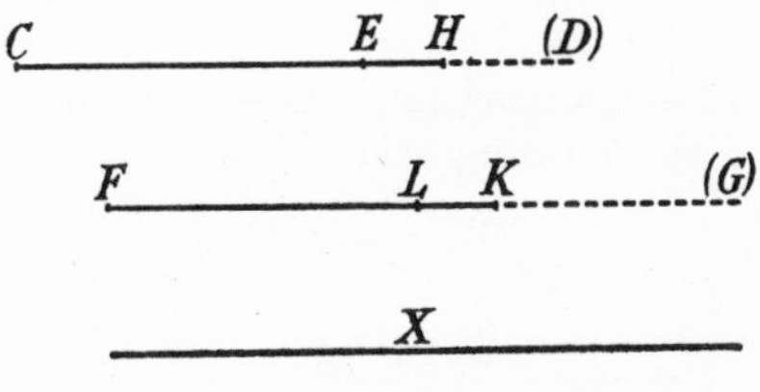

FIG. 26

$$CD : CH = FG : FK,$$

since in uniform motion the distances traversed are proportional to the times taken.

Hence, while obviously a more quickly moving object will traverse the same distance in less time than a slower, it may also describe a *greater* distance in less time.

In order to show the relation of the second part of the explanation to the first, we will use the same diagram as for the first part, with the necessary additions. It will be observed that *LNM* and *PR* respectively in Aristotle's second diagram correspond (not to *CED* and *FG* respectively, but) to *CEH* and *FK* respectively, no point corresponding to *D* appears, and instead of *FG* we have a separate line *X* (according to the better reading).

We have proved that A traverses the line CH in the time FK (less than the original FG).

Therefore A will traverse CE ($<CH$) in a time FL less than FK.

But FK is less than the original FG (now X), the time in which B traversed CE. Therefore *a fortiori* $FL<X$, or A describes an *equal* distance in less time than B does.

Instead of all this, it would have been sufficient to add to the first part of the explanation something to this effect: 'Since we have shown that A may traverse a greater distance in less time than it takes B to traverse a lesser distance, it follows, *a fortiori*, that A will traverse an equal distance in less time than B does.'

As if the proofs by means of the diagrams were not sufficient, Aristotle adds another proof by exclusion (232^b14-20).

Much neater and more happily expressed is his proof ($232^b20-233^a21$) that, if you have a series of lengths diminishing in a constant ratio, you can find a series of times diminishing in the same ratio, from which it follows that, as magnitude is divisible *ad infinitum*, so in precisely the same way is time. As Aristotle observes, you pass from the slower moving object to the faster in order to divide the time, and from the faster to the slower to divide the length, and you do the two things alternately.

Suppose that A is the quicker body, B the slower.

Suppose that B, the slower, traverses the distance CD in the time FG.

Then (passing to A) A will traverse CD in the shorter time FH.

Then (passing to B) B will, in the time FH, traverse a distance CK less than CD.

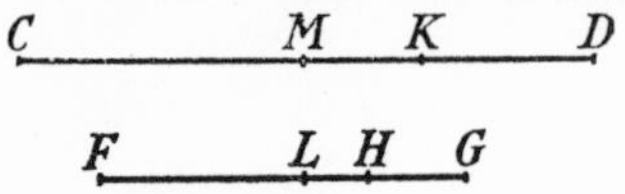

FIG. 27

Next (passing to A again) A will traverse CK in the still lesser time FL.

And so on. As Aristotle says (233^a7), 'the quicker divides the time and the slower the length'. The length and the time are both continually divided in the same ratio (that of the speeds).

Phys. VI. 2. 233^a13-31

'Again, it is manifest from the argument used in ordinary life that, if time is continuous, magnitude is continuous also, since a moving body traverses half a given distance in half of the time, and generally a lesser distance in a lesser time; for we shall have the same divisions of the time and the magnitude respectively. And if either of them is infinite, so will the other be, and the one is so in the same manner as the other; thus, if time is infinite in respect of its extremities [i.e. extends *ad infinitum* in both directions] length is also infinite in respect of its extremities; if time is infinite by way of division, length is infinite by way of division; and if time is infinite in both ways, so is magnitude.

'Hence it is that Zeno's argument makes a false assumption when it asserts that you cannot traverse an infinite number of things, or come in contact with an infinite number of things one by one, in a finite time. For there are two senses in which both length and time, and generally anything continuous, are called infinite; infinite may mean either (1) infinite by way of division or (2) infinite in respect of extremities. Now it is not possible to come in contact with things which are infinite in respect of quantity in a finite time; but it is possible to come in contact with things infinite by way of division; for the time itself is infinite in this sense. And so it turns out that the infinite is really traversed in an infinite, not a finite, time, and the contacts with the infinite things are made ⟨one by one⟩ by points of time ⟨or "nows"⟩ which are infinite, not finite, in number.'

Zeno's paradoxes are more fully dealt with in VI, c. 9, where they are all taken together. Here it is sufficient to note that the present criticism of Zeno undoubtedly implies that Zeno did not regard time as divisible *ad infinitum* like space, and no doubt this would be the idea of the 'man in the street'. But Zeno made no such mistake, he knew better; so did Aristotle himself, as he shows later,[1] where he admits that his answers to Zeno in Book VI are arguments *ad hominem* only and do not go to the root of the matter.

Aristotle goes on (233^a34 ff.) to prove that the time taken to traverse a finite distance cannot be infinite, using a diagram. Suppose, he says, that BA is a finite magnitude and C is an infinite time. Let some finite portion of the time be taken, as CD. Then, in the time CD, the moving object will have traversed part of BA, say BE. If BE be now taken as a measure and used to measure successive lengths along BA, it will, says Aristotle, 'either measure AB exactly or will leave a deficiency or an excess, it does not matter which' (233^b2-4). By this he means that, if the multiple of BE which is nearest to the total length of BA does not terminate at A itself, it will terminate either a little short of A (as at G) or a little beyond A (as at H), but so that the length AG or AH is less than BE. Taking the case where BA is an exact multiple of BE, Aristotle observes that, if each of the equal sections, BE, EF, etc., is traversed in the same finite time CD, it follows that the total time taken to

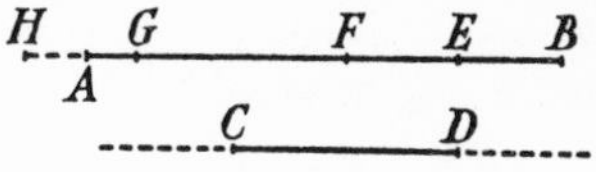

FIG. 28

[1] vi. 8. 263^a11-18.

traverse BA will be the same multiple of CD that BA is of BE, hence the total time must be finite, not infinite: Q.E.D. If he had thought it necessary, he would have added, as regards the two other cases, that the excess or defect by which the nearest multiple of BE differs from BA would be traversed in a time less than CD, so that, whether this has to be added or subtracted, the total time taken to traverse BA will still be finite.

To clinch the argument Aristotle says that we must exclude the hypothesis that the moving object takes an infinite time to traverse BE, the part of AB. That this is impossible is 'manifest if a time be taken which is limited in one direction; for if a part of the length is traversed in less time ⟨than the whole⟩, that time must necessarily be finite, one extremity of it anyhow being given'.

Simplicius raises a question here: 'If Aristotle assumes as obvious that the part is traversed in less time than the whole, and that what is less than the infinite must be finite, what more was necessary to establish that BE is traversed in a finite time, unless indeed ⟨it were implied⟩ that what is infinite in one direction only is less than what is infinite in both directions, though the former is itself infinite? Why then did he assume his infinite time to be infinite in one direction only?'[1] The answer is no doubt that Aristotle is not here concerned to compare two infinites, but that, just as the length traversed must be measured from a definite point (B), and the measure BE also, so must the finite time taken out of the infinite time also be measured from some point of time (C).

Aristotle adds that the same proof will show that neither can an infinite length be traversed in a finite time ($233^{b}14$–15).

The fact is of course that, if a moving object took an infinite time to traverse a finite length, its speed would have to be less than any assignable speed, which is impossible; in the other case the speed would have to exceed any assignable speed.

Aristotle continues as follows ($233^{b}15$): 'It is thus manifest from what has been said that no line, no plane, nor generally anything that is continuous, can be indivisible. This is so not only for the reason stated but also because on the contrary assumption it will be found that the indivisible is divided.'

This he shows with the help of a diagram. Let us assume two moving bodies, a quicker and a slower, and suppose that the former traverses $1\frac{1}{2}$ times the distance traversed by the latter in the same time, i.e. is $1\frac{1}{2}$ times quicker. 'Suppose that the quicker travels $1\frac{1}{2}$ times faster in the same time ⟨as is occupied by the slower⟩, and let the magnitudes be divided, that traversed by the quicker into the three ⟨equal⟩ indivisible parts AB, BC, CD, and that traversed

---

[1] Simpl. 951. 3–8.

by the slower into the two ⟨indivisible parts⟩ *EF*, *FG*. Then the time taken will also be divided into three indivisible parts, since an equal ⟨distance⟩ is traversed in an equal time. Let the time be divided into the parts *KL*, *LM*, *MN* accordingly.

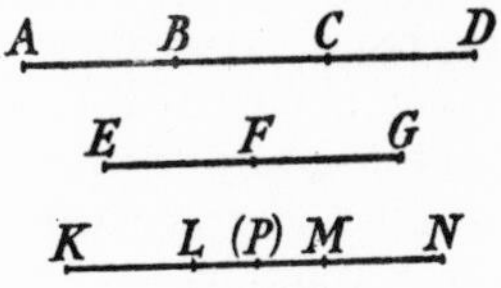

'Again, since the slower body has traversed *EFG*, the time also will be divided into two equal parts. Therefore the ⟨supposed⟩ indivisible will be divided, and that which has no parts will be

FIG. 29

traversed, not in an indivisible time, but in a greater time. It is manifest therefore that nothing continuous is without parts, i.e. indivisible.'

That is to say, since, in the time *KN*, the slower moving object traverses *EG*, divided into two equal parts at *F*, one of the parts of *EG*, say *EF*, must be traversed in half the time *KN*. Therefore *KN* must be bisected at a point *P*. And *P* must be at the middle point of *LM*, so that the supposedly indivisible *LM* is divided.

(*l*) *Zeno's arguments against motion*

I agree with Cornford that the first paragraph of c. 9 ought to have come at the end of c. 8, with which it is naturally connected, and the last sentences of which throw much light on Aristotle's argument in the first paragraph of c. 9.

Aristotle has explained in c. 8 that there is no '*first* period' of time during which a thing can be said to be in motion. If you assumed such a period, you could, since time is divisible *ad infinitum*, always take a smaller part of it instead, and the process would never end. Similarly for a state of rest. If we say that a thing is at rest, we mean that it is at a given instant where it was before (νῦν καὶ πρότερον); we do not judge by reference to one instant of time, but by reference to two instants at least; there can be no (minimum) indivisible period when a thing was first at rest (239ª10–17).

Phys. VI. 8. 239ª27–ᵇ4

'We say that a thing is at rest when it is true to say of it that, at one instant ⟨"now"⟩ after another, both the thing and its parts are in the same place. If this is being at rest, then a thing which is changing cannot as a whole, in the time primarily taken by the change, be ⟨exactly⟩ over against a particular thing, for in that case it would have to be true to say that in one part of the time after another both itself and its parts are in one place. If this is not so, and the thing only satisfies the condition at one instant during the time, it will not be over against something for any time at all. At any particular instant ⟨"now"⟩ it is over against something stationary, but it is not at rest—indeed at any *instant* there can be neither motion nor rest—it is only true to say that at the instant it is not in motion, and *is* over against something; it cannot be over against an object at rest during any time whatever; if it were, the moving object would have to be at rest.'

Phys. VI. 9. 239ᵇ5–9

'Zeno's argument is fallacious. If, he says, everything is at rest when it is over against that which is equal ⟨to itself⟩, and what is in motion is at a given instant ⟨over against that which is equal (to itself)⟩, then the flying arrow must be unmoved. This, however, is false; for time is not made up of individual instants ⟨"nows"⟩ any more than any other magnitude is made up of indivisibles ⟨points⟩.'

In the above I have adopted the suggestions made by Zeller, who omitted ἢ κινεῖται after πᾶν in 239ᵇ6 and proposed to insert κατὰ τὸ ἴσον after ἐν τῷ νῦν in ᵇ7. The pros and cons for the different readings suggested are fully discussed by H. D. P. Lee.[1] It is only necessary to add that the alternative ἢ κινεῖται has actually just been excluded by the last paragraph of c. 8, which has shown that, if a moving object is exactly over against a stationary object for any time at all (as distinct from an instant of time, which is only a limit or division of time) it is not in motion but at rest. There was, therefore, no need to mention the alternative ἢ κινεῖται again here. If, however, it *is* mentioned, there is nothing for it but to destroy it again, as is done by Diels and Lee, by reading εἰ γὰρ ἀεί, φησι, ἠρεμεῖ πᾶν ἢ κινεῖται, ⟨οὐδὲν δὲ κινεῖται⟩ ὅταν ᾖ κατὰ τὸ ἴσον. It is therefore best to omit ἢ κινεῖται. In any case it is necessary either to insert or to *understand* κατὰ τὸ ἴσον after ἐν τῷ νῦν, for this is the necessary meaning of ἔστι δ' ἀεὶ τὸ φερόμενον ἐν τῷ νῦν. I do not think it can be rendered, as Cornford suggests, by 'at every moment the moving thing is occupying *the moment (of the time occupied by the whole movement) which corresponds to* the space equal to its own dimensions'.

It is only necessary to add that Zeno's supposed argument rests on the tacit assumption that time is made up of instants, points of time, or 'nows'. Aristotle answers this in the passage above, where he denies that time is made up of indivisible 'nows' (239ᵇ8–9); he recurs to this in c. 9. 239ᵇ31–3.

---

[1] *Zeno of Elea*, pp. 78–83.

Ib. 9–33

'The arguments of Zeno which give trouble to those who try to dispose of them are four in number.

'The first is that which asserts that there is no motion because the moving object must arrive at the half-way point before it reaches the end. This we have dealt with in our earlier discussion.'[1]

'The second is the so-called "Achilles". This is to the effect that the slowest in a race will never be overtaken by the quickest because the pursuer must first arrive at the point from which the pursued started, so that the slower must always be some distance ahead. This is the same argument as that of the Dichotomy, only differing from it in that the divisions of the distance added ⟨from time to time⟩ are not into halves. The result that the slower is not overtaken follows from the argument as stated, and rests on the same ground as the Dichotomy, for in both cases it is a division of the distance in a certain way which causes the failure to arrive at the end; but in the case of the "Achilles" there is the added dramatic effect of the statement that not even the swiftest runner can succeed in his pursuit of the slowest; the solution must be the same in both cases. In fact the claim that that which is ahead cannot be overtaken is false; it is true that when it is ahead it is not overtaken, but it *is* overtaken all the same if you admit that a certain finite distance is in fact traversed ⟨by a moving object, however slow⟩.

'These are the first two of Zeno's arguments.

'The third is that just mentioned (b5–9) to the effect that the arrow while in flight is at rest. This result is consequent on the assumption that time is composed of instants ⟨"nows"⟩; for, if this be not granted, the conclusion will not follow.'

A summary account of the four paradoxes, the questions to which they give rise, and the latest attempts to deal with them on the basis of new theories of the infinite or otherwise, is given by Ross in his Introduction.[2] This account seems to me so admirable, and the writer's own judgements so sound, that it would be superfluous to add anything thereto. I shall therefore confine myself to a few points of detail, chiefly mathematical.

Aristotle saw clearly that the first two arguments, the Dichotomy and the Achilles, really come to the same thing so far as the summation of the series is concerned, the only difference being in the ratio of the successive subdivisions in the two cases. While I agree with Ross that one might be misled by the words προσλαμβανόμενον μέγεθος in 239b19–20, applied to both cases, into drawing the same

---

[1] The reference here is to c. 2. 233a13–31, as to which see pp. 130–3, above.

[2] pp. 71–85.

figure to represent the two cases, I am clear that we should not do so, because the point is that in the Achilles the series is arranged in the descending order of magnitude but in the case of the Dichotomy the same kind of series has to be put in the inverse order beginning from the smallest (if there is one). The argument is that before you reach the end of the whole distance you must first traverse its half. The implication is clear that, again, before you traverse *that* half (not the remaining half), you must have traversed half of *that*, and so on for ever. The two cases require different diagrams as

The Achilles A _____ C DE... _____ B

The Dichotomy A ...E D C B

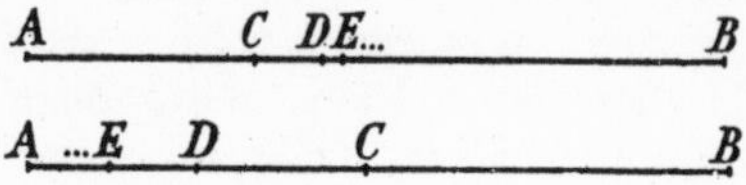

FIG. 30

shown. The whole point in distinguishing them as Zeno did is that in the first case the series of successive terms CD ,DE, ... will never *end*, but in the second case the series of terms ending with ED, DC, CB will never *begin*; there is *no* first term AX and the motion can never *begin*. If the figure is drawn as above (as it should be) there is no difficulty in προσλαμβανόμενον μέγεθος as applied to this case, because you begin measuring from the end (B) instead of from A, the beginning; CD is equally 'added', namely to BC, DE to CD, and so on.

The mathematics of the case may be put thus. We take first the Achilles. We know that in fact Achilles will catch the tortoise, and we can prove it by calculating the time it will take him to do so. If the tortoise has a start of a (say, feet), let v, w be the speeds of Achilles and the tortoise respectively (in feet per second), t the time taken. We must then have $vt = a + wt$; therefore $t = a/(v-w)$. In this time Achilles has travelled $av/(v-w)$, and the tortoise $aw/(v-w)$ feet, and the difference between these two distances, the amount Achilles has *gained* on the tortoise, is of course equal to a, the amount of the tortoise's start. Now, in the time that Achilles covered a, the tortoise covered $(w/v)a$; while Achilles travelled this further distance, the tortoise travelled $(w/v)^2a$; and so on. Let us for convenience put r for w/v ($r<1$); the distances covered by Achilles are then $a, ra, r^2a,...$ and those covered by the tortoise are $ra, r^2a,....$ The sums of these distances respectively are

$$a(1+r+r^2+...+r^n+...)   \text{(Achilles)}$$
$$ra(1+r+r^2+...+r^n+...)   \text{(The Tortoise).}$$

The sum of the series in the bracket to n terms is, by the usual algebraical formula, $\dfrac{1-r^n}{1-r}$, and the sum 'to infinity' is $\dfrac{1}{1-r}$. There-fore, when he is caught, the tortoise has travelled $ra/(1-r)$ and Achilles $a/(1-r)$, which are the same distances as those found above.

In the case of the Dichotomy we have simply to substitute $\frac{1}{2}$ for r, and the sum of the series $\frac{1}{2}+(\frac{1}{2})^2+\dots$ 'to infinity' is $\frac{1}{2}/(1-\frac{1}{2}) = \frac{1}{2}/\frac{1}{2}=1$.

Phys. VI. 9. 239ᵇ33–240ᵃ18

'The fourth is the argument about a set of bodies moving in a race-course and passing another set of bodies equal in number and moving in the opposite direction, the one starting from the end, the other from the middle ⟨of the race-course⟩, and both moving at equal speed; and the argument leads, he thinks, to the conclusion that the half-time is equal to its double [i.e. to the whole time].

'The fallacy in this reasoning lies in the assumption that two bodies moving at equal speeds take equal times in passing, the one a body which is in motion, and the other a body of equal size which is at rest: an assumption which is false.

'Suppose, let us say, that the bodies of equal size which are stationary are AA. ... Let BB... be the bodies which start from the

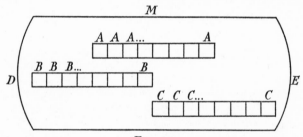

FIG. 31

middle [omitting τῶν A, "of the A's", with Ross], being equal in number and in size to the A's; and let CC... be the bodies which start from the end ⟨of the race-course⟩, being equal in number and in size to the A's, and moving at equal speed with the B's. The effect will be as follows.

'In the course of the movements of the B's and C's past one another, the first B will reach the last ⟨C⟩ at the same time as the first C reaches the last ⟨B⟩. It is then found that the first C has passed

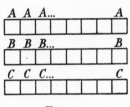

FIG. 32

all the B's [Ross brackets "the B's", τὰ B] while the first B has passed half that number ⟨of bodies⟩ [namely, half of the A's];

consequently the time ⟨taken by the first *B*⟩ is half ⟨that taken by the first *C*⟩, since each of the two bodies takes the same time to pass each body. At the same time the first *B* [reading τὸ πρῶτον *B* for the τὸ αβ or τὰ *B* of the manuscripts, after Ross] is found to have passed all the *C*'s; for the first *C* and the first *B* will be at the opposite ends ⟨of the *A*'s⟩ at the same moment,[†] because both the first *B* and the first *C* are for an equal time alongside the *A*'s [i.e. each *A*].'

[At the point marked [†] some manuscripts have the words ἴσον χρόνον παρ᾽ ἕκαστον γιγνόμενον τῶν *B* ὅσονπερ τῶν *A*, ὥς φησιν 'being as long opposite each of the *B*'s as it is opposite each of the *A*'s, as he says'. I have, after Ross, omitted these words as a gloss on the similar words in [a]12–13.]

'The argument then is as above, but it depends on the fallacy aforesaid.'

The first difficulty arising is in 239[b]35 where the bodies afterwards called *B* are said to start from 'the middle' and 'the end' respectively. This must mean the middle and the end of the race-course, whereas, with the figures we ordinarily draw in illustration, it would seem more natural to say that the *B*'s begin from one end of the stadium and the *C*'s from the other (see Fig. 31, above). To meet this point Ross suggests that the 'middle' means the middle of the complete course along the stadium and back again, that is to say, the *turning-point* (the καμπτήρ, as it was called), which gives the same point *D*. When, therefore, at 240[a]5–6 the *B*'s are said, according to the text of some manuscripts, to start from 'the middle *of the A's*' he thinks it necessary to delete τῶν *A* because the words 'would require us to take ἀπὸ τοῦ ἐσχάτου as meaning "from the end *of the A's*" also and thus imply a contrast between the *B*'s and *C*'s which does not exist'. I do not feel satisfied that 'of the *A*'s' cannot stand, as I do not think it would be unnatural that Aristotle, in his lecture-room style, pointing to a figure such as Fig. 31 above, should change his expression and describe the *B*'s as starting from the middle of the *A*'s (seeing that the *B* farthest to the right which leads the procession to the right *does* begin from there), while keeping to the expression 'from the end ⟨of the race-course⟩' for the *C*'s. In any case there seems to be general agreement that the figure assumed by Aristotle was of the nature of Fig. 31 as drawn.

It would be quite natural that at 240[a]9–10, Aristotle having drawn Fig. 32, should express the fact that the first *B* reaches the last *C* at the same time as the first *C* reaches the last *B* by the abbreviated phrase 'the first *B* and the first *C* are simultaneously ἐπὶ τῷ ἐσχάτῳ', meaning opposite the last of the other row respectively. Simplicius says ἐπὶ τῷ ἐσχάτῳ τῆς ἑαυτοῦ κινήσεως, 'at the end of its own motion', explaining that the rows are 'at the end of each other respectively'.

The greatest crux in the whole passage is presented by 240ᵃ10–12, where, according to the reading of the MSS. FKE² and Simplicius, Aristotle says that 'it will be found that ⟨the first⟩ C has passed all *the A's* while B has passed only half ⟨of them⟩'. What is at once obvious is that the first C has passed all the B's, not all the A's. Two manuscripts apparently have τὰ B, and it gives the easier reading; but there is this in favour of τὰ A that one can quite understand that a scribe might be tempted to alter πάντα τὰ A into πάντα τὰ B, whereas he would be unlikely to do the reverse. Simplicius naturally observes that it is easy enough to see that the first C has passed all the B's, but how has it passed all the A's too? It requires an argument to establish this, and Aristotle has not given it. The argument is suggested by Simplicius: 'The A's are equal to the B's; therefore, whatever time C takes to pass the B's, it will take the same time to pass the A's.'

No account is here taken of the fact that the B's are themselves moving (at equal speed) in the opposite direction to the C's, while the A's are stationary. If Zeno argued, as Aristotle says (240ᵃ1–4), that a body moving at equal speed takes the same time to pass a body moving in the opposite direction as it takes to pass an equal body at rest, he could only have based his argument on a particular assumption as to the nature of the moving bodies, namely that they are indivisible. The first two paradoxes of Zeno were based on the assumption that magnitude is divisible; the last two, the fourth as well as the third, are based on the contrary hypothesis, that matter, space, and time are made up of *indivisible* elements. The ὄγκοι are such indivisible elements; and there is much to be said for the view of R. K. Gaye that Zeno had in mind the ὄγκοι of Empedocles, for we are told by Stobaeus¹ that Empedocles composed his elements of ὄγκοι which were minute and indivisible particles of matter. Simplicius speaks of the ὄγκοι of this passage as ὄγκοι ἢ κύβοι, evidently figuring them to himself as cubes. The essence of Zeno's argument was clearly that, if the ὄγκοι and the spaces occupied by them are indivisible, C must pass as many A's as it passes B's in the same time. This may be shown in various ways. One was indicated (after Brochard, Noel, and Bertrand Russell) in my *History of Greek Mathematics;*² another is shown by Lee in *Zeno of Elea.*³ The case is also well put by R. K. Gaye⁴ as follows: 'Let us suppose then that the respective position of the B's and C's has changed from that represented in Fig. 1 to that represented in Fig. 2. Now,

¹ *Ecl.* i. 17.   ² i, pp. 282–3.   ³ pp. 100–2.
⁴ *Journal of Philology*, xxxi, 1910, pp. 115–16.

in reaching the position that it occupies in Fig. 32, *C* must have been opposite each of the eight *B*'s in succession, and at the moment when it was opposite each *B* it must have been opposite an *A*. But two moments are necessary to enable it to have been opposite two successive *B*'s; and it cannot have been opposite the same *A* at both of these moments (which would mean that it was at rest, whereas *ex hypothesi* it is in motion); nor can it at one and the same moment be opposite part of one *A* and part of another (which would mean that the ὄγκοι were divisible, whereas *ex hypothesi* they are ἀμερεῖς). Consequently at each of the two moments *C* must have been opposite a different *A*, and therefore at the moment when it has passed eight *B*'s it must also have passed eight *A*'s, notwithstanding the fact that the *B*'s are in motion while the *A*'s are at rest. Thus we see that the responsibility for regarding τὸ πρῶτον *Γ* as ἴσον χρόνον παρ' ἕκαστον γιγνόμενον τῶν *B* ὅσονπερ τῶν *A* [the gloss bracketed by Ross] must rest, not with Zeno, who makes no unwarrantable assumption, but with those who maintained the original absurdity that an ὄγκος can be ἀμερής. So interpreted, Zeno's argument is perfectly sound.'

(m) *Motion on a circle and on a straight line*

Phys. VII. 4. 248ᵃ10–13, 18–ᵇ7, ᵇ10–12

'The question may be raised whether every motion is comparable with every other or not. If all motions are comparable and things have the same speed when they move an equal amount in an equal time, then we may have a circular arc equal to a straight line, while of course it may be greater or less.'

Then, after explaining that a material change and a motion in space cannot be comparable because an affection cannot be equal to a length, Aristotle goes on:

'But how will the matter work out in the case of a circle and a straight line? For it would be absurd that it should not be possible for one particular body to move on a circle with a motion similar to that of another body on a straight line, and that we must forthwith conclude that the one is quicker or slower than the other, just as we might if one motion were uphill and the other downhill. Besides, it makes no difference to our argument whether anyone asserts that the one motion must inevitably be quicker or slower than the other; since in that case the circular arc will be greater or less than the straight line, and, if this is so, it is possible that the one may be *equal* to the other. For if in a given time *A* one body has described ⟨the arc⟩ *B* and the other ⟨the straight line⟩ *C*, then *B* may be, let us suppose, greater than C: this is what we assumed "quicker" to mean. It follows that a thing will also be quicker if it moves an equal distance in less time. Hence there will be some part of the time A in which B describes an arc of the circle equal to the distance described by C ⟨on the straight line⟩. [This is a carelessly written sentence, for B is used to denote the object moving on the circle B, and C for the object moving on the straight line C.] But, once more, if the motions are comparable, we are met by the difficulty aforesaid, namely that we shall have a straight line equal to a circle [really a circular arc]. But these are not comparable; therefore neither are the motions comparable: in fact, things are always non-comparable which are called by the same name but not in the same sense [reading, with Ross, ἀλλὰ ὅσα μὴ συνώνυμα πάντ' ἀσύμβλητα] . . .. Can it be then that "quick" has not the same meaning in the one case [motion on a circle] as it has in the other [motion on a straight line]?'

It is strange, as Ross remarks,[1] that Aristotle's idea of the non-*comparability* of a circular circumference with a straight line should lead him so far as to make him deny implicitly that such a circumference can even be *greater* or *less* than a straight line. But it is worth noting that he seems to admit as an axiom that, if such a circumference could be greater or less than a given straight line, it would be possible that some such circumference might be equal to it (whether it could be *found* or not). This is, however, an assumption precisely of the same kind as that which we must suppose Bryson to have made in his argument on the squaring of the circle, though only applied to areas and not straight lines. As we have seen,[2] Proclus[3] makes a similar statement, οὗ δὲ ἔστι μεῖζον καὶ ἔλαττον, τούτου ἔστι καὶ ἴσον (whatever its origin), though[4] in order to cover the case of the supposed 'angle of contact', he modified it by saying that 'it is not always that the transition from the greater to the less takes place through the equal'.

Ib. 249ᵃ8–13

'So too, in the case of motion, two things have the same speed when they are moved equal amounts in equal times. If, then, one body has been altered along such-and-such a part of its length, and another body moved locally over an equal length, in a certain time, is the alteration in this case equal to, and has it the same speed as, the local motion? This is absurd, for the reason that motion includes different species of motion. If ⟨to avoid this difficulty⟩ we confine ourselves to saying that things which are *locally* moved an equal

[1] p. 677.
[2] Note on pp. 49–50.
[3] ap. Philop. on *An. Post.* 112. 21–4.
[4] On Eucl. i, p. 234. 12–15.

distance in an equal time will have the same speed, even then [on our assumption that things moving on a circle and things moving on a straight line can have equal speeds] we shall have to admit that a straight line and a circular circumference can be equal.'

The Greek text of the last sentence (249ᵃ11–13) is, as Ross says, highly compressed and illogical, but is quite intelligible if expanded as above. Simplicius' interpretation (1092. 6–12) comes to the same thing.

Aristotle again implies that you cannot have a straight line equal to the circumference of a circle, for he goes on:

Phys. VII. 4. 249ᵃ13–17

'What is the reason [of this impossible conclusion]? Is it that locomotion is a genus (i.e. contains different species), or that "line" (i.e. the track) is a genus? We may leave the time out of account since that is one and the same ⟨in both cases⟩; but if the lines ⟨on which the local motions take place⟩ are different in species, the local motions must be so too, since local motion has different species if that on which the motion takes place has different species.'

As Simplicius observes, Aristotle seems to regard the difference in the 'lines' as the cause of the difference in the motions (1092. 31–1093. 3 and 1093. 25–7). He takes it as indisputable that a straight line and the circumference of a circle are not 'comparable'. Presumably, as Simplicius says, this was because of the doubt whether the circle could be squared. He observes that, in Aristotle's time, the circle had not been squared, and if in his own time it was thought to have been squared the solutions involved hypotheses that were disputed. The reason, he says, why the squaring of the circle and the discovery of a line equal to its circumference were still the subject of study was that the problem had not yet been shown to be *impossible*, as had the problem of finding a common measure of the side and diagonal of a square (1082. 27–1083. 3).

(n) Motion caused by different forces

Ib. 5. 249ᵇ27–250ᵃ27

'We take it for granted that a movent always moves something in something, and to some extent—by "in something" I mean in time, and by "to some extent" I mean a certain amount of distance—for when a thing is causing motion, it has always, at the same moment, also caused motion, so that there will be some amount of distance which it has traversed and some amount of time that it has taken.

'If now A be the movent, B the thing moved, C the distance traversed, and D the time taken, then, in the same time $\langle D \rangle$, an equal force A will move $\frac{1}{2}B$ the distance $2C$ and, in $\frac{1}{2}D$, A will move $\frac{1}{2}B$ the distance C; for so the due proportion will be maintained.

'And if the same force $\langle A \rangle$ moves the same weight $\langle B \rangle$ a certain distance $\langle C \rangle$ in such-and-such a time $\langle D \rangle$ and half the distance in half the time, then half the force will move half the weight an equal distance in an equal time [i.e. $\frac{1}{2}A$ will move $\frac{1}{2}B$ a distance C in time D].

'Thus let E be half the force A and F half the weight B; the force and the weight are then similarly related, that is, in the same proportion, in the two cases, so that $\langle$the respective forces$\rangle$ will cause the respective weights to move an equal distance in an equal time.

'But, if E moves F the distance C in the time D, it does not necessarily follow [reading οὐκ ἀνάγκη] that E will in the same time move $2F$ $[= B]$ the distance $\frac{1}{2}C$; that is to say, if A moves B the distance C in the time D, it does not follow that $\frac{1}{2}A$ or F will move B, in the time D, or in any part of it, some part of the distance C such as bears the same ratio to the whole of C that E bears to A [Aristotle, by a slip, says "A to E"]; in fact it may happen that E cannot move B at all. For it does not follow that, if the whole of a given force has moved $\langle$a thing$\rangle$ such-and-such a distance, the half of the force will move it any distance in any length of time whatever; were it so, we should have to suppose that one man could by himself move a vessel on the water, that is to say, if you have only to divide the total power of the hauliers and the distance they collectively moved the vessel by the number $\langle$of the gang$\rangle$. Hence Zeno's argument is false when he says that any grain of millet however small will make a sound $\langle$as it falls$\rangle$; for there is no reason why it should not fail, in any time whatever, to move the air which the whole bushel of grain has set in motion by falling; nay, it need not move even the same fraction of the whole of the air that it would move as part of the whole bushel if that fraction were by itself. For the whole in question has no parts except potentially.

'But if we have two forces acting on two weights, and each moves one of the two weights such-and-such a distance in such-and-such a time, then the forces added together will move the weight made up of the two $\langle$together$\rangle$ an equal distance in an equal time.'

For the first part of c. 5 we have a parallel in *De caelo*:[1] 'there being a certain force which moves $\langle$the body$\rangle$, a smaller and lighter body will be moved a greater distance by the same force': and $301^{b}11-13$: 'the speed of the lesser body will be to that of the greater

---

[1] iii. 2. $301^{b}4-5$.

as the greater body is to the lesser', the latter passage stating definitely that, if the force exerted is the same, the weights and the speeds are reciprocally proportional.

The only way to make the above argument easy to follow is to set out the steps in quasi-tabular form, thus:

If A moves B a distance C in the time D, then

(1) A will move $\frac{1}{2}B$ the distance $2C$ in the time D (250ª1–3)

(2) A ,, $\frac{1}{2}B$,, C ,, $\frac{1}{2}D$ (ª3)

(3) A ,, B ,, $\frac{1}{2}C$,, $\frac{1}{2}D$ (ª4–5)

(4) $\frac{1}{2}A$,, $\frac{1}{2}B$,, C ,, D (ª6–7)

But (5) $\frac{1}{2}A$ will not necessarily move B the distance $\frac{1}{2}C$ in the time D (ª9–12)

(6) $\frac{1}{2}A$ (or any fraction of A) may not move B the distance $\frac{1}{2}C$ (or the same fraction of C that we have taken of A) in time D (or any part of D) (ª12–15)

(7) If A moves B a distance C in time D
and G moves H a distance C in time D
then $A+G$ moves $B+H$ a distance C in time D (ª25–7)

Professor Cornford reads ἀναγκαῖον instead of οὐκ ἀνάγκη in 250ª10, regarding it as the original reading because otherwise the statements in ª9–12 and ª12–15 become mere duplicates. With the reading ἀναγκαῖον, however, the statements must appear flatly contradictory. To get over this difficulty Cornford takes τὸ διπλάσιον τοῦ Z to mean 'twice F' in the sense of two separate halves of B taken separately and moved separately, i.e. so that $\frac{1}{2}A$ would first take one F ($=\frac{1}{2}B$) and move it the distance in the time D and would then go back and fetch the second F the same distance in another time D, making $2D$ in all. I agree in Ross's objection to this interpretation because in the context the only natural meaning of τὸ διπλάσιον τοῦ Z is 'the double of F', that is to say the mass B itself. On the other point, namely that if we read οὐκ ἀνάγκη in ª10 the statements in ª9–12 and ª12–15 become mere duplicates, I would point out that there is this difference: the second adds in effect that the fraction of A to be taken need not be the $\frac{1}{2}$; the statement is equally true if we take *any* fraction of A and the *same* fraction of C. There is point in this, with reference to the illustration (ª17–19) of the boat and the hauliers; it is not a question of *two* hauliers in that case.

In the *American Journal of Philology* for January 1938 there is a comprehensive and useful article by Israel B. Drabkin[1] under the title 'Notes on the Laws of Motion in Aristotle', which gives a good account of the differences between Aristotle's elementary notions

[1] Vol. lix. i, pp. 60–84.

on the subject and modern theories based on Newton's Laws of
Motion. Though Aristotle attempts in a number of cases to give
mathematical form to his views regarding 'forces', 'speeds', etc., he
does not proceed on any really scientific basis. He does not begin
with definitions of the terms used or give them any precise technical
sense; he uses them as we use them in popular speech. A 'force'
is sometimes called ἰσχύς (literally 'strength'), sometimes δύναμις
('power'), sometimes by no name at all but 'A' or 'B' without any
description of what it actually is or how it is applied. He makes no
distinctions, such as we have, between 'force', 'power' (in the sense
in which we use it when we say 'horse-power'), and 'work'; we have
to gather the sense in which 'force' or 'power' is used from the content and context of the particular passages. Aristotle does not deal
with *acceleration* and forces producing it as a definite department
of the subject. Nor, in dealing with a subject like the resistance of
a medium, does he eliminate other conditions before venturing to
state a law about it. If he had correctly considered resistance as
involving a *subtraction* from a speed obtainable under ideal conditions instead of a *division* of the speed by a certain number or in
a certain proportion, 'and had he therefore been able to assume as
the ideal condition, not necessarily as an entity of nature but as
a limiting case for the purposes of a mathematical treatment of
motion, a medium devoid of resistance, he could then have deduced
that all heavy bodies fall naturally in this ideal medium with equal
and finite speed; in short he could have deduced a principle of
inertia. Such a principle of inertia for just such a medium he formu-
lated precisely enough,[1] only to reject it; from this a sound deductive
science of dynamics would not have been a far step.'[2]

In our present passages Aristotle says nothing about the initial
velocity of A; we are only told (249^{b}29) that, when the period of its
action on B under consideration begins, A is already causing motion
['it always *is* causing motion and *has* caused motion at the same
instant']; and the content of the passage generally implies that the
motion is at uniform speed.

As Drabkin observes, if a force is applied to a body, there are
three possible cases:

(1) If the force is insufficient to cover the forces tending to prevent
motion, no motion will take place.

(2) If the force exerted is greater than that required to overcome

---

[1] *Phys.* iv. 8. 215^{a}19–22: 'Further, no one would be able to say why a body
set in motion [in the void] would stop at any place, for why should it stop in
one place rather than in another? Hence a body must either remain at rest or be
moved *ad infinitum* unless something stronger obstructs it.' Cf. pp. 115–16, above.

[2] Drabkin, op. cit. (p. 144 *supra*), p. 86.

the forces tending to prevent motion, and if A represents the *excess* of force applied beyond that so required, we shall have, in the Newtonian system, *accelerated* motion. In this case, if A moves B a distance C in the time D, then

    (*a*) A moves $\frac{1}{2}B$ a distance $2C$ in the time D,

(*b*)	A	,,	$\frac{1}{2}B$	,,	C	,,	$D/\sqrt{2}$, not $\frac{1}{2}D$,
(*c*)	A	,,	B	,,	$\frac{1}{2}C$	,,	$D/\sqrt{2}$,
(*d*) $\frac{1}{2}A$		,,	$\frac{1}{2}B$	,,	C	,,	D.

(3) Where the force A is just sufficient to keep B moving at a uniform rate, the rules about accelerated motion do not apply. This is the alternative which seems definitely to be the sort of case that Aristotle had in mind (since there is no suggestion of acceleration, and it seems to be implied that the motion is uniform). It would exclude cases (*a*) and (*b*) because, if A were a force just sufficient to keep B moving at a certain rate, it would be more than sufficient to keep $\frac{1}{2}B$ moving at that rate, and there would be *acceleration*. We are therefore confined to cases (*c*) and (*d*). A case in point would be the lifting of a weight at uniform speed. In this case, if we omit the time element or consider equal units of time, then A (to which Aristotle applies the name δύναμις or ἰσχύς or no specific name) is, in the Aristotelian formulation, not what we call 'force', but what we call '*work*'.[1]

If we include the time element, we may under similar circumstances, e.g. in the case of the vertical lifting of a weight at a uniform speed, consider A in the Aristotelian formulations as the measure, not of the 'force' required but of the *power* as the term is used in modern mechanics (the power of an agent being 'the amount of work that would be done by the agent if working uniformly for the unit of time'.[2] Thus the 'power' represented in lifting B a distance C in the time D is equal to that represented by lifting $\frac{1}{2}B$ a distance $2C$ in the time D [(*a*) above], or by lifting a weight $\frac{1}{2}B$ a distance C in time $D/\sqrt{2}$ [(*b*) above].[3]

(*o*) *Circular motion and rectilinear motion; Zeno's dichotomy*

Phys. VIII. 8. 261ᵇ27–262ᵃ5

'We have now to explain that there may be an infinite motion, one and continuous, and that this is motion in a circle. Everything that is carried along moves in a circle or a straight line, or in a line compounded of the two; hence, if neither of the two is continuous,

---

[1] The unit of work being 'the work done by a force equal to the weight of one pound when it moves its point of application one foot in its own direction', Loney, *Elements of Statics*, 1925, p. 164.

[2] Ibid., p. 166.   [3] Drabkin, op. cit., p. 73.

neither can the line which is compounded of the two be so. Now it is manifest that that which is carried along a straight line finite (in length) cannot be so carried continuously; it must turn back, and that which does so in a straight line is moved with contrary motions, for in space up is contrary to down, forward to backward, left to right, these being respectively contraries in place. Now we have already[1] defined what the motion is which is one and continuous, namely, the motion of one thing, in one (period of) time and in a domain specifically invariable (throughout). For we saw that there are three things: (1) the thing that is in motion, as, for example, a man or a god, (2) the *when*, namely, the time, (3) that in which the motion takes place, the last being a place, or a quality, or form, or magnitude.'

'Motion in a circle' (κύκλῳ) in 261ᵇ28 means specifically revolution or rotation (cf. 262ᵃ5–7); it has to be translated 'motion in a circle' here because the *path*, the circle, is contrasted with a straight line. It is tempting to suggest, with Cornford, that, in speaking of the path which is a combination of a straight line and a circle, Aristotle had in mind such a thing as a spiral, or the path of a point on the wheel of a carriage moving along a road (a cycloid), or that of a planet describing an *epicycle*. Such a supposition would, however, I think, make him too close a forerunner of Archimedes, Apollonius, and Galileo. Aristotle does not elsewhere show any knowledge of higher curves than the circle; where he speaks of 'spirals' (ἕλικες), e.g. the 'spirals of the heaven', it is a vague term denoting some twisty path which he does not attempt to define.[2] I prefer to regard the phrase 'a circle or a straight line or a mixture of the two' as a mere echo of that of Plato, ἤτοι εὐθέος ἢ στρογγύλου ἤ τινος μεικτοῦ ἐξ ἀμφοῖν,[3] cited by Cornford. The point is, as he says,

that the claim of any compound motion to be continuous can be disproved by showing that rectilinear motion cannot be so; and this Aristotle proceeds to do, considering only a *finite* straight line, as, in his view, no actual infinite straight line exists.

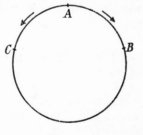

FIG. 33

After speaking of *contrary* motions, and showing how, on a straight line AB, motion from B to A is contrary to motion from A to B, and, on a circle, motion from A towards B is contrary to motion from A towards C, Aristotle goes on:

[1] v. 4.   [2] Cf. note on *Phys.* v. 4. 228ᵇ15–25, p. 124, above.
[3] *Parm.* 145 B.

Phys. VIII. 8. 262ᵃ12–ᵇ4

'But what makes it manifest that motion in a straight line is not continuous is the fact that anything which turns back must necessarily come to a stop, not only if the motion is rectilinear but also if it is on a circle, which is not the same thing as *circular* motion (revolution or rotation); in motion on a circle a thing may at different times either continue moving without break, or turn back again when it has arrived at the place from which it started. That it must come to a stop we may convince ourselves not only by the evidence of sense but also on theoretical grounds. We begin in this way. There are three things, beginning, middle, and end, and the middle is to each of the others in the relation of both beginning and end, and, though numerically one, is notionally two. Again, what exists potentially and what exists actually are different things. Hence any point whatever on a straight line between its extremities is potentially a middle point, but it is not so actually unless the moving thing divides the straight line at a point and, having stopped there, begins to move again. In this way the middle becomes both beginning and end, beginning of the later portion and end of the earlier portion of the motion. I mean, for instance, the case where the travelling point *A* stops at *B* and then travels onward again to *C*. When, however, *A* travels continuously, it is not possible that it should either have come to be at *B* or have ceased to be there; it can only *be* there in the "Now", not in any portion of time except the (whole) time in which the Now forms a point of division. Nay, if we say that *A* has come to be and ceased to be at *B*, then *A*, though moving, will continually be standing still; for it is impossible that *A* should simultaneously have come to be at *B* and ceased to be there. Therefore, the two events must occur at different points of time, and between them there will be time intervening. Hence *A* will be stationary at *B*; and similarly with all other points on the line, for the same argument applies to all.'

In short, as Cornford observes, all intermediate points such as *B* are only *potential* starting- or finishing-points unless or until *A* actually pauses at them.

Contrast with this the case of the body which, moving on a finite straight line, tries to keep up 'continuous' motion by continually going from end to end and back again.

Ib. ᵇ21–263ᵃ1

'As it is, then, we cannot, in speaking of continuous motion, use such terms [as "having arrived at" or "having left" an intermediate point *B*]. On the other hand, if *G* travels to *D* and then turns back

and travels downwards again, it *has* used the extremity *D* as both
end and beginning, that is to say, has used the one point as two;
it must therefore have halted and it cannot at the same moment
have come to be at *D* and ceased to be at *D*, for if this were possible,
it would simultaneously, in the same "now", both be there and not
be there. Nevertheless, we cannot apply the solution we gave of
the case above (continuous motion); we cannot say that *G is* at *D*
at a dividing point of time and has not come to be there nor ceased
to be there. For in this case the end to which *G* has come is necessarily one which exists actually, not potentially. Whereas, then, the
point which is in the middle is only potentially beginning or end,
this point *D* is actually an end; it is an end regarded from below
and a beginning regarded from above, and accordingly it is in the
same relations to the two motions respectively.'

(*p*) *Zeno's 'Dichotomy' (further)*

Ib. 263ᵃ4–ᵇ9

'It is in the same way that we must meet (1) those who ask in
the terms of Zeno's argument whether it is a fact that you must
always first traverse the half of the distance, that the halves are
infinite in number, and that you cannot traverse an infinite number
of distances, or (2) those who put this same argument in another
form and claim that, concurrently with the motion over the halves,
you must first count each half separately as it appears, so that,
when you have traversed the whole distance, you must have counted
an infinite number, which is admittedly impossible. Now in our
first discussions of the question of motion[1] we disposed of the
difficulty by means of the fact that time contains in itself an infinite
number of parts; there is, we said, nothing absurd in supposing that
you can traverse an infinite number of distances in a time infinite
in the same sense, seeing that the infinite (in the sense of infinite
divisibility) is equally present in length and in time. This solution,
however, though it is an adequate answer to the particular ques-
tioner—his question being whether an infinite number of things
can be traversed or counted in a finite time—is not adequate as an
explanation of the fact itself and the true state of affairs. For if
anyone, dropping the idea of length and the question whether it is
possible to get through an infinite number of things in a finite time,
should put the same question with reference to time by itself (for
time is susceptible of an infinite number of divisions), this solution
will no longer be adequate, and we must state the truth as we put

[1] vi. 2 and 9.

it in the argument just set out. If we divide a continuous line into two halves, we use the one point as two, for we make it beginning and end: this is the effect both of counting and of dividing into halves. If we divide in this way, neither the line nor the motion will be continuous, for continuous motion must be over what is continuous, and in the continuous there is an infinite number of halves, not actually but potentially. If you make the halves actual, you make a motion which is not continuous but has pauses in it. In case you count the halves, it is manifest that this is the result; for then the one point must be counted as two, since it will be the end of one half and the beginning of the other if you count, not the one continuous line, but the two halves. Therefore, to the question whether it is possible to get through an infinite number of parts whether of time or of length we must reply that in one sense it is possible, in another it is not. If the parts exist actually it is not possible; if they exist only potentially, it is possible. For one who moves continuously has incidentally traversed an infinite number (of parts), but he has not done so in an unqualified sense; for it is incidental to a line to contain an infinite number of half-lengths; but this is not its essence and real nature.'[1]

(q) *Circular motion* (κύκλῳ) *may be one and continuous*

In *Phys.* VIII. 8. 264ᵇ9–28 Aristotle argues that circular motion (κύκλῳ), unlike motion on a finite straight line, may be one and continuous. You may think of the moving object as moving *from* a point *A* on the circle *to* the same point *A* again, but it need not stop there; it may go on continuously, passing *A* again any number of times without interruption; *A* is a point you may think of or mark, but it is not an *actual* extremity like the extremities of a line. Passing *from A to A* does not involve two contrary (ἐναντίαι) or opposite (ἀντικείμεναι) motions; the intention, motive, or 'urge' (πρόθεσις) is throughout one and the same. Suppose, on the other hand, that the moving object moves along a finite straight line which has two actual extremities (as it might be, say, the *diameter* of a circle, which gives the measure of the longest possible distance between any two points on the circle). If the body, on reaching either end, is to continue to move, it must turn back, and moving backwards and forwards on a straight line is not *one* motion, but is made up of contrary (ἐναντίαι) motions alternating. There is nothing mathematical in the passage. The only point of difficulty is a rather obscure distinction between 'contrary' and 'opposite'

---

[1] Cf. *Metaph. a.* 2. 994ᵇ22–5, below (pp. 200–1).

motions. Aristotle here restricts 'contrary' (ἐναντία) to motions on a *straight line*; 'opposite' (ἀντικειμένη) motions need only cover the same length (τὸ αὐτὸ μῆκος) which presumably need not be straight.

(r) A finite movent cannot cause motion for an infinite time

Phys. VIII. 10. 266ᵃ12–24

'Nothing finite can cause motion for an infinite time. There are three things, that which moves, that which is moved, and thirdly that in which it is moved, namely, time. Now the alternatives are: (1) that all of these are infinite, (2) that all are finite, (3) that some of them are finite, say two or one of them. Let A be the movent, B the moved, C an infinite time. Let D (a part of A) move a certain part of B which we will call E. Then D will not move E in a time equal to C—for it takes longer to move the greater body—therefore the time F (in which D moves E) will not be infinite [see note following]. Proceeding in this way and adding to D (its equal), and to E (its equal), I shall use up A and B respectively; but by continually taking away from the time (C) an equal amount, I shall not use up C, for by hypothesis it is infinite. Hence the whole A will move the whole B in a finite time (which is part) of C. Therefore nothing can have an infinite motion imparted to it by a finite movent. It is manifest, therefore, that it is impossible for the finite (movent) to cause motion for an infinite time.'

Ross's note on this passage is closely and finely argued.[1] I agree with him that Aristotle's whole argument is vitiated by his failure to distinguish two meanings of κινεῖν ἄπειρον χρόνον: (1) to cause motion to go on for an infinite time, (2) to take an infinite time to cause a body to move (a certain distance). What he ought to be proving is that no finite body can do the former: what he purports to prove is that no finite body can, as in (2), take an infinite time in moving a body a certain distance.

But notwithstanding Ross's argument on ᵃ15–23[2] and Cornford's,[3] I feel sure that Simplicius[4] is right on the mathematical point, namely, that, if the proof is to be conclusive, D must bear a greater ratio to E than A does to B. It is true that Aristotle does not state this; but neither does he state that D is the *same* fraction of A that E is of B, which is what Cornford and Ross both assume.

Suppose that $A : D = B : E = n : 1$, where n is an integer

---

[1] pp. 721–2.
[2] pp. 722–3.
[3] In *Cl. Q.* xxvi (1932), p. 53, and *Physics*, vol. ii, pp. 408–11.
[4] p. 1322, 8–14.

greater than 1. Then, on Aristotle's principles: If A moves B a certain distance in time C, A/n will move B/n the same distance in the *same* time C (namely, the infinite time), and not in a lesser time as requires to be proved.

This principle is clearly laid down in 250ª4–9, and there is no getting away from it. What we want to arrive at is that D, the fraction of A, moves E, the fraction of B, in a time F which is finite. Aristotle clearly infers (266ª17–19) that F is finite, for he says that F is 'not a time equal to C—for a longer time is required to move the greater body—so that the time F is not infinite'. Aristotle's reasoning is naïve enough in itself, for he infers simply that anything (e.g. the time F) that is less than infinite is finite. Now, if D is to move E (the given distance) in any time less than C, E cannot be the same fraction of B that D is of A; it must be something less, as Simplicius observes. On the assumption that E is the same fraction of B that D is of A, Ross and Cornford interpret the words ἐν πλείονι γὰρ τὸ μεῖζον to mean that D would take a longer time to move any multiple of E, or B itself, which is $n.E$, than it takes to move E. D would, however, in fact, if it could move B at all, take a time to move B which is not n times F but n times C, or n times the infinite time; and it would scarcely be a proper inference (even for Aristotle) to say that any time less than nC must be finite, seeing that C itself (which is infinite) is on the face of it less. I think it is best to take the parenthesis ἐν πλείονι γὰρ τὸ μεῖζον to be quite general, without explaining it in terms of D and E. If we try so to explain it, we must observe that what is wanted is a time less than C, and therefore that, *if* D is supposed to be what moves τὸ μεῖζον ἐν πλείονι, πλείονι must mean the time C and τὸ μεῖζον must be B/n itself, and Aristotle must have meant it to be inferred (perhaps making it quite clear to his pupils by reference to a diagram) that E is something less than B/n, as Simplicius supposes.

In concluding that A after all must move B in a finite part of the time C (266ª21), Aristotle omits to say ὅπερ ἄτοπον (as he should, because by hypothesis A moves B in the infinite time C itself), but leaves it to be understood, passing on to state, as proved, the substantive proposition which contradicts the original hypothesis.

There is one statement of Ross's[1] to which I do not feel able to subscribe, namely, that Aristotle 'has in fact no conception of the First Law of Motion, that if a body has once been set in motion it will continue to move till it is acted on by some fresh force'. On the contrary, I think that, in *Phys.* IV. 8. 215ª20–2, Aristotle shows that he had a fair inkling of such a principle as that of the First Law of Motion.[2]

[1] p. 722.   [2] Cf. pp. 115–16, above.

Phys. VIII. 10. 266ᵃ24–ᵇ6

'And the general proposition that a finite magnitude cannot possess an infinite force is clear from the following considerations. Let us assume that it is always the greater force that produces an equal effect in less time, in heating, for example, or sweetening, or throwing, or generally in moving anything. Then that which is acted on must be affected in some way by the finite magnitude which we have supposed to possess infinite force, and that to a greater extent than it would be by anything else, for the infinite force is greater than any other. In that case the time taken must be no time at all. For let *A* be the time taken by the infinite force in warming or thrusting the object acted on, and let *A* + *B* be the time in which some finite force does the same; then, if I make this finite force greater and greater by continually adding another finite force, I shall sometime arrive at the point of having completed the motion in the time *A*, for if I add continually to a limited magnitude, I shall at length exceed any assigned magnitude whatever, and if I continually subtract from it, I shall similarly make it fall short of any assigned magnitude. Therefore, the finite force will move the object in the same time as the infinite force does. But this is impossible; therefore nothing finite can possess infinite force.'

This reasoning is, from a mathematical point of view, anything but shipshape; but it is quite intelligible. It is natural that Aristotle should make a point of quoting the axiom πρὸς πεπερασμένον γὰρ κ.τ.λ. (266ᵇ2–4) in full though the first part does not help him, his point being that the finite force, if added to in the prescribed manner, yet remains always *finite*. But the whole argument depends on the risky assumption in 266ᵃ33 that *some* finite force can be found which will, in some time *A* + *B* greater than *A*, do what the infinite force has done in the time *A*.

Ib. ᵇ6–24

'Nor again can a finite power belong to an infinite magnitude— you may of course find more force in a lesser magnitude (of a different sort), but you will find even more in a greater magnitude (of that same sort).

'Let *AB* be an infinite magnitude. Then (a part of it) *BC* has some force which can move *D* in a certain time, say *EF*. Now if I take the double of *BC*, it will move *D* in half the time *EF*, to take this particular ratio; that is, it will move

FIG. 34

D in the time *FH*. Then, if I continually add to *BC* in this way,

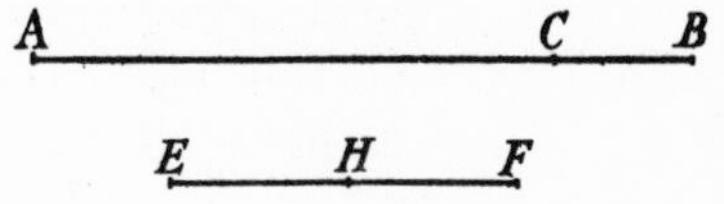

I shall never exhaust AB, but the time taken will continually be a smaller and smaller fraction of the given time. The force will therefore (ultimately) be infinite, since it will exceed any assigned finite force, ⟨our assumption being that⟩ with any finite force, the time occupied must also be finite. For, if such-and-such a force moves a thing in such-and-such a time, a greater force will move it in a lesser but determinate time, in reciprocal proportion. And of course every force, like every number and every magnitude, must be infinite when it exceeds any determinate amount.

'Our proposition may also be proved thus. We take a certain force, the same in kind as that possessed by the infinite magnitude, but subsisting in a finite magnitude, which is also such that it is an exact measure of the finite force subsisting in the infinite magnitude.'

This argument, like the foregoing, is not well arranged but is easily followed. There is little to add to Ross's note on 266^b8–20.[1] The first point arising is on ^b10–14 where Aristotle says 'take the double of BC' and then goes on to tell us to 'take [other magnitudes] in the same way' ($οὕτω\ λαμβάνων$). Does this mean that we are to *double* the double of BC and so on continually, thus making the series BC, $2BC$, 2^2BC, etc.; or may we simply add *once* BC each time, making the series BC, $2BC$, $3BC$, etc.? Simplicius takes the former view and is followed by Ross; Cornford chooses the latter alternative. I think it certain that Simplicius is right and that continual *doubling* is what is meant; this is distinctly implied by the words in ^b11–12, 'for let this be the ratio', indicating that the same ratio is followed throughout.

To make the argument down to ^b15 complete an intermediate step is wanted between 'I shall arrive at a time continually less than the given time' (^b13–14), i.e. less than any assigned time whatever, and the conclusion (^b14–15) 'therefore the force must be infinite'. By increasing the part taken ($2^n.BC$) continually, i.e. by increasing n continually, I diminish the time ($EF/2^n$) without limit. Aristotle should therefore have said: '⟨If the fraction of EF becomes less than any assigned time whatever, however small, the corresponding multiple of BC must exceed any magnitude whatever (of the same kind);⟩ therefore the force will be infinite.' Now the intermediate step is really implied in ^b15–20, and accordingly I agree with Ross that it is best to regard ^b15–20, not as a new argument, but as parenthetical and as intended to supply the missing link in the lines ^b12–15, and to read in ^b15–16 $εἴ\ γε\ πάσης\ πεπερασμένης$. Even then, after 'if with any finite force the time taken must also be finite, (^b15–17), or at some other point, we have to supply for ourselves

[1] pp. 724–5.

the actual link in the argument required at ᵇ14 to the effect that, concurrently with the reduction of the time taken to a time less than any finite time, the force must have increased so far as to exceed any finite force, i.e. must be infinite.

The second proof (ᵇ20–4) is similarly incomplete. Aristotle merely says, 'take a force of the same kind as that in the infinite magnitude but such as to be an exact measure of it'. To this we have to add something like the following. Let A, an infinite body, have a finite force B. Suppose that some finite body, as X, has a force which is an aliquot part of B, say, B/n. Then, on the proportional principle, nX will have a force equal to $n.B/n$ or B. Therefore a finite body nX has the same force as A, the infinite body: which is impossible. Therefore an infinite body cannot have a finite force.

(s) *Motion of things thrown*

Phys. VIII. 10. 266ᵇ27–267ᵃ20

'With regard to things which are moved in space, it will be well, first of all, to dispose of a certain difficulty. If it is true that everything that is moved, except things which are self-moved, is moved by something, how comes it that some things are moved continuously, though that which has caused them to move is no longer in contact with them, as, for instance, things *thrown*? If that which has caused their motion sets something else in motion too, say the air, which when set in motion also causes motion, it is no less impossible that it (the air) should be in motion when the original movent is no longer in contact with it or moving it; all the things (that are moved) must be moved, and must have ceased to be moved, at the same time, (their motion ceasing) whenever the first movent ceases to operate, even if, like the magnet, it communicates to what it has moved the power of causing motion. We must, therefore, hold that the original movent gives the power of causing motion to air, or water, or anything else which is naturally adapted for being a movent as well as for being moved. But this thing does not simultaneously cease to be a movent and to be moved; it ceases to be moved at the same moment as the movent acting upon it ceases to move it, but it is still a movent. Hence it moves something else contiguous to it (reading κινεῖ τι ἄλλο); and the same applies to that again. The motion comes to cease whenever the power of causing motion communicated to the next member of the series becomes less and less continually; and it finally ceases when the member of the series immediately preceding no longer makes the next a movent but only causes it to be moved. The motion of the last two, of the one as movent and of the other as moved, must cease simultaneously, and with this the whole motion. Now this kind of motion takes place in things that can be at one time in motion and at another time at rest, and the motion is not continuous, but only appears to be. For it is a motion of (a series of) things which are either successive or in contact, since the motion is not one but a series of movements contiguous to one another. This is why such motion occurs in air and water, and some thinkers call it "mutual replacement". But the difficulties involved cannot be disposed of in any way other than that which we have set out. The theory of "mutual replacement" makes the whole series of things move and cause motion simultaneously, so that they must also all cease to move at the same time; whereas the appearance presented to us is that of some one thing moving continuously. What then keeps it in motion, seeing that it cannot be the same movent (all the time)?'

Simplicius' commentary on the whole passage is useful.[1] Aristotle begins, he says, with the axiom 'Everything that is moved is moved by something'. If, says Simplicius, this were not granted at the outset, it would not even be necessary that what is moved in the eternal motion (of the universe) should be moved by anything, and Aristotle's doctrine about the prime mover would lose its point. Aristotle accordingly thinks it necessary to deal first with a possible objection to the axiom. If everything that is moved is moved by something, how can some things which have not the principle of motion (τὸ κινητικόν) in themselves, but are moved from outside, remain in continuous motion even when that which has moved them no longer does so, e.g. things *thrown*? For, when the thrower is not moving them, they nevertheless remain in motion continuously for a long distance. Consequently they will then appear to be moved by nothing, and the axiom will be falsified. Aristotle's phrase μὴ ἀπτομένου τοῦ κινήσαντος means that the thrower is no longer in contact with the moving body, and will not be so any more during the time taken by the motion. Next, Aristotle refers to the explanation given by some thinkers, namely, that 'the thrower moves, simultaneously with the object thrown, something else, say the air, and the air, being set in motion by the thrower, moves the object'. But the difficulty remains; the argument only substitutes the air for the thrower. If the air is not self-movent (this character is peculiar to living things), but is only moved by the thrower, it should, at the moment when the thrower had ceased to move it, have ceased to be moved. In like manner, the series of things that are necessarily moved (in the process) should all be moved, and all

---

[1] pp. 1344–52.

cease to be moved, respectively at one and the same moment, namely, when the first movent ceased to act as such. If the air remains longer in the state of being moved after the thrower has ceased to move it, the axiom will again be falsified. This applies even in a case like that of the magnet, which is able to make what it moves (say, a piece of steel) move something else. In that case the magnet gives the steel, not only motion, but also the power of moving the next thing. If the next thing is not also given the power of causing motion, as well as actual motion, the argument begins to apply, and the motion ceases when the last movent ceases to act as such. Aristotle insists that the first movent (in the case of the thing *thrown*, the thrower) must communicate to the air, the water, or whatever it is, the power to move the object thrown. The air does not merely follow the object thrown in its motion, but it gives what comes next [presumably more air] power to cause motion as well as to move. But the power of causing motion successively communicated diminishes at each transmission and is finally annihilated; and at that time the thing moved ceases simultaneously to be moved. When the last thing but one ceases to cause motion, the last thing ceases to be moved. In the particular case the thing thrown falls down.

The theory of ἀντιπερίστασις is next dealt with. Aristotle says (267ª18–19) that the theory of ἀντιπερίστασις makes it inevitable that all the terms in the series 'must move and be moved together, so that they must cease together'. Simplicius defines the term very lucidly and has some sound remarks supporting Aristotle's view of it. ἀντιπερίστασις is what happens 'when, as one body is extruded by another, there is interchange of places, and the extruder takes the place of the extruded, that again extrudes the next, the next the succeeding one (if there are more than one), until the last is in the place of the first extruder'. But the extrusion cannot be the cause of the further motion of the object thrown, unless we suppose, with Aristotle, that each term in the series imparts to the next, not only motion, but the *power to move* the next. As Simplicius says, the portions of the air which take the place of preceding portions of the air do not occupy more space than those do respectively, so that there is no question of the air being forced to occupy less space, and so cause a contraction and consequent *pressure* which might force forward the object which is being thrown. (This seems definitely to exclude 'elasticity', which Cornford takes to be the 'nearest equivalent' of ἀντιπερίστασις.[1])

There is an echo of the above explanation in two chapters of the *Mechanica* dealing with objects thrown.

[1] p. 418, note *b*.

Mechanica, c. 32. 858ᵃ13–16

'Why do objects *thrown* cease to move? Is it that they cease when the force which has sent them off ceases, or because they meet with resistance, or because of the bias or natural tendency (ῥοπή) of the object if that overcomes the force which has thrown it?'

τὸ ἀντισπᾶσθαι, 'suffering resistance', means literally 'being dragged in the opposite direction'. It is obviously not the same thing as ἀντιπερίστασις 'mutual replacement' (see above).

Ib., c. 33. 858ᵃ17–22

'Why does anything (still) move with a motion which is not its own, although the thrower does not follow it or continue to propel it? May we not clearly say that the thrower has made the first member of the series of things put in motion capable of propelling the next, and that again the next following; and that the whole motion stops when the member of the series which is actually propelling the object no longer communicates to the next the power of propelling the object, and when the bias inherent in the weight of the object thrown is stronger than the power which drives it forward?'

The effect of ἀντισπᾶσθαι in c. 32 seems to be much the same as that of ἀντιτείνειν and ἀντερείδειν, 'resist', or 'push the opposite way', in cc. 31 and 34 respectively. In c. 31 (858ᵃ3) the author asks, 'Why is a thing already moving easier to move than if it is stationary?' Most difficult of all, he says, is it, when a thing is already moving one way, to move it the opposite way. The difficulty depends on the resistance of the body itself 'which results in a deduction from the power of the moving force'; even when the body is stationary it 'resists' (ἀντιτείνει), with the same effect. Similarly (c. 34. 858ᵃ25–6), when a body is *thrown* or *pushed*, the body 'resists' (ἀντερείδει) with the effect of exerting a force in the direction of the place *from* which you try to move it. Here, as van Cappelle remarks,[1] it is clear that the author had some idea of what we call *vis inertiae*.

[1] p. 278.

VII
DE CAELO
(a) Bodies, dimensions, etc.

De caelo I. 1. 268ª4–13; 20–ᵇ5

'Of things constituted by nature some are bodies and magnitudes, some possess body and magnitude, and some are the principles of things which possess these. That is *continuous* which is divisible into parts continually divisible and that which is divisible every way is body. Of magnitude that which (extends) one way is a line, that which (extends) two ways a plane, and that which (extends) three ways a body. And there is no magnitude besides these, because the three dimensions are all that there are, and thrice extended means extended all ways. For, as the Pythagoreans say, the All and all things in it are determined by three things; end, middle, and beginning give the number of the All, and these give the number of the Triad. . . .

'Since all things and the All, and the perfect, do not differ from one another in respect of form but only, if at all, in their matter and in the things to which the terms are applied, body alone among magnitudes is perfect; for it alone is determined by the three dimensions, that is, is an All. Being divisible in three ways, body is divisible all ways: of the other magnitudes one kind is divisible in one direction only and another in two. Their divisibility and continuity correspond to the number of dimensions they have: one is continuous one way, another two ways, and the third is continuous all ways. Now all magnitudes that are divisible are also continuous. Whether continuous magnitudes are all divisible is not clear from our present argument. One thing, however, is clear, that you cannot pass from body to yet another genus in the way that you pass from length to surface and from surface to body; if you could, body could no longer be a perfect or complete magnitude. Any transition to a further genus could only be to make good a deficiency, but what is perfect cannot be defective, for it is complete every way.'

Aristotle's argument that there can be no more than three dimensions rests on nothing more than the associations of the number three: the Pythagorean distinction of the three things, beginning, middle, and end; the use of the number three in divine worship; and our common parlance in which we speak of two as 'both' and not 'all' and use the term 'all' for the first time when we come to three. Ptolemy, however, we are told,[1] set himself to prove by

[1] Simpl. on *De caelo* 9. 21 f. Heib.

geometrical considerations that there can be no more than three dimensions in space. The number of possible dimensions depends, he says, on the number of straight lines that can be drawn through a point mutually at right angles to one another. Three such straight lines can be drawn from any point, but no more. The word for dimension is διάστασις or some cognate form, e.g. Proclus says that a line is a magnitude ἐφ᾽ ἓν διαστατόν. Aristotle says ἐφ᾽ ἓν διαιρετόν 'divisible in one direction', or ἐφ᾽ ἓν συνεχές 'continuous in one direction'. Cf. *Metaph.* 1016ᵇ24–31 and 1020ᵃ11. Of the three dimensions length is associated with up and down, breadth with right and left, and depth with before and behind.

(b) 'Heavy' and 'light'

De caelo I. 3. 269ᵇ20–32

'We must first lay down what we mean by the terms "heavy" and "light", in a manner adequate for the present purpose, leaving a more accurate statement over for a future occasion when we come to consider their essential nature. Let us then define as "heavy" that which naturally moves towards the centre, and as "light" that which naturally moves away from the centre, the heaviest thing being that which takes its place below all the things which are carried downwards, and the lightest that which rises to the top of the things which are carried upwards. Now everything that is carried downwards or upwards must possess either lightness or weight or both, but not relatively to one fixed standard: things are heavy and light in relation to one another, as air for instance is light relatively to water, and water relatively to earth. That body, therefore, which moves in a circle cannot possibly possess either weight or lightness; for it is not possible for it to move, either naturally or unnaturally, either towards the centre or from the centre.'

The further discussion of the meaning of 'heavy' and 'light' here promised is to be found in Book IV, cc. 1–4.

(c) Agelessness of the Universe

Ib. 270ᵇ1–20

'Now the reason why the primary body among all others is eternal and not liable to increase or diminution, but ageless, unchangeable, and unmodified is manifest, to anyone who believes in our assumptions, from what has been said. The theory appears to confirm the results of observation and to be confirmed by them.

All men have some conception with regard to the gods and all, whether barbarians or Greeks, who believe in the existence of gods, assign the highest place to the deity, obviously because they think the immortal to be linked with the immortal, any other assumption being impossible. If then there is anything divine, as there undoubtedly is, it follows that what we have just said about the primary bodily substance is well said. This result is sufficiently brought out by the evidence of sense, and we may be, humanly speaking, convinced of it, for in the whole of past time, according to the records which have passed down from hand to hand, no change appears to have taken place either in the outermost heaven or in any whatever of its proper parts. Even the name which has been handed down from our distant ancestors to the present day seems to indicate that they conceived of it in the same manner as we have spoken of it. For it is not once, nor twice, but over and over again, that the same ideas occur to the minds of men.'

Aristotle explains in the next sentence that the name which he refers to as given to the highest region is 'aether' ($ai\theta\acute{\eta}\rho$, from $\dot{a}\epsilon\grave{\iota}$ $\theta\epsilon\hat{\iota}\nu$, 'running always' for an eternity of time), which all thinkers (except Anaxagoras) made separate from the four elements—earth, fire, air, and water. Anaxagoras alone used $ai\theta\acute{\eta}\rho$ as a name for fire (incorrectly, as Aristotle holds, deriving it from $ai\theta\epsilon\iota\nu$).

It is apropos of Aristotle's allusion to ancient records of observations that Simplicius observes that he has been told that 'the Egyptians had records of astronomical observations made during not less than 630,000 years, while the Babylonian records covered 1,440,000 years'.

(d) Two simple motions, circular and rectilinear

The simple bodies being the four elements together with the primary body to which the name 'aether' has been given, Aristotle goes on to remark that the natural motion of a simple body must itself be simple. Now there are only two simple motions, circular motion and motion in a straight line, and the latter is subdivided into motion towards the centre and motion away from the centre (270^b26–31). The two rectilinear motions are contrary to one another, but there is no other form of motion contrary to the circular, though, if there were, motion in a straight line would have the best claim to be so. Suppose, says Aristotle, that we have a circle with diameter AB, and consider first the upper semicircle. The motion along the circumference from A to B or from B to A is really equivalent to motion along the straight line from A to B or from *B* to *A*, and is not 'contrary' to these respectively; it is not even a unique alternative, for you may have any number of circu-

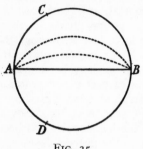

FIG. 35

lar arcs connecting *A*, *B*, whereas the straight path along *AB* is unique. 'Contrary' implies opposed *destinations*. Circular motion from *A* to *B* through *C* is not contrary to motion from *B* to *A* through *D*; motion from *A* to *C* is not 'contrary' even to motion from *A* to *D* (on the lower semicircle) because (if you continue them) you pass through all the same points (though in different order). If you have two (apparently) contrary motions round the whole circle, i.e. motions in opposite directions, one is only a deduction from the other, and the result is that either they neutralize each other (if these are equal) and there is no motion, or there is only one residual motion in one direction or the other, so that the 'contrary' motion might as well not be there: it is like a shoe with no one to wear it. The object of all this argument is to show that there is one body the natural motion of which is circular and continuous.

(e) *Is the universe finite or infinite? Is there an infinite body?*

Aristotle next takes up the question whether this body which naturally has a 'circular' motion continuous and changeless is infinite or finite. This is dealt with in c. 5, which contains first a preliminary general question and secondly some propositions, which Aristotle purports to prove, leading to his final contention.

De caelo I. 5. 271^{b}2–11

'Is there an infinite body as most of the ancient philosophers thought, or is this an impossibility? The answer to the question which of these alternatives is right makes no small difference, nay, it makes all the difference in the world, to research into the truth of things. This question has been the origin of nearly all the controversies between those who have expressed any views about nature as a whole, and it is likely to continue to be so, since the least departure from the truth will lead any who have made it myriads of times farther and farther away from it in the future. Take, for instance, the assertion that there exists a minimum magnitude; if you introduce this, small as it is, you raise the greatest issues in mathematics.'

Aristotle no doubt has in mind the sort of difficulties raised by Zeno's four puzzles, two of which are based on the hypothesis of indivisible lines and magnitudes.

Aristotle goes on ([b]17–26) to argue that every body must be simple or composite, and if the simple bodies are finite, so must that be which is compounded of them. He will, therefore, consider whether any one of the simple bodies can be infinite. He begins with the primary body the nature of which is to revolve circularly.

(f) A circularly moving body must be finite

Ib. [b]26–272[a]20

'That the body which is carried round in a circle (κύκλῳ, circularly) must as a whole be finite is clear from the following considerations. If the body carried round circularly is infinite, the radii drawn from the centre will be infinite. Hence the distance (διάστασις = intervening space) between the infinite radii must be infinite too: by "distance between the radii" I mean that outside of which no magnitude can be found which is in contact with the lines; this must necessarily be infinite. For between finite radii it will always be finite, and further you can always find a magnitude greater than a given one, so that, just as we say that number is infinite because there is no greatest number, the same argument applies also to the intervening space in question. Seeing then that the infinite cannot be traversed and that, if the body is infinite, the said space must be infinite, it will not be possible for the body to move circularly. But we actually see the heavens revolving in a circle, and we have decided by our argument that there is something to which circular motion belongs.

'Now, if from a finite time you subtract a finite time, the remainder too must be finite and have a beginning. If the time taken by a walk has a beginning, there is also a beginning to the movement and therefore to the magnitude (i.e. distance) covered, and similarly in other cases.

'Let ACE be a line infinite in one direction, that of E, and let BB be a line infinite in both directions.

'Then, if ACE describes a circle with centre E, ACE in its circular movement will sometime cut BB and continue to intersect it for a finite time. For the total time in which the heaven completes its revolution in a circle is finite. Therefore the time subtracted from it, during which the

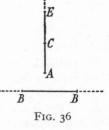

FIG. 36

revolving line continued to intersect the other, will also be finite. There will therefore be some initial point at which *ACE* first cut *BB*: which is impossible. Therefore an infinite body cannot be carried round in a circle, so that the universe could not either, if it were infinite.'

The argument is that an infinitely distant point *E* on *ACE* can, in its revolution, never reach *BB* (at a point on it infinitely distant in either direction as it would have to do) since it would have to traverse an infinite distance (an arc of a circle with a radius infinite in length) in a finite time (part of 24 hours, or whatever time the revolution takes). This contradicts the proposition that it is impossible that the moving object should traverse an infinite distance in a finite time, for the proof of which Aristotle (272ª30) refers to *Phys.* VI, c. 7.

De caelo I. 5. 272ᵇ25–8

'Further, if *C* be the centre *AB* an infinite line, *E* an infinite line perpendicular (to *AB*), *CD*, the moving straight line (also infinite),

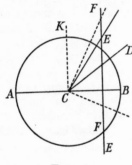

FIG. 37

will never be set free from *E*, but will for ever occupy a position like that of *CE*; for it will always cut *E* at a point *F*. Therefore the infinite line will not be able to complete a circular path.'

Aristotle's argument is that the points *F* in which *CD* successively cuts *E* during the revolution will continually move farther along the line *E* but can never reach the infinitely distant end of it; and therefore *CD*, if supposed infinite, can never complete a revolution about *C*. Mathematically we should have to say that *CD* would in a finite time reach the position *CK* perpendicular to *AB* when it would meet *E* 'at infinity'.

(g) *Bodies and weight*

Ib. 6. 273ª21–7, etc.

'From this it is clear that there cannot be an infinite body. But, in addition to this, there is the fact that, if there is no such thing as an infinite weight, neither can any of the bodies we know be infinite; for, if a body be infinite, its weight must be infinite too. The same argument applies also to the light; for if there is such a thing as infinite heaviness, there must be infinite lightness too, namely when that which floats on the surface is infinite. This is clear from the following considerations.'

The chapter is very long, and the wording very involved, not to say slipshod, but (as a matter of translation) not difficult to make out. We will confine ourselves to setting out shortly the mathematical arguments. The following is the type, a *reductio ad absurdum*.

Suppose that A (represented by the upper line), an infinite body, has a finite weight C.

Deduct from the infinite magnitude the finite part BD, and let its weight be E, which must obviously be less than C.

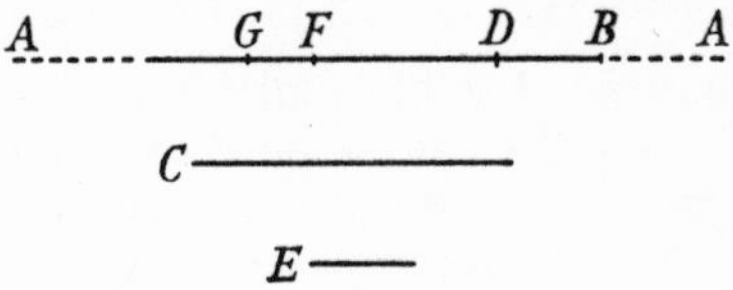

First, let E measure C (without remainder), i.e. let $C = n.E$.

FIG. 38

Take a multiple of BD, as BF, such that $BF = n.BD$.

Therefore, the weight of $BF = n.E = C$; and therefore the finite magnitude (BF) and the infinite magnitude A have equal weights: which is impossible.

A fortiori, (273^{b}5–8), if GB, still finite, is greater than FB, a finite magnitude GB has a *greater* weight than A, the infinite body: which is still more absurd.

(^{b}10–15) If C, E are incommensurable, the same argument still applies.

Take the smallest multiple of E that exceeds C.

Let it be $n.E$. Then n times BF (as GB) is a finite magnitude and has a *greater* weight than C, that of the infinite A.

Again, if the weights are *commensurable* (^{b}15–26), we can begin from the weights, and prove the same thing.

Let $C = (p/q)E$, where p, q are integers and $p > q$. We can then find a magnitude, still finite, which is equal to $(p/q).BD$ and the same result follows.

Aristotle goes on (273^{b}26–274^{a}3): 'It is clear then from what has been said that the weight of the infinite body cannot be finite. Therefore it must be infinite. If then this proves to be impossible, it is impossible that any infinite body should exist.

'But that infinite weight is impossible is manifest from the following considerations.

'If such-and-such a weight moves such-and-such a distance in such-and-such a time, such a weight with more added will move the same distance in a less time, *and the times will have a ratio to one another which is the inverse of that of the weights*; for example, if the half of the weight moves the distance in a given time, its double [i.e. the whole weight] will take half the time. Further, any finite weight traverses any finite distance in some finite time.'

These then are the assumptions (or axioms) on which Aristotle bases his proof. Presumably Aristotle refers to *falling* bodies, though he speaks of them only as 'moving', and not even as moving to their 'proper places'.

The proof amounts to the following:

If weights A, B move the same distance (a) in the times T, t respectively

$$A : B = t : T.$$

Suppose A to be infinite in comparison with B, a finite weight.

'Now there can be no ratio between the infinite and the finite.' In fact, the ratio $A : B$ must be greater than any finite ratio; therefore the ratio $t : T$ must also be greater than any finite ratio. As the time t is finite, it follows that T must be less than any finite time. In other words, as there is no minimum time (274^a9), T, the time in which the infinite A traverses the given distance, is no time at all. If there *were* a minimum time, it would be no use ($^a10$); for then we could find a *finite* magnitude which would traverse the given distance in that minimum time. If the said minimum is T, we have only to find a magnitude which is in the same ratio to B as t is to T, i.e. $(t/T).B$, which is finite. It would follow that this finite magnitude and the infinite magnitude A would move the given distance in the same time: which is impossible.

De caelo I. 7

The proofs in c. 7 are by *reductio ad absurdum* and of the same type as in c. 6.

Aristotle takes the case of an agent body acting on a patient body and moving it a certain distance or qualitatively changing it to a particular degree, and considers three things: (1) the amount of the agent operating, (2) the amount of the patient affected, (3) the time taken. His assumptions are:

    (*a*) that, if the time (3) remains unchanged, (2) increases or diminishes in the same ratio as (1);

    (*b*) that, if (1) remains the same, (3) and (2) increase or diminish in the same ratio.

He purports to prove the following propositions:

I. The infinite cannot be acted on by the finite (274^b33–275^a14.)

Let A be an infinite body, B a finite body, and suppose A moved or modified by B in the time C.

Let D be less than B, and let E be the amount of A affected by D in the same time. (Aristotle tacitly assumes that anything that is less than the infinite must be finite, and therefore that E is finite.)

The amount of A acted on by B in the same time will then be x, where $D : B = E : x$, and, since D, B, E are all finite, x must be finite.

But on our original assumptions we should have

$$D : B = E : A.$$

This is impossible, because the ratio of A, the infinite, to the finite E is no ratio at all.

II. The infinite cannot act on the finite in any time at all (275^a14–24).

Let A be an infinite, B a finite, body, C the time, and suppose A acts on B.

In the same time C, a finite magnitude, say D, will move or change some part of B, say F.

Take E such that $E : D = B : F$.

(As Simplicius observes, Aristotle here refers to B as BF ($=B+F$), perhaps because B contains F as a part of it.)

Then E must be finite, because D, B, F are finite.

Therefore the infinite A and the finite E will produce the same effect in the same time: which is impossible.

III. Nor can infinite be acted on in any way by infinite (275^a24–$^b3$).

Let A, B be two infinites, and let A produce a certain movement or modification of B in the time $C+D$.

A finite part of B, say E, will be similarly affected in a less time, say D.

The amounts of B affected being proportional to the times, take x such that

$$D : (C+D) = E : x.$$

Then, since D, $C+D$, E are all finite, x must be some finite part of B.

But the infinite A produces the same effect on the whole of B in the time $C+D$.

Therefore x must be equal to B, and a part of B is equal to the whole: which is impossible.

(h) *Falling bodies, etc.*

Ib. 8. 277^a27–$^b8$

'That locomotion cannot proceed to infinity is indicated by the fact that earth moves more quickly the nearer it is to the centre, and fire the nearer it is to the upper region. If movement had been through an infinite distance, the speed would have been infinite too, and if the speed, then the weight and the lightness respectively. For as that which by virtue of speed is lower than another body would have owed its speed to its weight, so, if its increase of weight had been infinite, the increase of its speed would also have been infinite.

'Further, in the cases mentioned (earth and fire), it is not by the action of something else that the one is carried upwards and the other downwards; nor is it compulsion such as the "squeezing-out" postulated by some thinkers. Had it been so, the greater mass of fire would have been carried upwards, and the greater mass of earth downwards, more slowly; as it is, on the contrary, it is the greater mass of fire and the greater mass of earth that are carried more quickly to their own place. Nor would their movement have been quicker towards the end if it had been due to compulsion or "squeezing-out"; for everything moves more slowly as it leaves the source of compulsion farther behind, and, if compulsion drives it from any place, it tends, if there is no compulsion, to that place.'

In his commentary on this passage Simplicius refers to a treatise by Hipparchus 'On things borne down owing to their weight' in which Hipparchus expressed a view contrary to that of Aristotle, holding that things are heavier, not lighter, the farther away they are (from the centre).

The theory of 'squeezing-out' as the reason for light bodies moving upwards was supported, we are told, by Strato and Epicurus after Aristotle's time. According to Simplicius, they held that all bodies are heavy and are carried towards the centre; but owing to the fact that the heaviest take the lowest place, those which are less heavy are forcibly 'squeezed-out' by them, and so go upwards; but if the earth were taken away water would go to the centre, if water were taken away so would air, and if air, then fire also.

I have quoted the passage because it is cited (especially 277^{a}32–3 and ^{b}3–5) among other passages as evidence that Aristotle thought that a weight of 10 lb. would fall ten times as quickly as a weight of 1 lb. Otherwise I have nothing to add to the notes in the Oxford translation.

(i) Mathematical 'impossibility'

De caelo I. 11. 281^{a}4–7

'The term "impossible" is applied to the "ungenerated" when used of that which cannot be generated in the sense that it was not before, but later is, e.g. the proposition that the diagonal is commensurable (with the side).'

Ib. 12. 281^{b}3–7

'One kind of "impossible" and "possible", and of "false" and "true",
is that which is relative to an hypothesis. I mean, for instance, that
it is impossible, if certain assumptions are made, that a triangle
should have its angles together equal to two right angles, or that,
on certain assumptions, the diagonal should be commensurable.'

Blancanus observes[1] that we should have to conclude that the
diagonal of a square is commensurable with its side if we assumed
that all lines are made up of indivisible elements, for then the
indivisible element would be a common measure of both. Cf. also
299^{a}2–11.

As regards the dependence of the two-right-angles theorem upon
a particular hypothesis see note on *Phys.* II. 9. 200^{a}15–19 (pp. 100–1).

(j) *Priority of circle and sphere among figures*

The circle, says Aristotle, is prior to all other plane figures, and
'perfect', because it is bounded by one line (whereas rectilinear
figures are bounded by three or more lines), and because you can
add nothing to it (whereas to a straight line you can add to any
extent). Similarly, a sphere is the primary and perfect solid figure,
because it is bounded by *one* surface (whereas rectilinear solids are
bounded by several). Aristotle goes on:

Ib. II. 4. 286^{b}27–33

'Again, those who divide (bodies) into planes and generate bodies
from planes seem to bear testimony to the truth of what we have
said. The sphere is the only one among solid bodies which they do
not divide up, for the reason that it has no more surfaces than one.
The division of bodies into planes, in fact, is not like dividing a
whole into its parts, but is by way of division into parts different in
form. It is clear then that the sphere is the first of solid figures.'

The allusion is, of course, to the passage in the *Timaeus*[2] where out
of two elementary triangles Plato makes up the faces of four out of
the five regular solids, and then shows how to fit the faces together
in order to give the outward shape of the solids respectively. The
triangles are (1) the right-angled triangle in which the hypotenuse
is double of the smaller of the other two sides (this is really the half
of an equilateral triangle), and (2) the isosceles right-angled triangle.

Out of six triangles of the first kind, put together as shown in
the accompanying figure, Plato forms an equilateral triangle. Three
of the four regular solids have equilateral triangles for faces; the

---

[1] *Aristotelis Loca Arithmetica*, p. 77.   [2] 54 C–55 C.

tetrahedron has four such faces, the octahedron eight, and the icosahedron twenty. The fourth regular solid, the cube, has six square faces all equal to one another, and each square face is made up of four of the second kind of elementary triangle put together as shown. The four solids are then appropriated as the ultimate constituents, or units, of the four elements, the tetrahedron of fire, the octahedron of air, the icosahedron of water, and the cube of earth. Plato then postulates the transformation of the four elements into one another according to the number of their triangular faces, as if the figures could be interchanged by merely separating the triangular faces and putting them together again differently; the unit of water (twenty triangular faces) is made to produce $2\frac{1}{2}$ units of air $(20 \div 8 = 2\frac{1}{2})$, the unit of air (eight faces) two of fire $(8 \div 4 = 2)$. This method of generating the regular solids is criticized by Aristotle in more than one place (cf. *Phys.* VI. 1 and *De caelo* III. 1; see below, pp. 174-5).

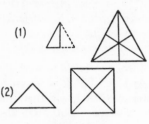

(1)

(2)

Fig. 39

The fifth regular solid, the dodecahedron, has for faces twelve equilateral and equiangular pentagons, but these pentagons cannot be divided up into triangles of either or both of the species used for composing the faces of the other four solids. Accordingly, God found a use for the dodecahedron in 'embroidering the universe with constellations',[1] i.e. forming twelve regions in the sky for mapping out the constellations.

(k) *A revolving heaven must be spherical*

De caelo II. 4. 287[a]11-22

'Again, since it appears and we assume that the universe revolves in a circle, and it has been shown that outside the outermost revolution there is neither void nor place, it follows, on these grounds, that it must be spherical. For, if it is in the shape of a rectilinear solid, it will be a necessary consequence that there must be place and body and void outside it. A rectilinear solid figure, if it revolves in a circle, will never occupy the same place (from moment to moment); but, where there was body before, there will not now be body, and where there is not body now, there will once more be body because of the "jutting-out" ($\pi\alpha\rho\acute{a}\lambda\lambda\alpha\xi\iota\nu$) of the angles. Similarly, too, if there were any other figure in which the radii are

---

[1] *Timaeus* 55 C, tr. Taylor.

unequal, e.g. a lentiform or an egg-shaped figure, the result in every such case would be that there would be both place and void outside the revolution, because the whole does not occupy the same place throughout.'

Simplicius observes, after Alexander, that the argument will not always apply if the figure revolves about an axis of symmetry, e.g. in the case of a spheroid revolving about its major or minor axis, or a cone or a cylinder revolving about its axis. Nor would it apply if the solid were what Archimedes calls a 'solid rhombus', which consists of two right cones with equal bases placed so that their bases coincide and their vertices point in opposite directions. But in the case of a rectilinear solid the argument would apply even if the axis of revolution were an axis of symmetry. Take the case of a tetrahedron revolving about a straight line joining two opposite angular points; then obviously the square section through the centre which is perpendicular to the axis would change its 'place' from moment to moment in the revolution, and the same would be true of the whole solid.

An instructive case of the use in mathematics of the word παραλ-λάττειν (from which παράλλαξις is derived) occurs in Eucl. I. 8. Two triangles with their sides respectively equal have to be proved, by superposition, to be congruent. Their bases being equal they are superposed so that their bases coincide. Then, says Euclid, if the other sides do not coincide, they will 'fall away' or 'askew' (παραλλάξουσιν), i.e. will fail to come together or to cover one another as in the annexed figure: which contradicts the previous proposition I. 7 and is therefore impossible. A similar use occurs in Eucl. III. 24.

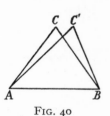

FIG. 40

(*l*) *Shortest line returning on itself*

Ib. ᵃ27–8

'Of lines starting from a point and returning to the same point the circle is the shortest.'

The statement as it stands is incomplete. It means, no doubt, that, of all lines with the same *content* (i.e. enclosing the same area), the circle is the shortest. This proposition was proved by Zenodorus, between, say, 200 B.C. and A.D. 90, in a treatise περὶ ἰσομέτρων σχημάτων, *On Iso(peri)metric Figures*, which is largely reproduced by Pappus.

Simplicius explains Aristotle's argument thus.[1] The movement of the heaven is the measure of movements in general; the movement which measures others is the quickest; the quickest movement, if the power used is the same, is that which has the least distance to go; the least periphery belonging to any of the different figures which enclose the same space is, in the case of plane areas, a circular circumference, and in the case of solids, a sphere; therefore the revolution of the heaven is that of a body which has the shape of a sphere.

It is the case of the sphere which is necessary to Aristotle's argument. As Simplicius says,[2] of all bodies of different shapes but of equal solid content, the sphere is that which has the least surface. If, therefore, we compare the effect of assuming different shapes for the heaven, subject to their solid content being the same, the sphere is the figure which will give, for the same power, the 'quickest and least' movement, and therefore the movement which is the best measure for all other movements whatever.

(m) *Surface of water at rest is spherical*

De caelo II. 4. 287ᵇ4–14

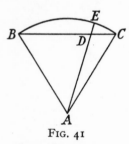

FIG. 41

'That at all events the surface of water is spherical is manifest if we assume as an hypothesis that it is the nature of water to collect in the hollower place, "hollower" in this case meaning nearer to the centre. Let radii AB, AC be drawn and let BC be joined. Then a line AD drawn to (meet) the base is less than the radii. Therefore the place (D) is hollower; and accordingly the water will collect all round it until equality is established.

'But AE is equal to the radii.

'Thus the surface of the water must come to be at the ends of (all) the radii; for only then can it rest.

'And the line which passes through the extremities of the radii is circular;

'Therefore the surface, BEC, of the water will be spherical.'

As usual, the language lacks precision. The line AD is probably supposed to be drawn perpendicular to BC, because in that case the point D would be the point in BC which is actually nearest to the centre and therefore the 'hollowest', and the water would tend

¹ p. 411.   ² p. 412. 20 f.

to that place first and flow round it, with the ultimate result that no place would be left on the surface of the water 'hollower' than any other, and the surface will pass through the ends of all the radii, as *AE*, between *AB* and *AC*.

A similar proof, but in a more precise form, was given by Adrastus and is reproduced by Theon of Smyrna.[1]

Archimedes has, in Prop. 2 of his treatise *On Floating Bodies*, I, the more scientific theorem that: 'The surface of any fluid at rest is the surface of a sphere the centre of which is the same as the centre of the earth.'

Archimedes proves this by the consideration of the pressure exerted upon any portion of the fluid below the surface by the portion which is above it, and which, in a postulate, he declares to be in 'a perpendicular direction'. He does not say what he means by a perpendicular direction, but in the course of Props. 1, 2 it becomes clear that he means in the direction of the centre of the earth. The following is a sketch of the proof.

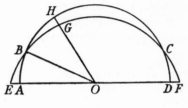

FIG. 42

Suppose that the surface of the fluid is cut by a plane through the centre, *O*, of the earth in the curve *ABHCD*.

Then shall *ABHCD* be the circumference of a circle.

If not, some of the radii from *O* to the curve will be greater than others. Let *OB* be greater than some of the others.

Draw a circle with radius *OB*. Let it be *EBF*, making *OE* greater than *OB*, and radii, as *OG*, beyond *OB* less than *OB*.

Draw the angle *BOG* equal to the angle *AOB*; let *OG* produced meet the surface of the fluid in *H*.

Lastly, draw in the plane an arc of a circle *PQR* with centre *O*, meeting *OE*, *OB*, *OG* in *P*, *Q*, *R*.

Then the parts of the fluid along *PQR* are uniform and continuous, and the part *PQ* is compressed by the part between it and *AB*, and the part *QR* by the part between it and *BH*.

But the compressing parts will be unequal because the arc *AB* is within, and the arc *BH* without, the circle *EBG*.

Consequently the parts along *PQ*, *QR* will be unequally compressed, and the part which is compressed the less will be set in motion by that which is compressed the more. Therefore there will not be rest: which is contrary to the hypothesis.

[1] pp. 123-4 H.

Therefore, the section of the surface will be the circumference of a circle with centre O, and so will all other sections by planes through O.

Therefore the surface will be a sphere with centre O.

(n) Construction of bodies out of planes

De caelo III. 1. 299ᵃ2–11

'The most superficial observation shows that those who hold this view and construct bodies out of planes assert, in effect, what is in several respects in contradiction to mathematics. One ought surely either not to disturb the hypotheses of science or else to replace them by others more convincing. Moreover, the same reasoning which maintains that solids are made up of planes would prove that planes are made up of lines and lines of points. Were this the case, a part of a line need not be a line. This matter has already been considered in the discussions on motion, where it was proved that there are no indivisible lines.'

Ib. ᵇ23–31

'Again, the idea that planes can only be put together so as to meet along a line is absurd. For just as line and line can be put together in two ways, namely lengthwise and breadthwise, so can a plane and a plane. A line and a line can be put together by being superposed linearly and not added. If similarly planes be put together so that their surfaces are in contact, their superposition in this way will produce a body which is neither an element nor composed of elements.'

The reference in 299ᵃ10 is to *Phys.* VI. 1.

As we have seen, Aristotle is clear that a line cannot be made up of points. Cf. *Phys.* IV. 8. 215ᵇ19; 11. 220ᵃ18–21; VI. 1. 231ᵃ21–232ᵃ22, and notes thereon; also *De gen. et corr.* I. 2. 317ᵃ10–12. For like reasons a plane surface cannot be made up of lines, or a solid body of planes.

The method adopted in the *Timaeus* for exhibiting the shapes of the regular solids by putting together equilateral triangles, squares, and regular pentagons with their sides in contact so as to form solid angles, and thereby solid figures, does not give actual solid figures but only hollow shells devoid of thickness.

Simplicius observes that some of the commentators on Plato, and notably Iamblichus, held that in generating the solids in this way Plato was speaking 'symbolically' and not literally. This is, I have no doubt, the true explanation; indeed, it may be inferred from the idea that three of the solids are such that one of them can be transformed into either of the others by rearranging the triangles so as to make different solid angles; this idea would be too fantastic on any other assumption.

Ib. 4. 303ᵃ31–ᵇ1

'Bodies differ in their figures, and all figures are made up of pyramids, rectilinear figures of rectilinear pyramids, and spheres of eight (pyramidal) parts.'

Here the pyramids are not in general *regular* pyramids (tetrahedra). The eight 'parts' of the sphere are evidently obtained by cutting a sphere by three planes mutually at right angles passing through the centre and are only *quasi*-pyramidal, being formed by three quadrants of circles for three faces and part of the surface of the sphere for the fourth face.

Ib. 5. 304ᵇ2–4

'If (the elementary figure assigned to each of the four elements) is divisible, those who give a figure to fire will have to conclude that a part of fire is not fire, because a pyramid is not made up of pyramids.'

The figure assigned to fire is the regular pyramid or tetrahedron, which cannot be divided into tetrahedra and nothing else. Euclid proves in XII. 3 that a pyramid with a triangular base can be divided into two pyramids equal and similar to one another and also similar to the original pyramid, and two equal *prisms*, and that the process of dividing the pyramids in this way can go on indefinitely. He also proves (Prop. 7) that any prism with triangular bases can be divided into three pyramids equal to one another in content but not similar.

In III. 7, after disposing of the views of Empedocles and Democritus on the generation of the elements from one another, Aristotle goes on:

Ib. 305ᵇ28–306ᵃ5

'The remaining alternative is that they should be generated by changing into one another. This may happen in two ways, either (1) by change of shape, as you may make a sphere and a cube respectively out of the same wax, or (2) by dissolution into planes, as some assert.[1]

'Now if (1) generation is by change of shape, we must perforce admit that the elementary bodies are indivisible. For, if they are divisible, we shall have a part of fire which is not fire,[2] and a part of earth which is not earth, since not every part of a pyramid is a pyramid nor every part of a cube a cube. If generation is by

---

[1] Plato in the *Timaeus*.   [2] See above.

dissolution into planes, it is in the first place absurd that the elements cannot *all* be generated from one another. Yet the supporters of the theory are obliged to maintain this and do maintain it. It is not reasonable that one only of the elements [earth] should have no part in the transformations, and it is not even consistent with sense-observation, which shows that they all alike change into one another.'

It is admitted in the *Timaeus*[1] that earth represented by the cube cannot be changed into any of the other three elements (though the latter can change into one another), because the elementary triangle (the isosceles right-angled triangle) out of which the square and cube are made up is different from the elementary triangle (the half of an equilateral triangle) from which the faces of the tetrahedron, octahedron, and icosahedron all arise.[2]

De caelo III. 7. 306ª20–3

'Nor even where the elements can be resolved into one another is it reasonable that triangles should be left in the air, so to speak. This, however, actually happens in the transition from one (of the three figures) to another, because they are made up of unequal numbers of triangles.'

This happens when, for example, the unit of water (the icosahedron with twenty equilateral triangles as faces) is broken up. The twenty triangles may be separated into two sets of eight and one of four, giving two octahedrons (units of air) and four triangles over, which latter Aristotle presumably regarded as 'in the air' (παραιωρούμενα, 'in a state of suspense' or 'stranded'). In this particular case Plato himself takes the four triangles to form one tetrahedron (or unit of fire); for in *Timaeus* 56 D he says that, if water is divided up it may become one particle of fire and two of air. He says even (56 E) that 'when air is vanquished and broken small, from two-*and-a-half* particles one whole figure of water will be composed'. This seems to show that Plato did not himself regard his units or particles as being indivisible. In any case they are, according to him, all of them so small as not to be visible to us; only when many are heaped together is their united mass seen (56 B–C).

Simplicius on this passage quotes from Alexander and, at length, from Proclus who, according to Simplicius, wrote a tract disposing of the criticisms of Aristotle. Alexander pointed out that, if you take three units of air (eight triangles each) and transform them into one of water (twenty triangles), there are four triangles remaining over; these we cannot suppose to become one of *fire*, since the transformation here is *downwards* as it were, i.e. by way of cooling and

[1] 54 C.   [2] Cf. pp. 160–1, above.

condensation, and it is inconceivable that the same transformation should have an upward element (a change from air to fire) at the same time; hence the four triangles *must* in this case remain for a time 'in suspense' till some other change absorbs them. Proclus thought this perfectly reasonable; and the principle is recognized by Plato himself in the case of earth. Since the elementary triangle appropriated to the earth, the isosceles right-angled triangle, cannot be transformed into the right-angled triangle appropriated to the other elements, the earth cannot be transformed into any of the other three; and 'when earth meets with fire and is dissolved by the keenness of it, it would drift about, whether it were dissolved in fire itself or in some other mass of air or water, until the parts of it meeting and being again united become earth once more; for it could never pass into any other kind'.[1]

De caelo III. 7–8. 306ª23–ᵇ8

'Further, those who hold these views must necessarily assume that generation does not begin from body, for where a thing is generated from planes it cannot have been generated from body. Further, they are obliged to maintain that not every body is divisible and so to come into conflict with the most exact sciences; for whereas these, the mathematical, assume that even the object of thought is divisible, the thinkers in question do not even admit that every sensible object is divisible, so anxious are they to save their hypothesis. For all who give to each of the elements a certain figure, and by that figure define their substances, must necessarily make them indivisible, since when the pyramid or the sphere is divided up in any manner the figure left over will not be a sphere or a pyramid as the case may be. Hence either a part of fire will not be fire, so that there will be something prior to the element—since everything must be either an element or composed of elements—or not every body is divisible.

'And, speaking generally, the attempt to give figures to the simple elements is irrational, first, because it will be found that they do not fill the whole (of a space). For, among plane figures, it is agreed that there are only three which fill up space, the triangle, the square, and the hexagon; while among solids there are only the pyramid and the cube.'

When in 306ª32–3 Aristotle says that a 'pyramid' cannot be divided into 'pyramids' and nothing else, he means *regular* pyramids or tetrahedra. As to the subdivision of tetrahedra see p. 175, above.

The fact (306ᵇ5–7) that only three kinds of regular rectilinear plane figures will fill up space in a plane round a point was no doubt known

---

[1] *Timaeus* 56 D.

to the Pythagoreans; for it is an obvious deduction from their theorems that the three angles of a triangle are together equal to two right angles, that all the angles that can be drawn in a plane round a point make up four right angles, and that the sum of all the interior angles of any polygon together with four right angles make up twice as many right angles as the figure has sides. Moreover, the fact that we can have a floor laid with bricks of the three shapes respectively must have been known long before the fact was proved geometrically, e.g. to the ancient Egyptians.

When, however, Aristotle passes to solid figures and says that the 'pyramid' and the cube will fill up three-dimensional space, he is correct as regards the cube, but incorrect as regards the pyramid if the pyramid is *regular*, i.e. a tetrahedron; see above.

Blancanus takes credit for having been the first to point this out, when all commentators before him, Greek, Latin, and Arabian, had accepted Aristotle's statement as correct. According to Blancanus, Benedetti (1530–90) did not succeed in vindicating Aristotle, nor did Maurolycus, who, however, maintained that pyramids and octahedra fitted together would fill up space.

A possible view is that Aristotle did not mean literally that pyramids alone would fill up space, but merely (say) that, if you put six tetrahedra together round a common point as vertex and all in contact with one another, the six plane faces that meet in this point form a *plane*, and not a solid angle, at it (cf. the explanation to this effect in Euclid XIII, addendum to Prop. 18). But it seems better to suppose that Aristotle simply made a slip.

(o) *Principles should be the fewest possible*

De caelo III. 4. 302^{b}26–30

'It is manifest that it is far better to make the principles finite in number. Nay, they should be the fewest possible provided they enable all the same results to be proved. This is what mathematicians insist upon; for they take as principles things finite either in kind or in number.'

(p) *Motion of falling and rising bodies*

Ib. 5. 304^{b}17–18

'Just as fire, in proportion as its amount becomes greater, is carried the more quickly upwards with the motion proper to it.'

Ib. IV. 1. 308^{a}29–33

'We define then as absolutely light that which is carried upwards or to the extremity, and as absolutely heavy that which is carried downwards or to the centre; while that which is light or lighter relatively to something else is that which, when the two have weight and are equal in bulk, is surpassed by the other in the speed of its natural downward motion.'

Ib. 2. 309^b12–15

'But of course the greater mass of fire is carried upwards faster than the lesser, and again, in the same way, the greater mass of gold or lead is carried downwards more quickly; and so with everything that has weight.'

Ib. 4. 311^b1–13

'It is because of the difference between the first elements of body that the same things appear to be not everywhere heavy or not everywhere light. For instance, in air, a log of wood weighing a talent will be heavier than a mina of lead, but in water it will be lighter. The reason is that all the elements except fire have weight, and all have lightness except earth. Earth, then, and such things as have the greatest admixture of earth must needs have weight everywhere, while water is heavy everywhere except in earth, and air everywhere except in water and earth; for in their own place all these bodies have weight except fire, even air. There is evidence of this in the fact that a bottle inflated weighs more than a bottle empty. Hence, if a thing contains more air than earth or water, it may in water be lighter, and in air heavier than another; for it does not float in air, but may float in water.'

Ib. ^b33–312^a1

'Further, the direction in which fire is carried upwards, and earth as well as everything that has weight downwards, is seen to make similar [i.e. equal] angles (with the earth's surface). Hence the heavy things must necessarily be carried towards the centre.'

That is, the direction of the fall of a heavy object is at right angles to the surface ⟨supposed spherical⟩ of the earth at the point of impact ⟨strictly speaking, at right angles to the tangent-plane at the point⟩.

The expression 'similar angles', meaning equal angles is, according to Proclus,[1] a relic of the view that angles come under the category of 'quality' rather than 'quantity'; Eudemus is referred to as having held this view.

The making of equal ('similar') angles (πρὸς ὁμοίας γωνίας) with a plane recalls the definition (10) in Euclid, Book I: 'When a straight line set up on a straight line makes the adjacent angles equal to one another, each of the equal angles is *right*, and the straight line standing on the other is called a *perpendicular* to that on which it stands.'

[1] On Eucl. i, p. 125 f.

VIII

METEOROLOGY

(a) *A geometrical proposition*

Meteor. III. 3. 373ª3–19

'Since the reflection takes place in the same way from every point, the result is necessarily a circle or a segment of a circle: for if the

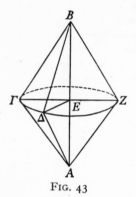

FIG. 43

lines start from the same point and end at the same point and are equal, the points where they form an angle will always lie on a circle.

'Let *AΓB* and *AZB* and *AΔB* be lines each of which goes from the point *A* to the point *B* and forms an angle. Let the lines *AΓ*, *AZ*, *AΔ* be equal and those at *B*, *ΓB*, *ZB*, *ΔB* equal too. Draw the line *AEB*. Then the triangles are equal; for their base *AEB* is equal. Draw perpendiculars to *AEB* from the angles: *ΓE* from *Γ*, *ZE* from *Z*, *ΔE* from *Δ*. Then these perpendiculars are equal, being in equal

triangles. And they are all in one plane, being all at right angles to *AEB* and meeting at a single point *E*. So if you draw the line it will be a circle and *E* its centre. Now *B* is the sun, *A* the eye, and the circumference passing through the points *ΓZΔ* the cloud from which the line of sight is reflected to the sun.'

Aristotle assumes that if a number of broken lines, as *ACB*, *ADB*, *AFB* (*AΓB*, *AΔB*, *AZB* of Aristotle) are drawn from *A* to *B* such that, if the lines form angles at *C*, *D*, *F* respectively, not only the total lengths of *ACB*, *ADB*, *AFB*, but also (1) the parts *AC*, *AD*, and *AF* are equal, and (2) the remaining parts *BC*, *BD*, *BF* are equal, the points *C*, *D*, *F*, etc., all lie on a circle.

If these assumptions are made it is easy to prove that *C*, *D*, *F*, etc., all lie on a circle. For, if we join the points *A*, *B* by the line *AEB*, all the triangles *ACB*, *ADB*, *AFB*, etc., will be equal in all respects (having all sides respectively equal). Hence, if from each of the points *C*, *D*, *F*, we draw perpendiculars to the line *AB* which is the base of all the triangles *ACB*, *ADB*, *AFB*, the perpendiculars will all be equal. Also they will meet *AB* in one point *E* because in each of the right-angled triangles formed by *AC*, *AD*, *AF* with *AB* and the three perpendiculars respectively we have two angles equal (the angles at A and the right angles) and one side (AC, AD, AF), so that the third sides are equal, i.e. they form the one line AE.

Now the lines EC, ED, EF, being all perpendicular to the one straight line AB which meets them, are in one plane (cf. Eucl. XI. 5); and since they are all equal, the locus of C, D, F is a circle.

(b) A locus-proposition

Ib. 5. $375^{b}16-376^{b}12$

This chapter is of the greatest possible interest to the historian of mathematics (in the sense of *pure* mathematics, geometry in particular, as distinct from physics and the physical explanation of the phenomenon of the rainbow) because it contains, and proves quite correctly, a theorem which was (as we learn from Eutocius' commentary on Apollonius' *Conics*[1]) given and proved in almost exactly the same way by Apollonius in a treatise (now lost) belonging to the 'Treasury of Analysis', presumably the work called *Plani Loci*.

The theorem does not appear in Euclid's *Elements*; but its occurrence in Aristotle shows that it was discovered and similarly proved before Aristotle's time.

Apollonius enunciated the theorem in these terms:

'Given two points in a plane and a ratio between unequal straight lines, it is possible to describe a circle in the plane such that the straight lines inflected from the given points to the circumference of the circle shall have a ratio the same as the given one.'

I called attention to this remarkable coincidence in my edition of *The Thirteen Books of Euclid's Elements*[2] and gave full details. But I have not seen it noticed either before or since; and I think that the more recent writers on our passage[3] have lost much by the omission.

It is worth while to see in the first place how the theorem can be deduced from that of Eucl. VI. 3 with an extension given by Robert Simson, which, however, is assumed by Pappus without proof.[4]

Euclid VI. 3 is to the effect that, if ABC be any triangle, and if the angle at A be bisected by AD meeting BC in D, then

$$BD : DC = BA : AC \qquad (a)$$

Simson's extension proves that, if BA be produced to F, and if

---

[1] *Apollonius*, vol. ii, pp. 180–4 Heib.   [2] Vol. ii, pp. 198–200.
[3] In particular, Fr. Poske in *Zeitschrift für Math. und Physik*, xxviii (1883), hist.-litt. Abtheilung, pp. 134–8, and Otto Gilbert in *Die meteorologischen Theorien des griechischen Altertums*, 1907, pp. 611–13.
[4] Pappus, vii. 730. 24.

the external angle CAF be bisected by AE meeting BC *produced* in E, then

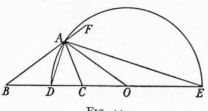

FIG. 44

$$BA : AC = BE : EC \quad (\beta)$$

From (a) combined with (β) we derive

$$BD : DC = BE : EC$$
$$= BA : AC \quad (\gamma)$$

Now, since the angle DAC is half of the angle BAC, and the angle CAE is half of the angle CAF, while the angles BAC, CAF are together equal to $2R$, the angle DAE is a right angle.

It follows that a circle described on DE as diameter will pass through A.

Therefore, if any ratio $h : k$ be given ($h > k$) and any straight line BC, and if BC be divided internally at D, and externally at E, in the ratio $h : k$, the points D, E are fixed points, and the circle described on DE as diameter will be the locus of all points A which are such that

$$BA : AC = BD : DC = BE : EC = h : k$$

The curious fact is that both Aristotle and Apollonius construct the locus in question without making any use of the points D and E. Starting with the given ratio (greater than unity) between the straight lines h, k and the straight line BC, they find (1) a point O, which is in fact the middle point of DE and the centre of the required circle, (2) the length of the radius of that circle ($= OA$ or OD or OE) and so construct it.

The *raison d'être* of their construction can be shown by the following analysis.

Let O be the middle point of DE.

By hypothesis,

$$h : k = BD : DC = BE : EC$$
$$\therefore \qquad EC : CD = EB : BD$$
$$\therefore \quad (EC + CD) : (EC \sim CD) = (EB + BD) : (EB \sim BD),$$
or $\qquad\qquad 2OD : 2OC = 2OB : 2OD,$
i.e. $\qquad\qquad OD : OC = OB : OD$
so that $\qquad\qquad BO \cdot OC = OD^2 \qquad\qquad (\delta)$

We have, therefore, the radius of the required circle (OD), but the position of O still remains to be found.

It follows from (δ) that, if A be *any* point on the required circle,

$$BO : OA = OA : OC \qquad\qquad (\epsilon)$$
so that $\qquad\qquad BOA, AOC$ are similar triangles.

Let us denote the radius of the circle ($= OD$) by r.
Then, by (γ) above,

$$h : k = BD : DC = BE : EC$$
$$= (BD+BE) : (DC+EC)$$
$$= (BD+BE) : DE$$
$$= 2BO : 2OD$$
$$= BO : r \qquad\qquad (\zeta)$$
$$= r : OC \qquad\qquad (\text{by } \epsilon)$$

∴ alternately $k : OC = h : r$

Now find a straight line x such that each of the last two ratios is equal to $x : BC$.
Since

$$x : BC = k : OC = h : r, \qquad\qquad (\eta)$$
$$(x+k) : BO = h : r,$$

and, alternately,

$$x+k : h = BO : r$$
$$= h : k \qquad\qquad \text{by } (\zeta) \text{ above} \qquad (\theta)$$

The last relation enables us to find x in terms of h, k, and (η) enables us to find r from x, h and BC.

Meteor. III. 5. 375ᵇ16–376ᵇ12

'The fact that a rainbow can never form a (complete) circle or any segment greater than a semicircle, and the other facts which emerge with regard to it, will on consideration be clear from a diagram. Let A be a hemisphere standing on the circle of the horizon, K the centre, and G some other point just rising. Then, if straight lines be drawn from K forming as it were a cone with GK as axis, and if lines joined from K to M are (there) inflected from the hemisphere to G (passing) over the greater angle [at K], the straight lines so drawn *will fall on the circumference of a circle*. If the inflexion takes place at the time of the rising or setting of the heavenly body, the part of the circle [of the rainbow] cut off above the earth by the horizon will be a semicircle; if the star be above the horizon, the part of the circle (so cut off) above the earth will be always less than a semicircle and it will be least when the body is on the meridian circle.

'Let it first be just rising, as at the point G, let KM be inflected to G, and let a plane A be set out, namely that determined by the triangle GKM. The section of the sphere will be a great circle; let it be A—it will make no difference which the plane drawn through the triangle KMG is of the (various) planes which pass through GK.

'The straight lines in a particular (given) ratio which can be drawn from G, K cannot be constructed to more than one point of the semicircle A. For, since the points K, G and the straight line KG are given, MG must be given also, and therefore the ratio of MG to MK. *Then M will lie on a given circular circumference.* Let this be NM. Hence *the point of intersection of the circles is given.* In fact no pair of lines in the same ratio can be constructed from the same points *in the same plane* to any point other than one lying on the circumference MN [lit. 'to any circumference other than MN'].

'Let a line DB [i.e. $D+B$] be set out and let it be so cut that

$$D : B = MG : MK.$$

MG is greater than KM because the inflexion of the cone [meaning the inflected line which is one of the generators of the cone] subtends the greater angle of the triangle KMG. Therefore D is greater than B.

'Let there be added to B the line F such that

$$(B+F) : D = D : B.$$

'Next let B be made to bear the same ratio to another straight line KP [i.e. let KP be taken of such a length that B bears to it the same ratio] as F bears to KG; and let MP be joined from P to M.

'P will then be the pole [really the *centre*] of the circle on which the lines from K fall, for,

as F is to KG, so is B to KP, and so will D be to PM.

'Suppose that D is not in the said ratio to PM, but (is in that ratio) to some straight line less or greater than PM—it will make no difference which—let it be (in the said ratio) to PR.

'Therefore GK, KP, PR will have the same ratio to one another that F, B, D have [Aristotle writes, carelessly, "D, B, F"].

'But the relations of D, B, F were such that

$$(F+B) : D = D : B,$$

so that $\qquad PG$ [$= PK+KG$] $: PR = PR : PK,$

⟨therefore the triangles GPR, RPK are similar⟩.

'If then we join GR, KR from G, K to R, these lines GR, KR will have the same ratio as GP to PR, for the (sides of the) triangles GPR, KRP [better RPK] about the same angle P are proportional, so that

[*alternando*] $\qquad PR : KR = GP : PR.$

[There is an error here. Two corrections are possible: either (1) we may alter the right-hand ratio to $GP : GR$ or we may change the left one ($PR : KR$) to $GR : KR$. The second is the better alteration because it follows Alexander and Olympiodorus. The Oxford translator adopts it.

We write therefore $GR : KR = GP : PR$.]

'But MG has this same ratio to KM, for both ratios are the same as the ratio $D : B$.

[We have in fact $MG : KM = D : B$ (by the original construction)

and $PG : PR = (PK + KG) : PR$

$$= (F + B) : D \qquad \text{(see above)}$$
$$= D : B, \qquad \text{by construction.}]$$

'Hence from the points G, K there will be constructed lines in the same ratio not only to the circumference MN but also elsewhere [ἄλλοθι, i.e. to some point *not* on the circumference MN]: which is impossible.

'Since then D has not the said ratio [equal to $F : KG = B : KP$— see above] to either a lesser or a greater line than MP—the proof being similar in either case—it is clear that D is in the said ratio to MP; therefore, as MP is to PK, so is $PG : MP$, and so lastly is MG to MK also.

'If therefore with P as pole and MP as distance a circle be described, it will pass through all the angular points made by the lines which are inflected from the circle MA. If not, we can show in like manner that lines in the given ratio can be constructed to different points on the semicircle: which was proved to be impossible.'

[There is some difficulty in the last paragraph, caused by the description of P as the 'pole' of a certain circle to be drawn. P is really the *centre* of the circle which is the locus of the points in which the pairs of straight lines in the given ratio set up from K, G meet, although it is the pole of the circle described by M when the plane of A is made to rotate bodily about KG as axis. Accordingly, Poske says[1] of the construction 'with P as pole and PM as distance' that what is described is 'rather the surface of a circular cone about PK as axis' than a circle. But the difficulty about this is that it is only in the next lines ($376^{b}12$ f.) that we are first asked to suppose the whole plane of A and the rest made to turn about GKP as axis.]

To enable Aristotle's proof to be clearly visualized I have drawn a new figure with G the *rising* heavenly body to the *right* (instead of the left) which seems more appropriate. As usual, *Roman* capitals are substituted for the Greek with F instead of Z, G for H, and H for Θ; this makes the proof easier to follow, especially as Π and H are easily confused.

GMR is a semicircle in a plane which for clearness sake we will suppose perpendicular to the horizon (Aristotle explains in $375^{b}33$

[1] $376^{a}1$, p. 136.

that it makes no difference what angle it makes with the horizon provided its diameter is the horizontal line *GK*). *K* is the centre of

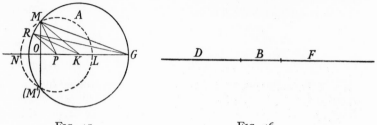

Fig. 45   Fig. 46

the semicircle. The radius *KM* is supposed to be reflected (or inflected) from the semicircle at *M* to *G*, the *rising* heavenly body. The inflexion is said to be 'over the greater angle' (375ᵇ24, ἐπὶ τὴν μείζω γωνίαν)—a requirement which is satisfied in my figure but not in that taken from the commentators, the angle being *MKG*.

Aristotle assumes that *KM*, *MG* have a constant ratio to one another (though he does not venture to assign a specific value to it), and he asserts that, the points *K*, *G* being given, straight lines 'in this ratio' can only be inflected from *K*, *G* to *one* point on the semicircle *GMR* (376ᵃ1–3), as *M* itself; this is because all the points to which straight lines in a given ratio can be inflected from two fixed points lie on a certain circle ('*M* will touch [i.e. lie on] a given circumference', ᵃ5–6). The intersection with the circle *GMR* determines *one* point *M* on it and one only (on one side of the diameter *GK*).

I have inserted in my diagram the extra letter *L* to show that, in my view, 'the circle *MN*' is clearly in the same plane as the circle *GMR*, whereas the way in which it is drawn in the figure taken from the commentators gives the impression that it is in a plane different from, in fact perpendicular to, the plane of the circle *GMR* (cf. the note by the Oxford translator that *MN* stands for 'a semicircle in a plane at right angles to the plane of *HMPN*'). Aristotle himself puts the matter beyond doubt when he says (376ᵃ7–9) that you cannot set up lines in the same ratio '*in the same plane* except to the circumference *MN*'; and it is not till 376ᵇ12 that any question arises of making the whole figure revolve about *GK* as axis.

To clinch the matter it is necessary to compare Aristotle's procedure step by step with that of Apollonius. For this purpose I substitute the lettering of my figure[1] for that of Apollonius as given by Eutocius.[2]

---

[1] Fig. 45.   [2] p. 181 *supra.*

Aristotle first says (376ᵃ10–11) 'Take D to B in the ratio of MG to KM' (the ratio supposed to be given). (Apollonius makes a similar assumption but the lines MG, KM are not yet drawn. Only the points G, K are given.)

Aristotle goes on (ᵃ14–16) 'Add to B the line F such that

$$D : B = (B+F) : D'$$

(cf. (θ) in the analysis on p. 183 above); Apollonius says exactly the same.[1]

Next, says Apollonius,[2] in effect: let P be a point on GK produced such that[3]
$$F : KG = B : KP$$
and take 'H' such that these ratios are equal to D : 'H'.

Then after observing that it is obvious that D is a mean proportional between $B+F$ and B, and 'H' a mean proportional between KP, PG (pp. 180. 25–182. 1), he describes a circle with P as centre and radius 'H' (182. 1–2).

This corresponds to the lines in Aristotle following, viz.

ᵃ16–18, where we are told to contrive that
$$B : KP = F : KG$$
and to join MP;

ᵃ18–19, stating that P is the 'pole' of the circle on which the lines from K meet (meaning KM, GM);

ᵃ19–21, where Aristotle says that the ratios $B : KP$ and $F : KG$ are also equal to $D : PM$ (this being what he has to prove); and

ᵃ21–2 putting the alternative: if the said ratios are not equal to $D : PM$, suppose them equal to $D : PR$, where PR is less or greater than PM.

ᵃ22–6, proving that $\quad PG : PR = PR : PK,$

the equivalent of Apollonius' statement that his 'H' is a mean proportional between KP, PG.

The last result means that the triangles GPR, RPK are similar, which fact Aristotle uses to deduce (ᵃ26–9) that

$$GK : KR = GP : PR$$

so that (ᵃ30–1), *alternando*,

$$PR : KR = GP : PR$$

[This, as we have seen, should rather have been

$$GR : KR = GP : PR]$$

on which Aristotle remarks (ᵃ32—ᵇ1) that this latter ratio is also equal to the ratio $GM : MK$ since both are equal to $D : B$. It follows that $GR : KR = D : B$.

---

[1] loc. cit. 180. 21–3.   [2] 180. 23–5.   [3] Cf. (η) on p. 183.

Apollonius reaches the same result but by a longer proof.[1]

Since then $GR : RK$, as well as $GM : MK$, is equal to $D : B$, it follows, says Aristotle ($376^b1–3$), that from the points G, K straight lines in one and the same ratio to one another can be drawn not only to the circumference MN (i.e. to M) but also to a point not on the said circumference [i.e. to R which is on the semicircle GMR but not on the circle LMN]: which is impossible. The conclusion is ($376^b3–5$) that the supposed PR can be nothing but PM itself: [in fact R can be nothing but M itself, which is the intersection of the circles GMR and LMN].

Apollonius completes his proposition[2] by a *reductio ad absurdum* showing that lines in the given ratio cannot be drawn from G, K to any point which is not on the circle LMN.

Poske remarks[3] that at the beginning Aristotle assumes without justification that in his figure $MK = KG$ and also that MG is given ($376^a4–5$). But with the diagram that he uses the first is a natural assumption. It is true that MG is not given until M is found.

It seems probable, therefore, that Aristotle's object was to give mathematical form to a vague sense-impression of the phenomenon of the rainbow. Thus, without venturing to enunciate any law of refraction, he assumed as a probable hypothesis that the length of the incident ray would be in some constant ratio to the length of the inflected ray. His problem, therefore, was to determine the position of M, the point of incidence, on the great circle which he had drawn passing through a horizontal line. To do this he used the theorem that the locus of a point (M) such that its distances from two fixed points G and K respectively are in a given ratio is a certain circle; he gave, therefore, the traditional construction for the circle in question, remarking at the outset ($^a7$) that the intersection of the two circles will be given, that is, the point M. The said circle obtained by the construction which he gives is that shown as LMN in my figure.

This is, I think, the answer to the suggestion of Blancanus,[4] repeated by Poske,[5] that there is a much easier way of finding the 'pole' P than the laborious one set out by Aristotle. P could be found, it is suggested, by simply drawing MP from M so as to make the angle KMP equal to the angle KGM, for this would make the triangles GPM, MPK equiangular and therefore similar. But this is only possible if the position of M is known. Aristotle, however, does not assume that M is known; by his construction he shows how to *find* it.

---

[1] p. 182; cf. *The Thirteen Books of Euclid's Elements*, vol. ii, p. 200.

[2] loc. cit., p. 184.   [3] p. 137.   [4] p. 122.   [5] p. 137.

We will now translate the passage in which Aristotle makes the semicircle A and the whole figure revolve round GK as axis.

Meteor. III. 5. 376^{b}12–22

'If then you make the semicircle A revolve about GKP as diameter, the straight lines from G, K inflected to M will occupy like positions in all the planes [successively occupied by the figure as it revolves] and will make (throughout) an equal angle KMG. And the angle which GP [this should be GM] and MP respectively make with GP will remain always equal (to itself). Therefore a series of triangles arises [lit. has been constructed], all of which are equal to the triangles GMP, KMP. The perpendiculars in all of them will fall on the same point of GP and will be equal. Let them fall on O. Then O will be the centre of the circle (traced by M in its revolution), and the part of it about MN cut off by the horizon is a semicircle.'

There is here no difficulty in the interpretation. The passage proves that in the course of the revolution of the figure about GK the line PM will describe a right cone with PG as axis and for base a circle with centre O in a plane at right angles to the axis. This circle shows the arc of the rainbow visible above the horizon when the sun or moon is rising or setting. When Aristotle says (at 376^{b}20–2) that O is the centre of the circle and the semicircle *about MN* is cut off by the horizon, we must suppose either that he is writing carelessly or that the words τὸ περὶ τὴν MN are, as the Oxford translator suggests, a gloss. What is meant is the semicircle 'which is half of the circle about MN (as diameter)' in the sense of the circle with O as centre and OM as radius in the plane at right angles to OG. The semicircle will of course contain all points on the rainbow corresponding to M in the particular plane taken.

Next Aristotle takes (376^{b}28—377^{a}11) the case where the luminary is at some height above the horizon, say at G in the figure below, where AC is in the plane of the horizon. Then, he says, in all other respects the above proof will apply, but the 'pole' (or centre) of the circle on which M lies will be below the horizon.

Ib. ^{b}28–377^{a}11

'Again, let AKC be the horizon and let G have risen above it; let the axes now be GP. The proof then will be in all other respects similar to the foregoing, except that P, the pole of the circle, will be below the horizon AC, because the point G has risen above it. Now the pole and the centre of the circle [i.e. P and O] and the centre [K] of the circle now defining the (position of the) risen body [lit. 'the rising'], are on the same straight line; the latter circle is

GP.[1] And, since *KG* is above the diameter *AC*, the centre, namely

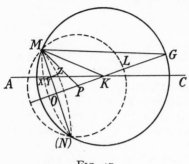

FIG. 47

O [*B* in Fobes's text should clearly be *O*] (of the circle representing the rainbow), will be below the former horizon, that is, *AC*, since it lies on the straight line *KP*: hence the segment *XY* (cut off) above (the horizon) will be less than a semicircle; for the (segment) *XYZ was* [in the former case] a semicircle but has now been (partly) cut off by the horizon *AC*. The (other) segment *ZY* (of the circle of the rainbow) will be invisible, since the sun is raised above the horizon. (The visible part) will be least when it is on the meridian circle; for the higher *G* is, the lower will be the pole and centre of the circle (of the rainbow).'

We may in conclusion point out some similarities between Aristotle's mathematical phraseology and that used by Euclid which tend to show how much of the latter was fixed and in use long before Euclid's time.

376^{b}7–8: 'If with the point *P* as pole and *distance MP* a circle be described'; the same word 'distance' (διάστημα) is also Euclid's word (cf. Eucl. I. 1, 2).

376^{a}1–3: 'Straight lines in such-and-such a ratio drawn from *G, K* respectively cannot be constructed (οὐ συσταθήσονται) to more than one point of the semicircle *A* (τοῦ ἐφ' ᾧ *A* ἡμικυκλίου πρὸς ἄλλο καὶ ἄλλο σημεῖον)', meaning 'cannot be drawn so as to meet at different points'; cf. the similar sentence in 376^{b}1–3.

We have only to compare Euclid's enunciation in I. 7: ἐπὶ τῆς αὐτῆς εὐθείας δύο ταῖς αὐταῖς εὐθείαις ἄλλαι δύο εὐθεῖαι ἴσαι ἑκατέρα ἑκατέρᾳ οὐ συσταθήσονται πρὸς ἄλλῳ καὶ ἄλλῳ σημείῳ ἐπὶ τὰ αὐτὰ μέρη τὰ αὐτὰ πέρατα ἔχουσαι ταῖς ἐξ ἀρχῆς εὐθείαις.

[1] The circle described as '*GP*' is the circle with diameter *GP* in the plane inclined to the horizon at an angle equal to *GKC*; in other words (as the Oxford translator describes it in a note) 'the great circle which would be the horizon if the sun were rising when it is at the point *H*'.

IX

DE ANIMA

(a) Straight line touching a (brazen) sphere

De an. I. 1. 403ᵃ12–16

'In the latter case it [the soul] would be like the "straight" (line), which, *qua* straight, has many properties, such as that of touching the bronze sphere at a point; but the straight, separated (from matter), will not touch it in this way; it is not separable at all, seeing that it is always conjoined with body of some sort.'

In the preceding lines Aristotle has said that, if there is no property or function of the soul which is not shared by the body, the soul will not have a separate existence. He goes on in the words ἀλλὰ καθάπερ τῷ εὐθεῖ without any expressed antecedent to καθάπερ, meaning thereby that '(it will be with the soul) as it is with the straight line'; for the mathematical straight line has no separate existence, but is only a conception arrived at by *abstraction* (from the matter, apart from which it is never found in nature). The straight line which touches the brazen sphere is the straight line which is embodied in the ruler or what not, and not the abstract straight line which is one of τὰ ἐξ ἀφαιρέσεως ὄντα or λεγόμενα, the so-called 'abstractions'. On the inseparability of mathematical entities cf. *Metaph.* E. 3, 1026ᵃ14, *Phys.* II. 2. 193ᵇ31–5.

(b) Definition of 'squaring'

Ib. II. 2. 413ᵃ13–20

'It is not enough that the defining statement should make clear the bare fact as most definitions do; it should also include and exhibit the cause. As things are, what is stated in definitions is usually of the nature of a *conclusion*. For instance, what is 'squaring'? The construction of an equilateral rectangle equal (in area) to a given oblong (rectangle). Such a definition is a statement of the conclusion, whereas, if you say that squaring is the finding of a mean proportional, you state the cause of the thing defined.'

With this should be read the following passage (to much the same effect).

Metaph. B. 2. 996ᵇ18–21

'Again, in the case of other things, namely those which are the subject of demonstration, we consider that we possess knowledge of a particular thing when we know *what* it is [i.e. its definition],

e.g. we know what squaring is because (we know that) it is the
finding of the mean proportional.'

To appreciate these passages it is necessary to refer to two propositions in Euclid. In II. 14 Euclid shows how to describe a square
(an 'equilateral rectangle') equal in area to any rectilinear figure.
After constructing a rectangle *BCDE*, which in general will have
its sides unequal (an 'oblong'), equal to the given rectilinear figure
A (a problem already solved in I. 45), Euclid proceeds as follows:

Produce *BE* to *F*, making *EF* equal to *ED*.
Bisect *BF* at the point *G*.
With *G* as centre and *GB* or *GF* as radius describe a circle *BHF*.

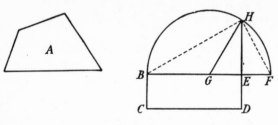

Fig. 48

Produce *DE* to meet the circle in *H*.

Then, since *BF* has been divided into two equal parts at *G* and
into two unequal parts at *E*, it follows that the rectangle *BE, EF*,
together with the square on *GE*, is equal to the square on *GF*.
(Eucl. II. 5.)

That is, since *GF = GH*,
the rectangle *BE, EF*, together with the square on *GE*, is equal
to the square on *GH*.

But, since *GEH* is a right angle, the square on *GH* is equal to the
sum of the squares on *GE, EH*.

Taking away from each side the square on *GE* which is common to
both, we have the rectangle *BE, EF* equal to the square on *EH*.

But the rectangle *BE, EF* is the rectangle *BD* which is equal to *A*.

Therefore the square on *EH* is equal to *A*.

If we now turn to Eucl. VI. 13, we shall find the same construction
used to find the mean proportional between two straight lines such
as *BE, ED*.

Place them in a straight line as *BE, EF (= ED)* and describe
the semicircle on *BF*. Draw *EH* at right angles to *BF* meeting the
semicircle at *H*.

Join *BH, HF*.

Then, since *BHF*, being the angle in a semicircle, is a right angle, it follows that the triangles *BHF, BEH,* and *HEF* all have their angles respectively equal, and are therefore similar.

Therefore in the triangles *BEH, HEF* the sides about the equal angles *BEH, HEF* are proportional,

that is $BE : EH = EH : EF.$

In other words, *EH* is a mean proportional to *BE, EF.*

Hence (VI. 17) the square on *EH* is equal to the rectangle *BE, EF* or *BE, ED.*

Aristotle's remark that squaring is better defined as the finding of a mean proportional than as the construction of an equilateral rectangle equal to a given oblong figure, because it states the cause, suggested to Heiberg that in Aristotle's time, i.e. before Euclid, the problem was solved by means of proportions rather than by the direct method of II. 14. This is the more probable, seeing that there is good reason to believe that the Pythagorean proof of the theorem of the square of the hypotenuse of a right-angled triangle was itself based on the theory of proportion (as known to the Pythagoreans). It was not in accordance with Euclid's plan to introduce the perfected theory of proportion (due to Eudoxus) so early as Book I in the *Elements*; he had, therefore, to give in I. 47 a proof of the Pythagorean theorem which did not employ proportions; and it is no doubt this fact to which we owe the *tour de force* presented to us in that proposition.

(c) 'Point', 'division', as 'privation'

De an. III. 6. 430^{b}20–1

'The point and every division and whatever is indivisible in the same sense, is made clear in the same way as privation.'

This sentence was quoted in the explanation of *Topics* VI. 6, where the cases were referred to in which a thing can only be defined by negation.[1] Plane or surface, line or point are arrived at by taking away from body the three dimensions one by one in succession. A surface has no depth, a line has no depth and no breadth, a point has none of the three dimensions: 'a point is that which has no part', as Euclid says (I, Def. 1). πᾶσα διαίρεσις, 'every division' (or dividing mark) includes, as part of its content, first the point which is a division of a line, and secondly the 'now' regarded as dividing time past from time future; it also includes line and surface but only in so far as they are 'privations', the surface in so far as it has no thickness, and the line in so far as it has neither breadth nor thickness. As explained in Mr. Hicks's note on the passage,[2] the point

---

[1] p. 89, above.   [2] p. 522.

and the 'now' are indivisibles of a kind different from those previously considered. They are indivisible not καθ' αὐτά, but by
absence or privation of extension and divisibility, by 'the absence
of the continuous' (as Themistius says), or 'in virtue of the shedding
of everything that is divisible', as Simplicius has it.

(d) The abstractions of mathematics

De an. III. 7. 431ᵇ12–16

The translation of this passage has been given above.[1]

The only difficulty is that of the text: the sense is quite clear.
The translation represents the received text, which reads as follows:
τὰ δὲ ἐν ἀφαιρέσει λεγόμενα νοεῖ ὥσπερ ἂν εἰ τὸ σιμόν, ᾗ μὲν σιμόν, οὐ
κεχωρισμένως, ᾗ δὲ κοῖλον, εἴ τις ἐνόει ἐνεργείᾳ, ἄνευ τῆς σαρκὸς ἂν
ἐνόει ἐν ᾗ τὸ κοῖλον· οὕτω τὰ μαθηματικὰ οὐ κεχωρισμένα ὡς κεχωρισμένα
νοεῖ ὅταν νοῇ ἐκεῖνα. The altered reading suggested by Bywater[2]
and in the main followed by the Oxford translator is: τὰ δὲ ἐν
ἀφαιρέσει λεγόμενα νοεῖ, ὥσπερ ἄν, εἰ ⟨τις⟩ τὸ σιμὸν ᾗ μὲν σιμὸν οὔ
[κεχωρισμένως], ᾗ δὲ κοῖλον [εἴ τις] ἐνόει, ἐνεργείᾳ ⟨νοῶν⟩ ἄνευ τῆς
σαρκὸς ἂν ἐνόει ἐν ᾗ τὸ κοῖλον, οὕτω τὰ μαθηματικά κ.τ.λ. No doubt
Bywater's suggested text is more shipshape; it gives, however, the
same sense, and on the whole I prefer the received text as being
thoroughly characteristic of Aristotle. The matter is discussed by
Hicks.[3]

---

[1] pp. 65–6.   [2] In *Journ. of Phil.* xvii, p. 62.   [3] op. cit., p. 541.

X

METAPHYSICS

(a) History of mathematics

Metaph. A. 1. 981ᵇ20–5

'Hence it was after all such inventions [the practical arts] were already established that those of the sciences which are not directed to the attainment of pleasure or the necessities of life were discovered; and this first happened in the places where men had leisure. This is why the mathematical arts were first set up in Egypt; for there the priestly caste were allowed to enjoy leisure.'

Greek tradition invariably ascribed the beginning of geometry to Egypt. Plato in the *Phaedrus*[1] makes Socrates say that he had heard that the Egyptian god Theuth was the first to invent arithmetic, the science of calculation, geometry, and astronomy (Proclus, on the other hand, says that arithmetic began among the Phoenicians because of its use in commerce and contracts). Herodotus[2] says that geometry arose out of mensuration or land-surveying, which became necessary to the Egyptians owing to the periodical flooding of the Nile, which would sweep away a portion of a plot of land subject to taxation, so that the area had to be recalculated in order to arrive at the proper assessment of tax. Or, as Proclus has it, the Nile would efface boundaries so that remeasurement of areas became necessary in order to replace them. Heron of Alexandria, Diodorus Siculus, and Strabo tell much the same story.

But in fact all these things, arithmetic, mensuration, and astronomy, were developed at least as early among the Babylonians. Cuneiform tablets recently discovered show that the Babylonians, as early as 2000–1800 B.C., were far ahead of the Egyptians in algebra and general arithmetic, solving quadratic equations, as a matter of routine, in accordance with a general rule (never set out as such in our surviving sources but actually identical with our modern formula for solution), and even particular cases of cubic equations. But the Babylonian achievements in geometry, algebra, and astronomy seem to have remained practically unknown to the Greeks till the time of Alexander the Great and even later.

Aristotle's implication that the first discoveries in mathematics were the monopoly of the priests is not confirmed by any of the surviving documents. Professor Peet[3] observes that there is no particle of evidence that in early times Egyptian mathematics were

---

[1] 274 C–D.　　[2] ii. 109.　　[3] *Rhind Mathematical Papyrus*, p. 31.

in any sense in the hands of the priests, whatever may have been the case in Aristotle's day. This is confirmed by O. Neugebauer.[1]

The orientation of temples, which would involve some geometry, no doubt rested with the priests, as also astronomical observations. There is evidence that on these subjects the priests kept their knowledge to themselves, if we may believe Strabo, who says that they were 'mysterious and not at all communicative',[2] and adds that Plato and Eudoxus only managed by means of entreaties and services rendered to induce them to explain certain theorems, while they made a secret of the rest. According to Porphyry, Pythagoras encountered similar difficulties with the priests, who at first sent him from pillar to post, and it was only when he had submitted to hard discipline and even undignified treatment that he was allowed to take some part in the priests' worship and routine. Iamblichus, on the other hand, says[3] that Pythagoras by his extraordinary enthusiasm and passion for exact inquiry so impressed the priests, and they conceived such an admiration and affection for him, that he remained twenty-two years with them studying astronomy and geometry and taking part in their ceremonies.

But no doubt the absence of documents may have caused the later Greeks to exaggerate the supposed secretiveness of the Egyptian priests. At any rate, now that more mathematical texts have been studied, both Egyptian and Babylonian, it is clear, says Neugebauer,[4] that in neither country was mathematics a secret science which the priests kept to themselves.

It is certain that Egyptian mathematics arose simply out of the necessities of administration and of daily life. When the Egyptians measured areas of land it was for the purpose of allocation of or dealings with land; when they measured the content of vessels of different shapes it was to find out how much corn, etc., they would contain; similarly, with pyramids of certain dimensions, they had to calculate how much stone they would require.

(b) Incommensurability of the diagonal

Metaph. A. 2. 983ª12–20

'As we said, all men begin by wondering that a thing should be so; the subject may be, for example, the automata in a peepshow, the solstices, or the incommensurability of the diagonal (of a square with its side). For it must seem a matter for wonder, to all who have not studied the cause, that there should be anything that cannot be measured by any measure however small. But it is necessary to

---

[1] *Vorgriechische Mathematik*, 1934, p. 121.   [2] *Geogr.* xvii. 1. 29.
[3] *Vit. Pyth.* 18–19.   [4] loc. cit.

arrive in the end at the contrary and better state, as the proverb
has it, which is what we do in these cases when we have been
instructed; for nothing would surprise a geometer so much as that
the diagonal should prove commensurable.'

(I have followed Ross in reading ⟨περὶ⟩ before τῶν θαυμάτων τὰ
αὐτόματα in ᵃ14 and transferring τοῖς μήπω τεθεωρήκασι τὴν αἰτίαν
from ᵃ14–15 to ᵃ16–17.)

According to Alexander and others the proverb is δευτέρων
ἀμεινόνων (meaning presumably 'the second state is the better'),
though in that form it scarcely brings out Aristotle's point that the
second state is *contrary* to the first (cf. the French and Italian
proverb that 'the better is the enemy of the good').

The allusion in τῶν θαυμάτων τὰ αὐτόματα is obviously to things
like the automaton-theatre. In later times Heron of Alexandria
wrote a treatise on the Automatic Theatre (περὶ αὐτοματοποιητικῆς),
and his *Pneumatica* is full of devices of the same kind using the force
of compressed air, water, and steam. In these works Heron was
following the lead of earlier mechanicians, notably Ctesibius of
Ascra and Philo of Byzantium. But the invention of such mechanical
devices goes farther back. Two in particular are attributed to
Archytas; one was a mechanical dove made of wood which would
fly,[1] the other was a rattle which according to Aristotle[2] was
calculated to amuse children and to keep them from breaking things
about the house.

The 'incommensurability of the diagonal' with the side is one of
the favourite illustrations of mathematical truths used by Aristotle.
There are at least eight allusions to it in the *Metaphysics*. The first
reference to it is in *An. Prior.* I. 23. 41ᵃ23–7, where Aristotle hints
at the well-known proof of the fact by *reductio ad absurdum*, which
evidently goes back to the Pythagoreans, who discovered the
property.[3]

(c) Pythagoreans and mathematics

Ib. *A.* 5. 985ᵇ23–986ᵃ3

'In the time of these philosophers (Leucippus and Democritus)
and before them the so-called Pythagoreans applied themselves to
the study of mathematics and were the first to advance that science;
insomuch that, having been brought up in it, they thought that its
principles must be the principles of all existing things. Since among
these principles numbers are by nature the first, and they thought

---

[1] Gellius x. 12. 8 after Favorinus.   [2] *Politics* viii. 6. 1340ᵇ26–8.
[3] See my note ad loc., p. 22.

they found in numbers—more than in fire, earth, and water—many resemblances to things which are and become—thus such-and-such an attribute of numbers is justice, another is soul and mind, another is opportunity, and so on, and again they saw in numbers the attributes and ratios of the musical scales—since, in short, all other things seemed in their whole nature to be assimilated to numbers, while numbers seemed to be the first things in the whole of nature, they supposed the elements of numbers to be the elements of all things, and the whole heaven to be a musical scale and a number.'

With this should be read:

Metaph. N. 3. 1090ᵃ20–5

'The Pythagoreans, because they saw many attributes of numbers to be present in sensible bodies, held that things are numbers, not however separately existing numbers—rather (they held) that existing things are made up of numbers. Why? Because the attributes of numbers are found in a musical scale, in the heaven and in many other things.'

So far as the purely mathematical part of the Pythagorean discoveries is concerned, I have made the utmost possible use of what we learn from Aristotle's various statements on the subject (including the above passages) in my *History of Greek Mathematics*;[1] and it is unnecessary here to repeat, on the occasion of the separate passages, what I have there set out. Nor do I propose to discuss the philosophical questions about the connexion of the Pythagorean doctrines with Plato's Theory of Ideas, the development of that theory itself, Plato's ideal numbers, Ideas as numbers, and *mathematica* as 'intermediates'. The literature on these subjects is immense and has been dealt with very fully by Ross in his edition of the *Metaphysics*. I can only express my admiration of his work, and my agreement, generally, in his conclusions.

A word may be added about the supposed Pythagorean identification of justice etc., with certain numbers. Alexander explains that the Pythagoreans took the characteristic of justice to be 'the reciprocal and equal' (τὸ ἀντιπεπονθός τε καὶ ἴσον), and, finding this character in numbers, said that the *first* square number ('equal-times equal', ἰσάκις ἴσος) is justice—for the first in each set of things having the same definition has the best claim to the description. The number in question some maintained to be 4, since that is the first square, being twice 2; others made it 9, which is the first square obtained from an *odd* number.

The non-mathematical meaning of ἀντιπεπονθός is 'requital'; in mathematics ἀντιπεπονθέναι is 'to be in reciprocal proportion'. If

---

[1] i, ch. 3, etc.

A, B, C, D are four magnitudes of which A, B are of one kind and C, D also of one kind (not necessarily of the same kind) they are proportional if $A : B = C : D$; they are 'reciprocally proportional' if $A : B = D : C$. A good illustration is found in Eucl. VI. 15, where it is proved that, if two triangles have one angle equal to one angle and are equal in area, the sides about the equal angles are reciprocally proportional, and conversely.

It seems probable that by ἀντιπεπονθός in their definition of justice the Pythagoreans meant pure retaliation or requital, 'an eye for an eye'; for Aristotle, who in *Nic. Eth. E.* 5. 1132ᵇ22 quotes their definition as τὸ ἀντιπεπονθὸς ἄλλῳ, objects to it because it does not fit either 'distributive justice' (τὸ διανεμητικὸν δίκαιον) or 'corrective justice' (τὸ διορθωτικὸν δίκαιον). We shall recur to the subject later when we come to the *Nicomachean Ethics*.

(d) Plato on 'points' and indivisible lines

Ib. *A.* 9. 992ᵃ10–24

'When we wish to refer (ἀνάγειν, "carry up") substances to their principles, we derive lengths from the long and short, that is, from a sort of small and great, a plane from the broad and narrow, and a body from the deep and shallow. How then can the plane contain a line, or the solid a line and a plane? For the broad and narrow is one genus, the deep and shallow another; therefore, just as number is not present in these because the many and few are different from them, it is clear that neither is any other of the higher classes present in the lower. Again, the broad is not the genus of the deep; if it were, a body would be a kind of plane. From what principle then will the points (contained in lines) be derived? Plato actually objected to this class (that of points) as a "geometrical dogma" and applied the name "principle of a line"—a thing he often posited—to "the indivisible lines". Yet they must have a limit, so that the argument which establishes the existence of the line establishes that of the point also.'

On this vexed question of Plato's attitude with regard to the class of *points* (according to him a 'geometrical fiction') and his support of the doctrine of 'indivisible lines', it is difficult to add anything of value to Ross's admirable survey of the whole subject.[1] I confess, however, that I feel some doubt whether his proposal to read ἀλλ' ἐκάλει ἀρχὴν γραμμῆς—τοῦτο δὲ πολλάκις ἐτίθει—τὰς ἀτόμους γραμμάς, instead of the common reading ἀλλ' ἐκάλει ἀρχὴν γραμμῆς, τοῦτο δὲ πολλάκις ἐτίθει τὰς ἀτόμους γραμμάς, is an improvement. Without

[1] Especially in vol. i, pp. 203–8.

stressing the point unduly, I think 'he called the (supposed) indivisible lines' (in the plural) 'the beginning or principle of the line'
(in the singular) is a little awkward. Why should Plato have *called*
'indivisible lines' the principle or beginning of lines? What he really
did, according to the passage, was seemingly to lay it down that they
were the 'principle of lines', and ἐτίθει is the better word for explaining
this. I am more inclined to regard the sentence as being in two
parts, purposely made distinct, the first stating that Plato *called*
the point (in the singular, understood from the 'class (of points)') the
beginning or principle of the line, and the second stating that he
posited indivisible lines, the latter being a separate statement
intended to meet the query that might be made on the first statement, namely, 'If a point is only the beginning of a line, and you
cannot make up a line out of points, how else do you make up a
line?' To which Plato is supposed to reply by positing or assuming
indivisible lines ('so-called', τάς). In that case we should naturally
take τοῦτο δέ in the sense of 'and for this purpose' (= διὰ τοῦτο)
or 'in these circumstances' (namely in order to meet the difficulty
as to the generation of a line), or 'on the other hand' (with practically
the same effect).

The evidence that Plato denied the existence of 'points' seems
strong enough. No use of the word στιγμή by Plato is given in
Liddell and Scott. Ast's dictionary to Plato does not contain the
word στιγμή at all, nor any instance of σημεῖον used in the sense of
'point'. In *Laws* 894 A Plato seems purposely to omit to say what
the ἀρχή (principle or beginning) is which 'receiving an increase
advances to the second dimension ("change of place", μετάβασιν),
from that to the next, and then, when it has reached three dimensions, makes us perceive sensible objects'. Here, by the 'second
dimension', he really means the first dimension, for the point or
the indivisible line does not constitute a first dimension.

The first extension from the point or indivisible line to the
measurable line is very much like (if not identical with, as Burnet
supposed) the 'fluxion' (ῥύσις) of a point: cf. *De anima* I. 4. 409ᵃ4,
'since they say that it is by its motion that a line generates a plane
and a point a line'.

I agree that it is most probable that it was through feeling the
difficulty of meeting Zeno's 'argument from bisection' that Plato
thought it necessary to resort to indivisible lines (Ross, vol. i,
pp. 206–7).

Metaph. a. 2. 994ᵇ22–5

'For how can one think of things which are infinite in this sense
[i.e. actually infinite]? The case is not parallel to that of the line;

the line does not stop at its points of division, though you cannot apprehend them unless you stop; hence, if you are traversing the infinitely divisible line you cannot be counting the points of section.'

This should be read with *Phys.* VIII. 8. 263ª4–11 and notes thereon.[1]

I translate κατὰ τὰς διαιρέσεις 'at the points of division', this being the mathematical sense of κατά.

(e) Beauty in mathematics

Ib. *B.* 2. 996ª29–ᵇ1

On those who decried mathematics on the ground that the mathematical sciences take no account of a final cause, or of goods and evils, it is worth while to refer to a paper by O. Apelt, 'Die Widersacher der Mathematik im Altertum'.[2]

Admitting that mathematics says nothing of a final cause and bases none of its proofs on the consideration that a thing is 'better so', Aristotle in *Metaph. M.* 3. 1078ª31—ᵇ5 distinguishes between τὸ καλόν and τὸ ἀγαθόν and holds that mathematics shares in the former if not the latter:

'For the chiefest forms of the beautiful are orderly arrangement, symmetry, and definiteness, and the mathematical sciences have these characters in the highest degree. And, since these characters (such as orderly arrangement and definiteness) are the causes of many things, it is clear that mathematicians could claim that this sort of cause is in a sense like the beautiful acting as cause.'

(f) Axioms

Ib. ᵇ26–33

'Further, with regard to the first principles of demonstration, it is questionable whether they belong to one science or several. By first principles of demonstration I mean the *common opinions* on which all men base their proofs, e.g. that one or other of two contradictories must be true, that it is impossible for the same thing both to be and not to be, and all other propositions of this kind. Does one science deal with these as well as with substance, or do the two things belong to different sciences, and, if so, which of the two must we name as that which we are now looking for?'

Ib. 997ª10–11, 19–21

'All the demonstrative sciences use the axioms. . . . Every demonstrative science investigates, with regard to some subject-matter, the essential attributes, (starting) from the common opinions.'

---

[1] See pp. 149–50, above.
[2] *Beiträge zur Gesch. der gr. Philosophie*, Leipzig, 1891, pp. 253–70.

'Common opinions' is in Aristotle an alternative term for 'axioms'. Elsewhere he calls them κοινά simply (1061ᵇ18). We recognize here the same idea as in Euclid's term for axioms, 'common notions' (κοιναὶ ἔννοιαι). 'The axioms', says Aristotle (997ᵃ12–13), 'are the most universal (propositions) and are principles in all things alike.'

The answer to the question what science is concerned with any discussion of the axioms or common opinions is not given in Book *B* but in *Γ*, c. 3 and *K*, cc. 3, 4.

Metaph. Γ. 3. 1005ᵃ19–27

'We have now to declare whether it is the duty of one science or of different sciences to consider the so-called axioms in mathematics and substance respectively. It is manifest that the inquiry into the axioms also belongs to one science, and that the science of the (first) philosopher, for they hold good of all existing things and are not peculiar to some one genus apart from the rest. Everyone makes use of them because they belong to being *qua* being, and each genus has being. But men use them just so far as is sufficient for their purpose, that is, within the ambit of the genus to which their demonstrations relate.'

Similarly:

Ib. *K.* 4. 1061ᵇ17–25

'Since the mathematician too uses the common (axioms) in a special application, it must be the business of first philosophy to investigate the principles of mathematics also. For that, when equals are subtracted from equals, the remainders are equal is common to all quantities, but mathematics singles out and investigates some portion of its proper matter, as e.g. lines or angles or numbers, or some other sort of quantity, not however *qua* being, but in so far as each of these things is continuous, in one, two, or three directions' (i.e. dimensions).

The axioms are *indemonstrable* (*B.* 2. 997ᵃ5–9):

'If there is a demonstrative science which deals with them, there will have to be some subject-matter underlying it, attributes of the same [the things to be proved] and axioms applicable to it [from which the proof must start]—for it is impossible that there should be demonstration about everything—since all proof must start from some (premisses), must be about something, and must be (a proof) of some things (i.e. properties).'

The unexpressed conclusion is the *reductio ad absurdum* that, if axioms are the subject-matter of a science, there must be properties to be proved to belong to them, and other axioms to base the proof upon: which would involve an infinite regress.

Ib. *Γ*. 3. 1005ᵇ11–20

'The most certain principle of all is that in regard to which it is impossible to be mistaken; such a principle must be at once the best known (for all men are liable to be deceived about things which they do not know), and non-hypothetical. For the principle which must be grasped by one who understands anything whatever that exists is not an hypothesis; that which it is necessary for a man to know who knows anything at all he must bring with him at the start. It is clear that such a principle is the most firmly established of all. . . . It is that the same attribute cannot both belong and not belong to the same thing at the same time and in the same respect.'

Ib. *Γ*. 4. 1006ᵃ5–15

'Some indeed claim to demonstrate this; but this they do through want of education, for not to know of what things we ought to look for demonstration, and what not, simply argues want of education. Now it is impossible that there should be demonstration of absolutely everything, for there would then be an infinite regress, so that even then there would be no proof. But, if there are some things of which we should not look for a demonstration, these persons could not say what principle they regard as more indemonstrable than that above stated. It is in fact possible to prove negatively that even this view is impossible, if the disputant will say anything; and if he will not, it is absurd to attempt to reason with one who has no reason to give for anything . . . . Such a man, as such, is no better than a vegetable.'

I have thought that it would be useful to collect in one place the above passages from the *Metaphysics* regarding axioms. On the part played by axioms (along with definitions, hypotheses, and postulates) in mathematics and other sciences there are full discussions in *Anal. Post.* I, cc. 2, 6, 10, which see. I may also refer to the summary in my *Euclid*.[1]

(g) *Geometry and geodesy*

Ib. *B*. 2. 997ᵇ26–34

'If geometry differs from mensuration only by being of non-sensibles, there will be a medical science intermediate between the ideal medical science and that which we know, and therefore intermediate healthy objects. It is not the case that mensuration is of sensible objects: if it were, it would have perished when they perish' (Ross's summary, I. 227).

The word for mensuration is γεωδαισία, literally 'division' or

---

[1] Vol. i, esp. pp. 117–19.

'allocation' of land. But the term was not confined to land-measuring: it covered generally the practical measurement of surfaces and volumes (Geminus ap. Proclus on Eucl. I, pp. 39. 20–40. 2 F). It is different from geometry in that geometry deals with lines, planes, and solids in abstraction from matter and all other attributes (ἐξ ἀφαιρέσεως), while mensuration deals with planes and solids not in abstraction from matter but in abstraction from any particular kind of matter, as Ross observes (I, p. 232).

(h) Protagoras and contact with a circle

Metaph. B. 2. 997^b35–998^a4

'Neither are sensible lines the sort of lines of which the geometer speaks (for no sensible thing is straight or circular in the way that he assumes); a circle in fact touches a straight-edge, not at one point only, but in the way that Protagoras, in his refutation of the geometers, said that it did.'

We know that the Epicureans and Sceptics objected to the whole of mathematics on the very same ground, namely that no mathematical points, lines, or planes exist or can exist in nature. No doubt it was on the same lines that Protagoras argued. He is said to have written a book περὶ τῶν μαθημάτων, and it may have been in that book that the contention quoted by Aristotle occurred. Appealing to the visible circle touching a visible straight line, he would no doubt argue that the line has actually more than *one* point common to it and the circle; it must in fact touch it over some (small) *length*, in other words, in a *line* however short. Mathematically the argument has no validity, and it was probably against such arguments that Democritus directed his tract, 'On a difference of opinion, or on the contact of a circle and a sphere'. In this book Democritus would no doubt discuss the nature of the contact between a circle and a tangent (and between a sphere and a tangent plane), and presumably the nature of the supposed 'angle of contact' between the circle and the straight line, which later became the subject of so much controversy. But he is certain to have done so in the light of his distinction between two kinds of opinion described in a fragment (11 D.) from Democritus preserved by Sextus Empiricus:

'There are two kinds of γνώμη (opinion or knowledge), the one genuine, the other dark or blind; to the latter belong sight, hearing, smell, taste, touch; the former (the genuine) is entirely distinct from these. When the dark or blind kind can no longer see, hear, smell, taste, or touch a thing in any further minuteness of detail, but finer penetration ⟨is yet required, then the genuine kind comes to the

rescue, since it possesses a more refined organ of apprehension⟩'
(so Diels).

We can, therefore, imagine Democritus replying to the view of
those who thought like Protagoras: 'It is true that, owing to the
imperfection of our instruments, we cannot *draw* a mathematical
circle and a mathematical straight line touching it in *one* point,
and hence we cannot *visualize* such contact. But, none the less, we
can see this with the eye of the *mind*; and we know, by force of
demonstration, that it cannot be otherwise.'

The sentence with which we are dealing continues thus (998ª4–6):
'nor are the movements and spirals of the heavens like those of
which astronomy discourses, nor have points the same character
as the stars.'

On the meaning of 'spirals' in various passages in Aristotle see my
note on *Phys.* 228ᵇ15.[1] The reference here seems clearly to be to the
spirals of Plato's *Timaeus* 39 A–B, where Plato says that the independent movements of the planets in the Circle of the Other are turned
into spirals by the motion of the Circle of the Same 'because the moving bodies have two motions which are in opposite directions', i.e. the
independent revolutions in the ecliptic and the daily revolution of
the heaven. The statement about the difference between the actual
movements and those of which astronomy treats reminds us of
Republic VII. 529 C–530 B; cf. *Aristarchus of Samos*, pp. 136–7 f.

(i) Elements

Ib. *B*. 3. 998ª25–7

'And, among geometrical propositions, we apply the term "elements" to those the demonstrations of which are present in (ἐνυπάρχουσι, i.e. "form part of" or "form *steps* in") the demonstrations
of other propositions, either all or most of them.'

Ib. *Δ*. 3. 1014ª31–ᵇ3

'Similarly those who speak of the "elements" of bodies mean the
bodies into which they are ultimately divided, while the latter are
no longer divided into others differing in species; and they call
these "elements" whether they are one or more in number. It is
in a similar sense that we speak of "elements" of geometrical propositions and generally of demonstrations; for the demonstrations
which are primary and are present [i.e. form steps] in a number of
demonstrations are called elements of those demonstrations; the
primary syllogisms constructed of three terms, i.e. using one middle
term, are of this nature.'

[1] p. 124, above.

On the utility of elements see also *Topics* VIII. 14. 163^{b}17–28.[1]

When Aristotle says that the *proofs* of the primary propositions are *present* (ἐνυπάρχουσι) in the proofs of further propositions, he does not, of course, mean that they are repeated in the later propositions; what happens is that they are simply taken for granted, and the results cited without proof, as already known. The point in making a collection of elements is that those elementary propositions must be selected which have the widest possible application, i.e. are most often required in proving further and more advanced propositions.

Euclid's *Elements* emphatically satisfy Aristotle's requirements; no wonder that they immediately ousted all previous collections such as those of Hippocrates of Chios, Theudius, and others, and became the universally recognized authority for the fundamentals.

(j) Senses of 'one'

Metaph. Δ. 6. 1016^{b}11–13, 16–17

'Again, we say of anything whatever that it is in a sense one if it is a quantity and continuous, but in a sense it is not one unless its form is one . . .. This is why the circumference of a circle is of all lines the most truly one, because it is a whole and perfect.'

ἡ τοῦ κύκλου is, of course, ἡ τοῦ κύκλου γραμμή, 'the line (i.e. circumference) of a circle', not a circle. Cf. *Meteor*. III. 3. 373^{a}4–5: 'the equal straight lines will be inflected (at points which are) always on the circumference of a circle' (ἐπὶ κύκλου γραμμῆς). Cf. also Eucl. I, Def. 15: 'A circle is a plane figure contained by one line (ὑπὸ μιᾶς γραμμῆς περιεχόμενον) such that all the straight lines falling upon it from one point among those lying within the figure (i.e. the centre) are equal to one another.' With Aristotle, as with Euclid, the circle is the *plane figure*, meaning the whole area bounded by the circumference, not the circumference itself. Cf. *De caelo* II. 4. 286^{b}15 'the circular (περιφερόγραμμον) plane figure bounded by one line', and *Rhetoric* IV. 6. 1407^{b}27, 'the plane equal (i.e. extending equally all ways) from the middle' (ἐπίπεδον τὸ ἐκ τοῦ μέσου ἴσον), meaning a circle. Only occasionally does Euclid say 'circle' when he means its circumference or an arc of it, e.g. III. 10, 'A circle does not cut a circle in more points than two.'

(k) Dimensions

Ib. 23–31

'Everywhere the one is indivisible either in quantity or in species.

[1] p. 93, above.

That which is indivisible in quantity and *qua* quantity is called, when it is indivisible all ways and is without position, a unit; when it is indivisible all ways and has position, a point; when divisible one way only, a line; in two ways, a plane; and that which is divisible in respect of quantity all ways, that is, three ways, is body. Conversely, that which is divisible two ways is a plane, that which is divisible one way only is a line, while that which is divisible in respect of quantity *no* way whatever is a point or a unit, a unit of it is without position, a point of it has position.'

Here (as in *De caelo* I. 1) the dimensions are distinguished with reference to *divisibility*. In a later passage (*Δ*. 13. 1020ᵃ7–14) they are distinguished with reference to *continuity*, and that which is continuous one way only is called 'length', in two ways 'breadth', and in three ways 'depth', with the explanation that limited 'length' is a line, 'breadth' a surface, and 'depth' a body.

Aristotle's word for dimension is διάστασις. He says (*Topics* 142ᵇ25) that the definition of body is 'that which has three dimensions'. In *Phys.* III. 5. 204ᵇ20 body is 'that which has dimension *every* way'; in *De caelo* I. 1. 268ᵇ6; it has 'all the dimensions'. Theon of Smyrna[1] uses the word διαστατόν in the same sense: 'a magnitude extended (διαστατόν) and divisible one way is a line'; so Proclus on Eucl. I, p. 97. 7 F: οἱ δὲ μέγεθος ἐφ' ἕν διαστατόν. Aristotle does not apparently use the word διαστατόν, but he has διεστηκός in the same sense (*Phys.* III. 5. 204ᵇ21, 22).

Euclid does not use the word διάστασις, but merely speaks of length, breadth, and depth.

In a single book περὶ διαστάσεως Ptolemy tried to prove that the possible number of dimensions is limited to three.[2]

(*l*) δύναμις, *etc., in geometry*

Ib. 12. 1019ᵇ33–4

'It is in virtue of a change of meaning that a "power" in geometry is so called.'

In geometry δύναμις means a 'square', in accordance with the similar geometrical use of δύνασθαι. A straight line is said δύνασθαι a certain area when it has the power of producing a certain area by being *squared*. To say of a straight line that it ἴσον δύναται τῷ περιεχομένῳ ὑπὸ . . . means that the square on the straight line is equal to the ⟨rectangle⟩ contained by ⟨two straight lines⟩. The substantive δύναμις is generally used in the dative: thus δυνάμει ἴση, 'equal in square', is an alternative for ἴσον δύναται.

---

[1] p. 111. 17 Hiller.
[2] Simpl. on Arist. *De caelo*, p. 710. 14 Heiberg.

This sense of δύνασθαι and δύναμις was doubtless fully established before Euclid's time. It is probable that Eudemus, when describing in his history of geometry the squaring of lunes (μηνίσκοι) by Hippocrates of Chios, was largely using Hippocrates' own language. Hippocrates began his tract by assuming as known the theorem that 'similar segments of circles have the same ratio to one another as their bases have in square' (αἱ βάσεις αὐτῶν δυνάμει). Again, he uses a trapezium in which three sides are equal and the fourth side (the larger of the parallel sides) is 'the triple, *in square*, of each of the other sides' (τριπλάσια ἐκείνων ἑκάστης δυνάμει), i.e. the square on that side is equal to three times the square on any one of the other three sides. Again, '*BC*, *CD* together are greater *in* square than *BD*'.

As Ross says, Plato uses δύναμις of a square in *Rep*. 587 D, *Timaeus* 32 A, but in *Theaetetus* 148 B it means what we call a *square root* in the sense of a straight line the square on which is equal to a non-square number of square feet, e.g. three or five square feet, i.e. it is the equivalent in geometry of what in arithmetic we call a *surd*.

δύνασθαι, in its orthodox sense of being 'equal in square to' (a certain other square or area), occurs in Euclid's Book X, where (Def. 4) αἱ δυνάμεναι αὐτά means the straight lines the squares on which are equal to them (i.e. certain areas) and ἡ ΒΓ ἄρα τῆς Α μεῖζον δύναται τῇ ΔΖ (X. 17), '*BC* is greater in square than *A* by *DF*' means that 'the square on *BC* is greater than the square on *A* by the square on *DF*'.

It is curious, however, that Euclid does not use δύναμις and δύνασθαι in this technical sense in the books preceding Book X. In Books I–II he uses the word τετράγωνον: thus he speaks of the *square on* (τετράγωνον ἀπό with the genitive) one side of a triangle being equal to, or greater or less than, the sum of the squares on the other two sides, and even in XII. 2 he says that circles are to one another as the squares on their diameters, ὡς τὰ ἀπὸ τῶν διαμέτρων τετράγωνα (contrast with this the proposition about similar segments of circles quoted by Eudemus from Hippocrates). It seems possible that the exceptional use in Book X of δύνασθαι in the technical sense is due to the immediate influence of Theaetetus, who is said to have discovered and developed a considerable part of the theory of irrationals as expounded in that book.

(m) *Mathematica as 'quality'*

Metaph. Δ. 14. 1020ᵃ35–ᵇ8

'A circle is a figure of a certain quality because it has no angles [ἀγώνιον], which implies that a differentia of essence is a quality. This is one sense in which quality is called a differentia of essence;

another sense is that in which immovable mathematical objects are qualities: thus numbers have a certain quality, e.g. numbers which are composite and not of one dimension only, namely those of which the plane and the solid are copies (these are numbers which are so many times so many, or so many times so many times so many); and generally that which is inherent in the essence besides quantity ⟨is quality⟩. For the essence of a thing is what it is *once*; the essence of 6 is not what it is two or three times, but what it is *once*; for 6 is once 6.'

As Ross observes, it is odd that a circle should be given as an instance of the first sense of quality, while τὰ μαθηματικά generally come under quality in a second sense; but this need hardly trouble us, as the case of the circle is parallel enough to the other illustrations given of the first sense: 'angleless' (used of a circle) is a differentia of figure just as two-footed (of a man) and four-footed (of a horse) are differentiae of animal. In any case the two senses are practically reduced to one in 1020ᵇ15. (It is curious that, in *Categories* 8. 10ᵃ11, Aristotle places 'figure' itself in the category of quality; but in that passage 'figure' appears to mean *shape* (μορφή) rather than figure in our sense.)

'Linear', 'plane', and 'solid' numbers were distinguished by the Pythagoreans. Prime numbers were called 'linear', γραμμικοί,[1] and, alternatively, 'rectilinear', εὐθυγραμμικοί, by Thymaridas or 'euthy-metric', εὐθυμετρικοί, by others; they were regarded as having one dimension only, because they are measured by no number but by unity only. They are so defined by Euclid[2] and Theon.[3] Euclid defines plane and solid numbers as follows: 'When two (three) numbers having multiplied one another make some number, the number so produced is called *plane* (*solid*), and its *sides* are the numbers which have multiplied one another.'[4] Of 'plane' numbers, Plato recognized the *square* and the *oblong*.[5] As regards solid numbers he merely refers to a 'similar' distinction. Nicomachus, Theon of Smyrna, and Iamblichus further subdivide plane and solid numbers.[6]

(n) 'Relative' as applied to numbers

Metaph. Δ. 15. 1020ᵇ26–1021ᵃ7

'We apply the term "relative" to different things: (1) things like "double" in relation to its half, "triple" to a third of it, and in general

---

[1] Theon of Smyrna, p. 23. 12 H.   [2] vii, Def. 11.
[3] p. 23. 9.   [4] vii, Defs. 16, 17.
[5] προμήκης, *Timaeus* 54 A, or ἑτερομήκης, *Theaet.* 148 A.
[6] See *Euclid*, iii, pp. 289–91.

multiple in relation to submultiple, and that which exceeds to that which is exceeded; (2) things like that which is capable of heating in relation to that which can be heated, . . . and in general the active to the corresponding passive; (3) things like that which can be measured in relation to the measure, the knowable in relation to knowledge, and the perceptible to perception. The first kind have a numerical relation, either (a) indefinite or (b) definite, to numbers; or to 1: a multiple has a numerical relation to 1 but not a definite relation, such as that of one or other particular number. Again $1\frac{1}{2}$ has to its reciprocal the definite relation of a number to a number;

while $1 + \dfrac{1}{n}$ is to its reciprocal $\left[\dfrac{n}{n+1}\right]$ in an indefinite relation like

that of a multiple [say n times] to 1. The relation of that which exceeds to that which is exceeded is numerically quite indefinite; for number is commensurable and number has no application to what is not commensurable, whereas what exceeds is, in relation to what is exceeded, simply so much and something over, which is indefinite.'

The gist of this passage is fairly clear. When Aristotle speaks of 'double' being relative to 'half', he seems to mean the half of the *double*, in other words, the 'half' is the thing itself of which the 'double' is double, not the half of *that*; the relation is the numerical one of 2 : 1. Similarly the relation of a multiple (n times a thing) to *its* submultiple is the relation of n times a thing to the thing itself, i.e. n : 1, which is clearly numerical but indefinite in that n is un-determined and may be any number. ἡμιόλιον (*sesquialter*) too I take to be $1\frac{1}{2}$ times *its* ὑφημιόλιον (inverse or reciprocal of ἡμιόλιον), so that the relation between them is that of $1\frac{1}{2}$ to 1, or 3 to 2, a ratio between definite numbers.

The ἐπιμόριος (*superparticularis*) number is formed in the same

way as $1\frac{1}{2}$; it is the whole *plus* some submultiple of it as $\dfrac{1}{n}$, i.e. $1 + \dfrac{1}{n}$

where n is any integer, or $(n+1)/n$. Nicomachus[1] defines ἐπιμόριος as being the number 'which contains in itself the whole with which it is compared and some one part (i.e. aliquot part) of it'. Its

reciprocal is ὑπεπιμόριος (*subsuperparticularis* which is $1\Big/\Big(1 + \dfrac{1}{n}\Big)$ or

$\dfrac{n}{n+1}$. The ὑπεπιμόριον of the ἐπιμόριον is of course 1, and the relation

of the latter to the former is that of $1 + \dfrac{1}{n}$ to 1 or of $n+1$ to n, which

is a ratio between numbers but is indefinite until n has been given a specific value, as 3, 4, etc.

When we are given two magnitudes of which we only know that

[1] i. 19. 1.

one exceeds the other, the relation is not necessarily that of one number to another; the magnitudes may be incommensurable. Thus the diagonal of a square exceeds the side—it is the side and 'something over', but the excess over the side has to the side a ratio that cannot be expressed as a ratio between numbers.

I agree with Ross that, if in 1021ᵃ5 we had to translate the reading κατὰ μὴ σύμμετρον δὲ ἀριθμὸν λέγεται we should have to say '(the expression of the excess) may involve a non-commensurable number', and this would be to credit Aristotle with some wider conception of number not limited to integers or ratios between integers. There is no evidence that he had any such idea, and it seems best, therefore, to read κατὰ μὴ συμμέτρου δὲ ἀριθμὸς οὐ λέγεται.

(o) Physics and mathematics

Metaph. E. 1. 1025ᵇ18–1026ᵃ5

'Since physics, the science of nature, deals with one class of being (for it is concerned with that sort of substance which has in itself the principle of motion and rest), it is clear that it is neither "practical" nor "productive". . . . Hence, if all thought is either "practical" or else "productive" or "theoretical", physics must be a species of theoretical science, which must, however, study the sort of being which is capable of being moved, and substance as notion of form, for the most part only as inseparable (from matter). Now we must not fail to notice the nature of the essence and the definition, for, without this, inquiry is fruitless. And of things that are defined, i.e. of essences, some exist in the way that "snub" does, and others in the same way as "hollow"; the difference is that "snub" is bound up with matter (for snub is a hollow *nose*), whereas hollowness is independent of sensible matter. If then all natural objects are described in the same way as snub, e.g. nose, eye, face, flesh, bone, and in general animal, or again leaf, root, bark, and, in general, plant (for none of these things can be defined without reference to movement, and all contain matter), it is clear how in physics investigation of the essence and definition should proceed . . . .'

Ib. 1026ᵃ6–19

'It is clear from these considerations that physics is a theoretical science. But mathematics too is a theoretical science, though whether it is concerned with things immovable and separable is as yet not clear; it is clear, however, that some branches of mathematics study things *qua* immovable and *qua* separable. Now, if there exists anything that is eternal, immovable, and separable, it is manifest that knowledge (of it) belongs to a theoretical science—not, however, to physics (physics being concerned with a certain class of movable objects), nor yet to mathematics, but to a science prior to both. For physics deals with things separable [i.e. existing separately, though not separable from matter] but not immovable; and some branches of mathematics at all events deal with things immovable but probably not separable, being as it were embodied in matter, while the first science [i.e. the science which is prior to both physics and mathematics, "first philosophy" or "theology"] deals with things which are both separable and immovable. Now all causes must be eternal, but especially these, for they are in the relation of causes to so much as is visible to us of the divine. Hence there will be three theoretical sciences, mathematics, physics, and theology.'

At 1026ᵃ10, εἰ δέ τί ἐστιν ἀΐδιον καὶ ἀκίνητον καὶ χωριστόν, φανερὸν ὅτι θεωρητικῆς τὸ γνῶναι, I confess I would rather translate εἰ by 'whether' as Natorp does; for if it had simply meant 'if', it would have seemed more natural to write τὸ γνῶναι αὐτό than τὸ γνῶναι by itself.

I have translated the above passages in full because they should be read with (a) the passage in the *Physics* (193ᵇ22—194ᵃ15) dealing with the difference between the objects of the sciences of physics and mathematics, and (b) the passages in which the abstractions of mathematics are explained by means of the same parallel of the 'snub' contrasted with the 'hollow', in *De an.* III. 4. 429ᵇ18–20 and III. 5. 431ᵇ12–16.

In the passage of the *Physics* Aristotle, while admitting that physics, in addition to discussing the constitution of the heavenly bodies, must also know about the *shapes* of the sun, moon, etc., and the universe, goes on to say (193ᵇ31–5) that the mathematician too studies these shapes, 'but not *qua* limits, in each case, of a natural body. Nor does he investigate their attributes *qua* attributes of natural bodies. This is why he separates (the mathematical objects) since they *can* be separated in thought from motion, and this makes no difference, nor does any error (ψεῦδος, false statement) arise through the separation.'

In the second passage from the *Metaphysics* Aristotle says that whether mathematics deals with things immovable and separable is as yet not clear (1026ᵃ8–9). The question is further considered in Books *M*, *N*, and the conclusion is that mathematical objects are *not* actually separable. The passage in the *Physics* is not inconsistent with this; for the statement there (193ᵇ34) is that it is *in thought* (τῇ νοήσει) that *mathematica* are separable from motion. So, too, according to *De an.* (431ᵇ15–16: as to which see pp. 65–7, above), *mathematica*, though not separable, are *conceived of* as separate.

(p) 'Figure' (form and matter): 'bronze sphere'

Metaph. Z. 7, 8

In *De caelo* I. 9. 277ᵇ33—278ᵃ10, a distinction is drawn between the sphere in itself, as such, and the bronze sphere: 'The form of a sphere and a golden or bronze sphere are different things. . . . When we describe the essential nature of sphere or circle we do not include gold or bronze in the definition because these things do not belong to the essence. If, on the other hand, we are describing the bronze or golden sphere, we do use the words.' The case would be the same even if the one particular circle were the only one that could be found: 'none the less, the being of circle and the being of this particular circle are different things, the one being form, the other being the form (embodied) in the matter, that is, a particular thing'.

Similarly in *Metaph. Z* 7. 1033ᵃ2–4, we are told that 'we describe what bronze circles are in both ways; we say of its matter that it is bronze, and of its form that it is such-and-such'.

In *Z*. 8. 1033ᵃ24 ff. Aristotle asks the question how the bronze sphere 'comes to be'. It is made out of the substratum in the full sense of the word (i.e. including form as well as matter). 'The maker does not make the substratum, . . . nay, we do not even make the sphere except incidentally, i.e. because the bronze sphere is a sphere; what we make is the bronze sphere' (1033ᵃ28–31). 'To make the bronze round is not to make the round or the sphere, but to make something else, that is to say, to produce the said form in something else' (ib. ᵃ32–4). 'It is manifest then that the form, or whatever else we must call the shape in the sensible object, is not produced (γίγνεται), nor is coming-to-be (γένεσις) true of it; the essence, that is, is not produced, the essence being what is produced in something else by art, by nature, or by (some) power. That there *is* a bronze sphere, *this* is what we "make"; we make it out of "bronze" and "sphere", for we put the form into such-and-such matter, and the result is a bronze sphere' (1033ᵇ5–10). 'If then a sphere is that figure which extends equally (all ways) from the centre, there will be included in it, first, that in which what is made is to be, second, what is in it, and, third, the whole product—say, the brazen sphere' (ᵇ14–16).

In the last sentence Aristotle says that even the mathematical sphere, the sphere of the definition, is a combination of matter and form. The 'matter' in this case Alexander calls the ὑποκείμενον, *substratum*, which he evidently regarded as being of the nature of ὕλη νοητή, *'intelligible* matter', as distinct from ὕλη αἰσθητή (cf. 1036ᵃ10, 1045ᵃ34), for he has spoken just before of the essence of a sphere being universal and intelligible and being produced in something else, say the soul, as the bronze sphere is made in bronze. Bonitz, on the other hand, interprets the first constituent or aspect of the mathematical sphere as the *genus*, comparing 1033ᵃ4 and 1024ᵇ4 f. for the treatment of the genus as matter. Ross follows Bonitz, taking the two constituents to be genus and differentia.

Metaph. Δ. 10. 1035ᵇ33–1036ᵃ12

'Only the parts of the form are parts of the definition, and the definition is of the universal, for "being a circle" (the essence of circle) and circle are the same thing, as are also "being a soul" and soul. But when we come to the concrete thing [the combination of form and matter], say *this* individual circle, i.e. some particular circle either sensible or intelligible (I mean by "intelligible" circle, the mathematical, and by "sensible" circles those made, say, of bronze or of wood), there is no definition of these circles, but they are known by means of thought or perception; and when they go out of our actual awareness it is not clear whether at a given time they exist or do not exist; but they are always described and known by the universal definition. Their *matter*, however, is in itself unknowable. Matter may be either sensible or intelligible, sensible matter being, say, bronze and wood and all matter that is changeable, and intelligible matter being that which subsists in sensible bodies but not *qua* sensible, such as the objects of mathematics.'

I have quoted this passage in full because Aristotle here sets out clearly the distinctions which he makes between (1) the generic or universal circle which is the subject of the definition of a circle, (2) particular mathematical circles which are non-sensible but are present in sensible things not *qua* sensible, (3) particular circles made of wood, bronze, etc. I agree with Ross's note on ὕλη νοητή.[1] In this particular passage it is equivalent to the ὕλη of mathematical objects (see *K.* 1059ᵇ15). In the case of the mathematical circle which is *in* sensible objects but not *of* them, so to speak, Alexander suggests that the ὕλη νοητή is διάστασις, *dimension*, i.e. extension.

(*q*) Definition of a whole in relation to definition of its parts

Ib. *Z.* 10. 1034ᵇ20–4

'Since a definition is an account or description, and every description has parts, and as the description is to the thing so is the part of the description to the part of the thing, the question at once arises whether the description of the parts must be contained in the description of the whole, or not.'

[1] Vol. ii, pp. 199–200.

The difficulty in answering the question, Aristotle goes on to say (^{b}32), is due to the fact that the word 'part' is used in several senses. One of these is 'that which measures a thing in respect of quantity'. This we can leave out of account. But substance consists of form and matter. Take the case of snub-nose: the flesh is part of 'snub-nose' but not of 'hollowness'; it is part, as matter, of 'snubness'. So with a bronze circle; the circle can be resolved into bronze and the bronze is part of it as *matter* ($1035^{a}25$–7).

In a particular immaterial circle the segments are parts, as matter, on which the form supervenes, though the segments are nearer to the form than the bronze is when the circle is of bronze ($1035^{a}12$–14). Such parts (in the sense of matter) do not come into the definition of the whole. On the other hand, 'parts which are parts of the definition and into which the definition is analysed are prior, either all or some of them. Now the definition of a right angle is not analysed into that of an acute angle, but the definition of the acute angle *is* resolved into that of the right angle; for he who defines an acute angle must make use of the right angle, since an acute angle is "less than a right angle". Similarly with the circle and the semi-circle; a semicircle is defined by means of the circle as a finger is defined by means of the whole (man), such-and-such a part of a man being a finger' ($1035^{b}4$–11).

The Euclidean definition of a right angle will be remembered (I, Def. 10): 'When a straight line set up on a straight line makes the adjacent angles equal to one another, each of the equal angles is right, and the straight line standing on the other is called a perpendicular to that on which it stands.' Euclid goes on: 'An obtuse angle is an angle greater than a right angle (Def. 11) and an acute angle is an angle less than a right angle' (Def. 12). Similarly, after defining a circle, Euclid goes on: 'A semicircle is the figure contained by a diameter and the circumference (of the circle) cut off by it' (Def. 18).

As regards the acute angle and the semicircle Aristotle makes a further point in c. 11. $1036^{b}32$–$1037^{a}5$.

'But, to return to the objects of mathematics, why are the definitions of parts not included in the definitions of the wholes, e.g. that of the semicircle in that of the circle? True, they are not perceptible things [like the hand as part of a man]. But surely that makes no difference; some things will be found to have matter, though they are non-sensible; in fact, there is some sort of matter in everything which is not an essence and pure form but is some individual thing. The semicircles will in that case not be parts of the universal circle, but they will be parts of individual circles, as we said before; for one sort of matter is sensible but another is intelligible.' That is to say, the semicircles are not part of the universal circle, the subject of the definition, but they are parts of individual mathematical circles, and these, though non-sensibles, have a matter of their own, namely the 'intelligible matter' (ὕλη νοητή) of mathematical objects. This intelligible matter in the case of geometrical objects is perhaps best described as 'extension' or 'dimensions'.[1]

Thus an acute angle is, so far as form or notion is concerned, not prior but posterior to the right angle; it is only as *matter* that an acute angle may be prior to a right angle, because a right angle can be divided up into acute angles (*Metaph. M.* 8. 1084ᵇ7–9).

(r) *Angle in a semicircle, etc.*

Metaph. Θ. 9. 1051ᵃ21–31

'Propositions too in mathematics are discovered by an activity (i.e. by actual working); for it is by a process of *dividing-up* (διαι-ροῦντες) that we discover them. If the division had already been performed, the propositions would have been manifest; as it is, they are present only potentially. Why does the triangle imply two right angles [i.e. that the angles are together equal to two right angles]? Because the angles about one point are equal to two right angles. If, therefore, the straight line parallel to the side had been drawn upwards, the reason why would at once have been clear [i.e. by simple inspection]. Why is the angle in a semicircle a right angle, universally? Because if there are three equal straight lines, and the base consists of two of them, while the perpendicular erected from the middle point is the third, the truth is at once clear by simple inspection to anyone who knows the aforesaid theorem [namely that the angles of a triangle are together equal to two right angles]. Hence it is manifest that relations subsisting potentially are discovered by being brought to actuality; the reason is that the exercise of thought is a (bringing to) actuality.'

In the above translation I have followed Ross's text. I feel no doubt that τὰ διαγράμματα in 1051ᵃ22 are, as in *Categ.* 14ᵃ39 and *Metaph. Δ.* 10. 1014ᵃ36, geometrical *propositions* including the proofs of the same, and not merely 'diagrams' or even 'constructions'.

διαιροῦντες, 'dividing up', is evidently meant in a non-technical, and even a literal sense, and there is no reference to the method of mathematical *analysis*. The dividing up is effected by inserting additional lines, etc. Given a figure in which it is required to prove a certain relation, our ordinary procedure is to join certain points by straight lines, to draw perpendiculars from certain points to certain lines, to bisect certain angles, to draw certain circles, and the like,

---

[1] Cf. p. 214, above.

all in the hope that certain relations will then emerge, the use of which will lead to the result desired.

I have already given and discussed the method of proof which Aristotle has in mind in the case of the right angle in a semicircle.[1]

The two well-known proofs, the Pythagorean and the Euclidean, of the proposition that the angles of a triangle are together equal to two right angles have been described already.[2] It is Euclid's proof in which the 'parallel to the side' of the triangle can be said to be 'drawn *up*' (ἀνῆκτο), and it is from this fact that I conclude that it was Euclid's proof that Aristotle had in his mind. The word ἀνάγειν in the sense of being drawn *upwards* is quite usual in Greek geometry; Apollonius of Perga uses it regularly. In his *Conics* the *ordinate* of a point on a conic is a straight line drawn *ordinate-wise* (τεταγμένως, meaning, no doubt, in the regular or recognized manner) to meet a diameter; the *ordinate* is in fact parallel to the tangent at the extremity of the diameter. Now when the ordinates are drawn *down* from the point of the curve to the diameter, they are called by Apollonius αἱ καταγόμεναι τεταγμένως; when they are drawn *upwards* from points on the diameter, the word ἀνάγειν is used.[3]

(s) *Measures*

Ib. I. 1. 1052ᵇ20-7

'A measure is that by which quantity is known; and quantity *qua* quantity is known by a 'one' or a number, all number is known by a 'one'. Hence all quantity *qua* quantity is known by the 'one', and that by which quantities are primarily known is itself the one; therefore the one is the beginning of number *qua* number. Hence comes it that, in other cases too, that by which each thing is primarily known is called a measure, and the measure of each is one—whether in length, breadth, depth, weight, or speed.'

Ib. 1052ᵇ31–1053ᵃ18

'In all these things, therefore, the measure or beginning is something that is one and indivisible, for even in the case of lines we treat as indivisible a foot-length. Thus everywhere we seek as the measure something that is one and indivisible; and this is that which is simple either in quality or in quantity. Now where it is not thought possible to subtract or add anything, our measure is exact; accordingly the measure of number is most exact; for we posit the unit as indivisible every way; and in other things we imitate this sort of

---

[1] pp. 71–4, above. [2] pp. 29–30.

[3] Cf. *Conics* i. 26: καὶ ἀπὸ τοῦ Γ τεταγμένως ἀνήχθω ἡ ΓΘ, and similarly in i. 35, etc

measure. Now with a stade or a talent or anything relatively large, any addition or subtraction would be less noticed than with something smaller. Hence the first thing from which it appears to our sense that nothing can be subtracted is taken by everyone as the measure, of liquids or solids or weights or magnitudes; and we think that we then know the quantity when we know it in terms of this measure. Thus motion is known by the motion which is at once simple and the quickest; for it is this that takes the least time. Hence in astronomy, we take a unity of this kind as the beginning and measure; for we take the motion of the heaven to be uniform and the quickest and we judge of other motions by reference to it. In music it is the quarter-tone because it is the smallest interval, and in speech the letter. . . . But the measure is not always numerically one; there may be more than one, e.g. the quarter-tones are two (not according to the ear but to the ratios), and the sounds by which we measure are more than one; the diagonal of a square and its side too are measured by two quantities, and so are all magnitudes.'

The measure of speed of motion is given by the time taken by the apparent daily rotation of the heaven. This time being taken to be roughly 24 hours, one twenty-fourth of it gives an hour in time; then the speed of any motion along a line or a track can be determined by ascertaining the distance covered in an hour. Angular motion can be measured in the same way by observing the angle through which the revolving object has revolved in an hour.

The statement that 'the diagonal and the side of a square and all magnitudes are measured by two (measures)' remains a complete puzzle. Alexander thinks that the two measures are (1) the notion or definition of the measure as conceived in our minds, e.g. the form of a cubit; (2) the concrete measure, e.g. the cubit in wood or any such material with which we measure in practice. The context does not seem to support this view in any way. Bonitz tentatively suggested that the meaning is that 'both the ratio which subsists between the diagonal and the side, and the size of any plane figure, are not determined by means of one measured line, but by two measured lines and the product of the numbers representing the measures when multiplied together'. But in the first place Aristotle does not speak of the *ratio* of the diagonal to the side, but of 'the diagonal and the side' (as two different things), nor can τὰ μεγέθη πάντα be restricted to plane figures: it must mean all spatial magnitudes, lines and solids as well as plane areas.

For the rest see Ross's note on the passage. It occurred to me that Aristotle might have in mind that the relative lengths of the diagonal and the side can be approximated to by forming the successive approximations to $\sqrt{2}$ in accordance with Theon of

Smyrna's rule; these are $\frac{7}{5}$, $\frac{17}{12}$, $\frac{41}{29}$, etc. If therefore we took the side to be 1, we could say that the diagonal was one of these fractions, so that two numbers (one divided by the other) are required to measure it; but in that case (as in Ross's conjecture) καὶ ἡ πλευρά is in the air and would have to be rejected as a gloss.

(t) The geometer's hypotheses

Metaph. N. 2

Aristotle is here discussing the Platonists' construction of numbers out of (*a*) the one, (*b*) the material element, variously described as the Unequal, the Great and Small, and the Indefinite Dyad. Aristotle says that the Platonists took to this type of element in order to oppose Parmenides' doctrine of the One which alone is Being. Since, if things are many, numbers must be composed of Being and of something else which is only potential and may not be actual, the Platonists thought it necessary to prove that not-being exists. Now one kind of not-being is the 'false or that class of thing' (ταύτην τὴν φύσιν), 1089ª20. What Plato actually says in the *Sophist*[1] is that there cannot be ψεῦδος, the false, unless there is not-being, and it must therefore be from *this* and Being that the many things that exist are constructed.

Ib. 1089ª21–5

'This is why it used to be said that you must make some false assumption, just as the geometer does when he assumes a line to be a foot long although it is actually not a foot long. This, however, cannot be the case. The geometer makes no false assumption; what he sets forth (ἡ πρότασις) is no part of his syllogism.'

Alexander explains that the last phrase is equivalent to saying, 'It is not the line put forward and drawn which is used in the syllogism, but the line they think of.' That is, the proof they give does not depend on the line which they draw and which is not a foot long but on the line of which they think and which *is* a foot long. I think this is undoubtedly the right explanation. It does not seem possible to take πρότασις in the sense of the technical term in geometry for the (general) 'enunciation' of a proposition (like those of Euclid). It is not the 'enunciation' which would be wrong in the case supposed; it is the ἔκθεσις (*setting-out*) which would be wrong, ἔκθεσις being the technical term for the second step in a Euclidean proposition, that in which the enunciation is put in a concrete form with reference to an illustrative diagram, e.g. 'Let *ABC* be the given

[1] 237 A, 240.

triangle'. Moreover, the 'enunciation' does in fact 'appear in the syllogism', namely as the *conclusion*.

For other passages on the same subject see *An. Pr.* I. 41. 49^{b}33–7 and *An. Post.* I. 10. 76^{b}39—77^{a}3 (pp. 26–7, above).

(*u*) *Numbers: Pythagorean and Platonist views*

Book *N* of the *Metaphysics* is a continuation of Book *M* and discusses certain views about mathematical objects, especially numbers, held by the Pythagoreans, Plato, and certain Platonists, to which views Aristotle opposes his own. The standpoint of *N* and the latter part of *M* from 1086^{a}21 onwards is that of Aristotle's early period (that of *A*, *B*), the period of his stay at Assos, 348–345 B.C. On the theory of numbers Aristotle distinguishes the views of (1) the Pythagoreans, (2) Platonist views, the first of which (*a*) separated ideal numbers from mathematical numbers (the view of Plato), the second (*b*) identified the two (Xenocrates), while the third (*c*) recognized mathematical numbers only (Speusippus). I do not propose to enter at all into the vexed questions connected with Plato's generation of numbers from the One with the Indefinite Dyad or the Great and Small, which have evoked a whole literature.

In Book *N* the first thing that especially interests the historian of mathematics is any further detail about the Pythagorean theory of numbers that can be gathered in addition to what is stated in Book *A*. 5. 985^{b}23—986^{a}3, as to which see pp. 197–9, above. We have first the remark (*N*. 3. 1090^{a}20–5) that the Pythagoreans were induced to conclude that all things are numbers by the fact that they found numbers in the musical scale, in the heaven, and in many things besides. They held that numbers were not separable, i.e. had no separate existence, but were the material out of which things are made (1090^{a}22–3). Aristotle goes on to say that he holds, as before stated, and that it is obvious, that the objects of mathematics are not separable from sensible things (1090^{a}28–30). In this respect, therefore, the Pythagoreans are open to no criticism; but 'in respect that they make physical bodies out of numbers, that is, things which have lightness and weight out of things which have them not, they would seem to be speaking of another sort of heaven and of bodies different from those perceptible to sense'.

The next passage of interest is

Metaph. N. 5. 1092^{b}8–15

'They have not anyhow defined in which of two ways numbers are the causes of substance and of being, whether (1) as boundaries, like points in relation to magnitudes, or in the way that Eurytus decided what number belonged to which thing, e.g. that this parti-

cular number is the number of a man, that number the number of
a horse, and making, with the aid of pebbles, likenesses in the shape
of plants, after the manner of those who bring numbers into the
form of triangle or square—or (2) because harmony is a ratio of
numbers and similarly man and everything else is a ratio of
numbers.'

With reference to alternative (1) there is nothing to be added to
Ross's note except that the figured numbers and their formation
are fully set out by Nicomachus in his *Introductio Arithmetica*.[1]
The plane figures include not only triangles, squares, and oblongs,
but regular pentagons, hexagons, and so on up to regular polygons
of any number of sides. The figured solid numbers include pyramids
having for bases triangles, squares, and regular polygons with any
number of sides; other solid numbers are cubes and parallelepipeds.
I have given in my *History of Greek Mathematics*[2] a full account of
the figured numbers with diagrams; and it would be superfluous to
repeat the details here.

Passing to alternative (2) Aristotle continues:

Ib. ᵇ15–23

'But in that case how are attributes such as white, sweet, and hot,
numbers? It is clear that the numbers are not the essence of the
things nor the causes of the form; the ratio is the essence, the number
is the matter. For example, the essence of flesh or bone is number
in this way, say three parts of air and two of earth. And, whatever
the number may be, it is always a number of something, of parts
of fire or of earth, or of units, while the essence is being "so much
to so much" by way of mixture; but this is no longer a number, but
a ratio of a mixture of numbers, which are corporeal or whatever
else they may be. . . .'

Ib. 6. 1092ᵇ26–32

'We may also well ask what is the good that comes from numbers
in respect that the mixture is expressible in number, whether it be
easily calculable or disproportionate (περιττῷ, perhaps "excessive"
rather than "odd"?). For, as it is, it is no more conducive to health
that watered honey should be mixed in the ratio "three by three"
(lit. three times three, τρὶς τρία); nay it would do more good if it
were in no (particular) ratio but decidedly watery than if it were
practically unmixed honey (though diluted) in a (definite) numerical
ratio. Moreover, the ratios of mixtures come of *adding* numbers

---

[1] ii, cc. 7–12 for plane figures and in c. 17 as regards numbers forming solid
figures.
[2] Vol. i, pp. 76 ff.

(sc. of other things, e.g. parts of earth or fire or units, b20); they are not relations in numbers as such; they mean e.g. "three parts to two" not "three times two".'

Aristotle implies that the Pythagoreans, when they spoke of a ratio of 'three parts to two', said 'three times two' (or 'three by two'). This is remarkable. There is no trace of such phraseology in Euclid, Book VII, in which the arithmetical theory of proportion is systematically set out, nor in Books VIII, IX; in all these books numbers are indicated by separate straight lines usually drawn parallel to one another; this applies even to 'plane' numbers, squares, cubes, and parallelepipedal numbers. It occurs to me that at some period before Euclid's time it may have been customary to represent two numbers bearing a certain ratio to one another by straight lines perpendicular to one another in the form, say, of two adjacent sides of a rectangle. This might be useful for denoting pairs of numbers in the same ratio, which would then be shown as two corresponding sides of similar rectangles. Now 'thrice three' or 'three by three' and 'thrice two' or 'three by two' is a natural way of referring to a square or a rectangle with sides in those ratios.

In 1092b27 the phrase ἢ ἐν εὐλογίστῳ ἢ ἐν περιττῷ (ἀριθμῷ) is difficult. Alexander takes εὐλογίστῳ to mean 'even' in contrast to 'odd', περιττῷ. But εὐλόγιστος in itself obviously means 'easily calculable' or 'easy to reckon with'. It naturally excludes the irrational, but otherwise is quite general; it need not be confined to numbers 'easily formed as products, by multiplication, e.g. squares, cubes, etc.', as Bonitz supposes. But in any case 'odd' is no proper correlative to it, and it seems more probable that περιττός here means 'excessive', 'disproportionate'. The 'easily calculable' ratio would then be like m, n, where m, n are ordinary manageable numbers, while 'excessive' might, in view of ἄκρατον 'unmixed' (b30) be an inconveniently large number, though determinate.

(v) 'Universal' mathematics

Metaph. E. 1. 1026a23–7

'The question may be asked whether first philosophy is universal or deals with some particular genus or some one class of thing. For not even in the mathematical sciences is the method one and the same; geometry and astronomy, for instance, deal with a certain class of thing, but the universal science of mathematics is common to all branches.'

Ib. *K.* 7. 1064b8–9

'For each of the mathematical sciences is concerned with some distinct genus, but universal mathematics is common to all.'

Ib. *M.* 2. 1077ᵃ9–10

'Further some propositions are proved universally by mathematicians, which extend beyond these substances' [the objects of special mathematical sciences such as geometry, astronomy, optics, harmonics].

Ib. 1077ᵇ17–22

'Just as the universal propositions in mathematics do not relate to separate entitiesa part from magnitudes and numbers but relate to these things, not, however, *qua* such as to have magnitude or to be divisible, it is clear that it is possible to have not only statements but demonstrations about sensible magnitudes, not however *qua* sensible but *qua* possessing such and such attributes.'

In speaking of universal propositions in mathematics applying to a wider class of entities than those of magnitudes, numbers, and the objects of particular mathematical sciences, Aristotle no doubt had in mind such propositions as that in which it is proved that, if four terms are in proportion, they are also proportional *alternando*. Aristotle pointed out[1] that this proposition used to be proved separately for numbers, lines, solids, and times, 'but is now proved universally for all'.[2] The reference is obviously to the proof forming part of Eudoxus' new theory of proportion. What Aristotle would have called the more general category of things to which the proof would apply does not appear, but it seems most likely that it would have been ποσόν, quantity. What was the word used by Eudoxus in his proposition we do not know; Euclid, who reproduced Eudoxus' theory, speaks of 'magnitudes'. If Eudoxus' word was 'magnitudes' it is odd that, in 1077ᵇ17–20, Aristotle should say that the general theorems referred to do not relate to a separate class of entities different from magnitudes, numbers, etc., and yet apply to these things *not qua* such as to have magnitude or to be divisible; for, as Ross says, one would have thought that divisibility was an essential characteristic of all the objects of mathematics (except points and units). Yet Aristotle does seem to say that general mathematics treats magnitudes, numbers, etc., as being members of some more general category (ποσόν, or whatever else Aristotle would have called it).

Perhaps the best analogy for the sort of 'general' or 'universal' mathematics which Aristotle seems to have had in mind is our *algebra* which supplements arithmetical notation and operations by the use of general symbols for things known or unknown, and for operations. (Even so, the things denoted by the symbols are generally spoken of as 'quantities'.) But algebra in our sense was

[1] *An. Post.* i. 5. [2] See pp. 43–4, above.

impossible for the Greeks in Aristotle's time, because no symbols had been invented, and such problems as are equivalent to the algebraical solution of quadratic or cubic equations the Greeks could only solve by geometry.

(w) Objects of mathematics, physics, and first philosophy

Metaph. K. 1. 1059^{b}9–20

'If, on the other hand, it is not as they say [the thinkers who make *mathematica* a separate class intermediate between Forms and Sensibles], with what sort of things must we assume that the mathematician deals? Not surely with the things in this world; for none of them is the sort of thing which the mathematical sciences investigate. Nor again does the science of which we are now in search [metaphysics or "theology"] treat of the objects of mathematics, for none of them has separate existence. But neither does it deal with sensible substances, for they are perishable. And, generally, it may be questioned to what sort of science it belongs to discuss the difficulties connected with the *matter* of mathematical objects. For it pertains neither to physics—because the whole study of the physicist is concerned with the things which have in themselves a principle of motion and rest—nor yet to the science which inquires about demonstration and science [logic], for this is the very subject of its own inquiry.'

In *E.* 1. 1026^{a}8–9, we were told that the answer to the question whether mathematics deals with things immovable and separable 'is not so far clear'. So far as separability is concerned the question is now answered: *mathematica* have no separate existence apart from things in nature, physical objects. More to the same effect appears in the passages next to be quoted.

The *matter* of mathematical objects (1059^{b}15–16) is the ὕλη νοητή, 'intelligible matter' (*Z.* 10. 1036^{a}9 f.) as distinct from 'sensible matter', ὕλη αἰσθητή. The best description of this intelligible matter appears[1] to be space or 'extension'.

Ib. 2. 1060^{b}12–17

'If we suppose lines or what immediately follows them (I mean the primary surfaces) to be principles, these are at all events not separable substances but are sections and divisions, the one of surfaces, the other of bodies (as points are of lines); they are also extremities or limits of the same things; but all of them subsist in other things, and no one of them is separable.'

---

[1] As we have seen, pp. 43–4.

Ross interprets 'primary' in 'primary surfaces' as meaning 'intelligible' and compares 'primary' length, breadth, and depth respectively in *De an.* 404^b20.

Metaph. K. 7. 1064^a30–^b3

'Physics then [the science of nature] is concerned with things that have in themselves a principle of motion; mathematics is theoretical and is a science dealing with things that are unchanging but have no separate existence. Therefore that which is separable and immovable must be the subject of some science different from the two mentioned—that is, if any substance of this kind exists, I mean separable and immovable, as I hope to show later. And, assuming that there is anything of this kind in the world, here must surely be the divine, and this must be the primary and most sovereign principle. It is clear, therefore, that there are three kinds of theoretical science, physics, mathematics, and theology.'

In Book *M*, c. 1, Aristotle returns to the question of the nature of mathematical objects. If, he says, mathematical objects exist, we have to consider the alternatives: (*a*) they may exist in sensible objects as some maintain, (*b*) they may be separate from existing things (a view which also has its supporters), or (*c*) they must exist in some other way. In c. 2 the first two alternatives are disposed of. In c. 3 Aristotle gives his own solution of the problem. He illustrates first by moving objects. You may have arguments about moving objects without reference to what the moving objects are or what attributes they possess, but treating them merely *as* moving objects, and it is not necessary to assume that there exist any movable entities separate from sensible ones, or that these have in them some natural character separate from their matter. In like manner you may have a science dealing with these same sensible moving objects not *qua* moving but *qua* bodies, and again, *qua* planes only, *qua* lengths only, *qua* divisible, *qua* indivisible but having position [points], and *qua* indivisible only. This science is mathematics.

Ib. *M.* 3. 1078^a2–31

'If geometry happens to be concerned with sensibles but does not treat of them *qua* sensible, it does not follow on that account that the mathematical sciences are sciences of sensibles, nor again of other things separate from sensibles. Many essential attributes attach to things in virtue of what they severally are. Thus animals have attributes peculiar to them as male and female respectively; yet there is nothing female or male existing apart from animals; thus essential attributes may attach to things merely *qua* lengths or *qua* planes. . . . Hence if we assume things separated from their accidental properties, and consider any question about them as so separated, we shall not on that account be guilty of any falsehood, any more than we are if we draw a line and say it is a foot long when it is not; the falsehood forms no part of our premisses [i.e. the premisses on which we base a proof]. And it would actually be the best method of investigating a particular thing to suppose that which is not separate to be separate, and this is what the arithmetician and the geometer do. A man as man is one and indivisible. The arithmetician treats him as an indivisible one, and inquires if he has any attributes *qua* indivisible; the geometer considers him neither *qua* man nor *qua* indivisible but *qua* a solid . . . .

'Thus geometers argue quite correctly; they speak about real things and their subjects do exist; for that which exists is of two kinds; it may exist either in actuality or by way of matter' (ὑλικῶς).

Ross is obviously right in taking the sense of ὑλικῶς, as contrasted with ἐντελεχείᾳ, to be that mathematical objects, straight lines, etc., though not actually and substantially present in sensible things, are potentially present, and their presence can be made actual by the geometer's power of χωρισμός, 'separation' (= abstraction).

X

MECHANICS

(a) Mechanics

THE *Mechanica* included in the Aristotelian corpus is not indeed by Aristotle, but it must be near in date, as we conclude from the terminology; this shows more general agreement with the terminology of Euclid than Aristotle's own writings do, but certain divergences from Euclid's terms are common to Aristotle and the author of the *Mechanica*. We must suppose, therefore, that the *Mechanica* was written before Euclid had made the terminology of mathematics fixed and convenient, or alternatively that it was composed after Euclid's time by persons who, though they had largely assimilated his terminology, were close enough to Aristotle's date to be still influenced by his usage. Again, the Aristotelian origin of many of the ideas in the *Mechanica* is proved by parallels found in Aristotle's genuine writings.

The book begins with generalities, remarking how, in the case of natural occurrences, we marvel at those of which we do not know the cause, and again we marvel when arts directed to the service of mankind appear to win a victory over nature; for nature's action is always uniform and unchanging, whereas our requirements from time to time vary in all sorts of ways. Hence, in order to produce some particular utility, we have to do something 'contrary to nature' or 'out of the natural order' (παρὰ φύσιν), and for this purpose to resort to art (τέχνη). The particular art that constantly helps in such cases is the *mechanical*, which we call by a name derived from μηχανή, a 'contrivance', a mechanical device, a *machine*. The commonest problems of a mechanical kind are those connected with the use of the *lever*. It seems strange that we should be able to move a great weight by applying only a small force; yet this is possible with the help of a lever, although the lever itself adds a little more weight.

The principle of the lever is made to depend on the circle.

Mech. 3. 850ᵃ39–ᵇ6

'As the weight moved is to the moving [weight or force], so is the length [or distance] to the length inversely. The moving weight or force will always move the weight to be moved the more easily the farther it is away from the fulcrum. The reason is that aforesaid, namely that the line which extends farther from the centre describes the greater circle, so that, if the force [or power, ἰσχύς] applied is the

same, that which moves the system will change its position the
more the farther away it is from the fulcrum.'   Cf. p. 235 *infra*.

Mech. 3. 848ᵃ11–19

'What happens with the balance is reduced to the circle, and the
phenomena of the lever to the balance; and practically everything
concerning mechanical movements is referable to the lever. Further,
it is the fact that, given a radius of a circle, no two points of it move
at equal speed, but the point more distant from the centre always
moves more quickly, and this is the reason of many remarkable
facts about the movements of circles which will appear in the
sequel.'

The idea seems to be that (assuming the force to be always
applied at right angles to the lever, in other words, along the tangent
to the circle described by the end of the lever) the action of the
force or 'power' is equivalent to a smaller weight traversing a greater
distance and balancing the larger weight which traverses a shorter
distance. This is much the same idea as emerges from the passages
which are often quoted as containing the germ of the 'principle of
virtual velocities', namely: *De caelo* III. 2. 301ᵇ4–13: 'A smaller
weight will be given more movement if the force acting on it is the
same. . . . The speed of the lesser body will be to that of the greater
as the greater body is to the lesser', and *Phys.* VII. 5. 249ᵇ30—
250ᵃ4: 'If A be the movent, B the thing moved, C the length over
which it is moved, D the time taken, then

A will move $\frac{1}{2}B$ over the distance $2C$ in the time D
and A „ $\frac{1}{2}B$ „ „ C „ $\frac{1}{2}D$,
and the proportion is maintained.'

In other words, if in a given time a force F moves a mass M over
a space S, it will in the same time move a mass m over a space s,
where $M : m = s : S$.

And of course, if v, V are the velocities respectively, $V : v = S : s$,
and therefore $M : m = v : V$.

This is what happens with a system of frictionless pulleys. The
smaller weight has, during the operation, to act over a longer distance (or move at a higher speed) than the larger weight which it
has to pull up, precisely in the ratio which the larger weight bears
to the smaller.

Suppose now that the weight W hangs at A, the extremity of the
lever which is nearest the fulcrum O, while the force F is applied at
B, the end of the lever farthest from the fulcrum, the lever being
to begin with in a horizontal position. Then if B with the weight
F hanging vertically from it describes a circle and the lever takes
the position $A'B'$, the force required to be applied vertically at B'

in order to balance, about O, the weight W is not F but a smaller force. Let the (vertical) line of action of the force applied at B' meet AB, the original position of the lever, in N so that $B'N$ is perpendicular to AB; and let $A'M$ be perpendicular to AB.

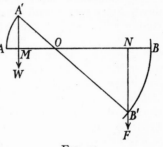

Then the force F may be regarded as acting at N and its effectiveness for turning the system is measured by the product of the force by the perpendicular distance from the fulcrum to the line of action, namely ON. This product $F.ON$ is what is called the *moment* of F about O,

FIG. 49

and this has to balance, not $W.AO$ but $W.OM$. The first person in medieval times to evince a clear conception of the *moment* of a force was apparently an unknown person whom P. Duhem[1] calls 'the precursor of Leonardo da Vinci' (1451–1519), and who was the author of a work which is contained in a manuscript of the thirteenth century,[2] and apparently bears the title *Liber Jordani de ratione ponderis*, but is a great improvement upon, and far more original than, Jordanus' own work. The treatise cannot be later than the thirteenth century, and Duhem[3] gives good reason for thinking that it was drawn upon by Leonardo da Vinci himself. But the whole idea, so far as weights and forces acting vertically are concerned, is found very clearly stated in Heron's *Mechanica* preserved in the Arabic[4], and no doubt goes back to Archimedes, since Heron bases himself on works of Archimedes, one of which, 'On Levers', is evidently the περὶ ζυγῶν now lost, and the other is in the German translation from the Arabic entitled 'Das Ausgleichen der Neigungen' (περὶ ἰσορροπιῶν).

(b) Motion in a circle: supposed two motions

The first problem in the *Mechanica* asks: Why do longer balances weigh more accurately than the shorter? The fundamental principle, says the writer, is, 'Why is it that the line (radius) which extends farther from the centre travels more quickly than the smaller (radius), though the latter is moved by the same force? . . . But the greater (radius) in an equal time describes a greater circle; for the outer circle is greater than the inner. The reason of this is

[1] *Les Origines de la Statique*, 1905, i, p. 134, etc.
[2] Paris, Bibliothèque Nationale, fonds latin 7378 A.
[3] i. 164.
[4] *Heronis Opera*, Teubner, vol. ii, Pt. i, cc. 33, 34, pp. 88, 90.

that the straight line (the radius) which describes the circle has two motions of translation' (848^{b}1–10).

The idea that a radius moving about the centre as fixed point and describing a circle with its other extremity has two motions of translation is odd, because (assuming that the motion is in one plane) it is clear that it has only one motion, and that an angular one (rotation). There must, therefore, have been some confusion in the writer's mind between (1) a constrained rotatory motion to which the moving radius is limited owing to one end being fixed and (2) *free* motion in a circle such as, for example, the motion of any one of the heavenly bodies. Cappelle refers to a genuine work of Aristotle,[1] where he describes a circular motion of this kind. This case is, however, irrelevant here, because it is a question there of the combination of two circular motions in different planes, those of the daily rotation and the separate motion of the sun, moon, and planets in the ecliptic.

Here the author seems to be trying to account for free motion of a body in a circle on the principle of the 'parallelogram of velocities'. This principle he states thus:

'When (a body) is carried (with two velocities) in a certain ratio, the body so carried must be carried in a straight line, which straight line is the diameter (diagonal) of the figure (a parallelogram) formed by the straight lines in the said ratio put together [with their extremities at one point]' (848^{b}10–13).

He goes on to give a proof of this in terms almost such as we might find in any elementary text-book to-day:

Mech. 2. 848^{b}13–26

'Let the ratio of the two motions (i.e. speeds) be that which AB has to AC. Let AC be moved (parallel to itself) towards B, and let

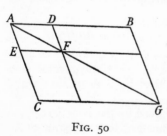

FIG. 50

AB be moved down (also parallel to itself) towards GC. Let A have reached D and B have reached E. Then, if during the two motions the speeds have been in the ratio of AB to AC, AD must bear to AE the same ratio. Therefore, the small quadrilateral (parallelogram) [$ADFE$] must be similar to the greater one so that they have the same diameter [AFG] and A (at the moment in question) will be at F. The same proof will apply at whatever point the motion is interrupted. The moving object will always be on the diameter.

[1] *De gen. et corr.* B. 10. 336^{a}33 and ^{b}2.

'It is clear, therefore (conversely), that, if a body moves along the diagonal (of a parallelogram) with (a motion made up of) two motions, those motions must be in the ratio of the sides. For if the ratio of the two motions is some different one, the body will not be carried along the diameter.'

The author goes on to the case where the motion is on a curve (a circle):

Ib. 2. 848^{b}26–35

'But if the two motions of translation are in no definite ratio for any length of time, the resultant motion cannot be in a straight line.

'For suppose the path *is* a straight line. Then, if this is made a diameter (sc. of a parallelogram) and the sides are filled in, the motion of the moving body must be (compounded of two motions) in the ratio of the sides. This has already been proved. Therefore the body carried by two motions in a ratio which does not remain the same for any time will not describe a straight line. For if the body is moved by two motions in any ratio for any length of time, the motion must, for the reasons aforesaid, for that length of time be in a straight line. So that ⟨if the ratio does not remain the same for any length of time⟩ the path must be an arc of a curve (περι-φερές).'

The author continues:

Ib. ^{b}35–849^{a}1

'That the straight line (radius) describing the circle'—meaning the *extremity* of the radius—'has two motions of translation is manifest from what has been said, and also because the moving body reaches the perpendicular (to its original direction) (but) so as to be itself again perpendicularly over the centre.'

This is apparently the best that can be made of the text of these lines after leaving out, with Cappelle, the words κατ' εὐθεῖαν in the clause ὅτι τὸ φερόμενον [κατ' εὐθεῖαν] ἐπὶ τὴν κάθετον ἀφικνεῖται. The idea seems to be that the extremity B of the radius OB in the annexed figure would, if it had a simple motion in the direction of the tangent at B, reach D, a point on the tangent parallel to OB and therefore perpendicular to the original direction of its motion. But in fact B will arrive at C, the extremity of the radius perpendicular to OB, in consequence of

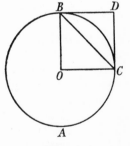

FIG. 51

a second motion being always combined with the first (along BD), a second motion which has 'never for any time whatever a definite ratio to the other'.

Mech. 2. 849ᵃ2–6

'Let *ABC* be a circle, and let the extremity *B* of the radius *OB* be carried towards *D*; it will, however (actually), some time arrive at *C*. Now, if it had been carried (by two motions) in the ratio which *BD* has to *DC*, it would have been carried along the diameter *BC*. But, as it is, since the motions are in no definite ratio for any length of time, it is carried along the circumference *BEC*.'

The explanation purports to be given in the following passage:

Ib. ᵃ6–38

'If, of two bodies carried along by the same force, one were more, and the other less, forcibly diverted, it is reasonable that that which is more diverted should move more slowly than that which is less diverted; this is what appears to happen in the case of the greater and lesser radii which describe circles (respectively). For, because the extremity of the lesser radius is nearer the fixed centre than that of the greater radius, the former, being as it were pulled back in the contrary direction, moves more slowly towards the centre.

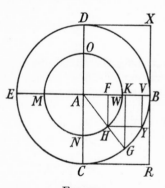

Now this happens with every straight line describing a circle; it (i.e. its extremity) is carried along the circumference, its natural translation being laterally (i.e. along the tangent) and its unnatural (i.e. constrained) translation being towards the centre. The unnatural translation is always greater in the case of the lesser radius; for, owing to its being nearer the centre which pulls against it, it is the more overpowered. And that the lesser of two radii describing

FIG. 52

circles is moved more than the greater in respect of its unnatural motion is clear from what follows.

'Let there be a circle *BCED* and another, *WNMO*, within it, about the same centre *A*. And let diameters be drawn [at right angles], *CD*, *BE* in the greater, and *MW*, *NO* in the lesser circle; and let the oblong (figure) *DXRC* be completed. If then *AB* describes a circle and comes back to the position from which it started, it is clear that it is carried towards itself; and similarly *AW* will come back to *AW*. And *AW* is carried round more slowly than AB because the forcible diversion and the pulling is greater for AW.

'Let (the radius) AHG be drawn, let HF be drawn perpendicular to AB in the circle, and again from H let HY be drawn parallel to AB [meeting the outer circle in Y].

'Let YV, GK be drawn perpendicular to AB.

'Now YV, FH are equal; therefore BV is less than WF; for, of equal chords in unequal circles drawn at right angles to the diameter, that in the greater circle cuts off a lesser segment of the diameter.'

[This can be seen as follows:

By Eucl. III. 31, VI. 8,

$$YV^2 = EV.VB$$

and $$FH_2 = MF.FW$$

But $YV = FH$; therefore $EV.VB = MF.FW$,

and $$EV : MF = FW : VB.$$

But EV is greater than MF;
therefore FW is greater than VB.]

Ib. ^{a}38–^{b}19

'Now in the time taken by AH [really AW] to describe WH the extremity of BA [B] has described in the greater circle an arc BG, greater than BY. For the natural motion is equal, the unnatural less, since BV is less than FW.

'But, proportionally [of the four motions] as natural is to natural, so should unnatural be to unnatural. Therefore (AB) has traversed an arc GB greater than YB. And it must have traversed GB in the aforesaid time, for that is the place (it should reach) when in both cases the proportion of natural to unnatural is the same.

'If therefore the natural motion is greater in the greater circle, the unnatural motion would agree in being proportionally greater only if B described BG in the time that W takes to traverse WH [reading, ἐν ᾧ τὸ ἐφ' οὗ χ σημεῖον τὴν χθ instead of Bekker's ἐν τῷ ἐφ' οὗ χ σημεῖον]. For then the point B by its natural motion comes to G, and by its unnatural motion to K, since GK is perpendicular from G, and, as GK is to KB, so is HF to FW. This will be manifest if B, W be joined to G, H respectively [the triangles BGK, KHF being similar].

'But if the arc described by B is less or greater than GB, the natural motion will not be similarly or proportionally related to the unnatural in the two cases.'

The above long passage (848^b26—849^b19) is rambling and ill arranged, with much repetition; but it is interesting as an attempt to account for the free motion of a body in a circle as the resultant of two simple motions, one of them directed along the tangent at a particular point in the motion, the other along the radius from that point to the centre, the latter being due to the impulse or tendency (ῥοπή) of a heavy body towards the centre, or (as here described) the 'pulling' (ἀντισπᾶσθαι) exerted by the centre on the body. It is shown that the pure application of the principle of the parallelogram of velocities will not serve because, if the ratio between the two assumed velocities remained the same for any length of time whatever, the path from one point to another would be along the chord joining them and not along the circumference, the inference being that the assumed constituent velocities 'are in no (definite) ratio for any length of time', so that the path cannot be rectilinear for any distance and must, therefore, be a curve of some kind. The curve is assumed to be a circle, but there is no attempt to determine what quantitative (if any) relation between the two speeds would make it a circle. It is also assumed that, if A, B be points on two concentric circles, the ratio of the 'natural' to the 'unnatural' component of the motion must be the same for A, B in their respective motions. The writer passes on to

Problem 1

Mech. 2. 849^{b}19–34

'The reason why the point which is farther from the centre is moved more quickly by the same force, and the greater radius describes the greater arc, is clear from what has been said. The reason why greater balances are more accurate than the lesser is manifest from the following considerations.' The explanation amounts to saying that the same angular displacement is more visible to the eye if the arm is longer. Also 'the impulse (ῥοπή) of the same weight is the greater the farther it is placed on the arm away from the centre', i.e. its power to move the arm of the balance is greater.

Problem 2

Ib. 850^{a}3–29

The language here offers no difficulty, and it is not necessary to add to or modify the Oxford translation. The question is, What difference, as regards position and stability of equilibrium, does it make in the case of a lever of some thickness suspended from the middle, whether (1) it is suspended by (say) a string from the middle point on the *top* side or (2) by means of a loop or a small ring with a pin through it which is horizontal and at right angles to the axis of symmetry of the lever, so that the point of suspension is at L, the middle of the bottom side of the lever, but so that the lever can move round L in a vertical circle without falling off in any position?

When the author speaks of putting a weight or *bias* ($\dot{\rho}o\pi\dot{\eta}$) on one end of a lever and taking it off again, he merely means using such small force as is necessary to depress that end of the lever.

Neglecting friction and regarding the point of suspension (above or below) as a mathematical point, the whole thing depends on the position

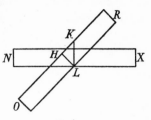

FIG. 53

of the centre of gravity of the system, at any particular moment, in relation to the point of suspension. The author does not speak of the 'centre of gravity', and he was probably unaware of the theory of it, which no doubt Archimedes was the first to work out fully. As it is, he appears to be in error in saying that, in the second case, the lever will remain where it is when let go, because, if the centre of gravity of the portion OKL has not then reached a new position vertically under L, the lever will not rest but will turn farther until it has, when of course the triangle KHL will vanish again.

Guido Ubaldi (1545–1607) applied to this problem the consideration that, if a body suspended freely from a point be in equilibrium, its centre of gravity and the point of suspension must be in the same vertical line.

(c) *The lever*

Ib. 3. 850ᵃ30–ᵇ9

The translation of this chapter offers no difficulty. One sentence (850ᵃ39–ᵇ2) is very tersely expressed: 'As the weight that is moved is to the moment, so reciprocally is ($\dot{a}\nu\tau\iota\pi\acute{e}\pi o\nu\theta\epsilon\nu$) the length to the length.' $\dot{a}\nu\tau\iota\pi\acute{e}\pi o\nu\theta\epsilon\nu$ is the regular Euclidean expression for 'is reciprocally proportional'.[1] The meaning, of course, is that as the power P is to the weight lifted, so is the distance from the fulcrum of the point where W is applied to the distance from the fulcrum of the point of application of P (P and W being both assumed to act in directions perpendicular to the lever and so parallel to one another).

Here again the principle of the lever is referred to the motion of radii of concentric circles. Heron, doubtless following Archimedes,

---

[1] Eucl. vi. 14. 15, etc.

does the same but shows more clearly how the cases are parallel.

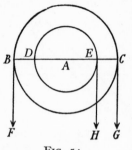

In connexion with the five mechanical powers, Heron[1] takes two concentric circles (rigidly connected) in a vertical plane with centre A and common diameter $BDAEC$ placed horizontally.

If, he says, we hang equal weights F, G at the points B, C respectively, BC is like a balance with A as point of suspension and, since $BA = AC$, the equal weights will balance and the circles will not turn in either direction. But if we move the point of suspension of G from

FIG. 54

C to E, the extremity of the diameter of the smaller circle, the weight F will descend and the circles will turn. If, however, we replace G suspended at E by a weight H increased to such an extent that

$$H : F = BA : AE,$$

there will again be equilibrium. This, he says, is proved by Archimedes in a work the title of which appears in the German translation from the Arabic as 'das Ausgleichen der Neigungen' which may very well represent περὶ ἰσορροπιῶν (cf. the two extant books of ἐπίπεδοι ἰσορροπίαι). Then[2] Heron observes that the force and the weight in the case of the lever present the same phenomenon as the two weights acting perpendicularly to the common diameter of two concentric circles.

Our author gives only the case of the lever of the 'first class', that in which the fulcrum O is between A and B, the points of application of the force P and the weight W respectively.

In a passage of the *De architectura*[3] Vitruvius describes not only

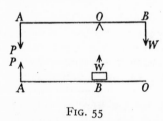

the lever of the first class but also that of the 'second', where AO is the lever and the end O resting on the ground is the fulcrum, while the weight W rests on the lever at a point between A and O. The power P then acts upwards and the weight is lifted. A pair of nut-crackers is a double lever of this kind. Vitruvius finally

FIG. 55

mentions the case where the power acts at a less distance from the fulcrum than the weight does. In this case, of course, the power must exceed the weight. A case of this 'third' kind is the treadle of a lathe.

---

[1] *Mechanics*, ii, c. 7.   [2] c. 8.   [3] x. 3–5.

Mech. 3. 850ᵇ10–27

The question is why the rowers who are amidships move the boat more than the others (nearer the prow or the stern). The answer is that, the boat being wider amidships, there is room to get a longer portion of the oar inside the thole-pin. Consequently with this greater length the rower can exert more power at the blade end of the oar, so that the blade will 'divide the most water' (πλείστην θάλασσαν διαιρεῖ ἡ κώπη (850ᵇ23).

The ground is (850ᵇ10–11) that the oar is a lever. But the author gives a wrong description of how the lever works. He says that the thole-pin, which is 'fixed', is the fulcrum, and the water at the blade-end of the oar is the weight, the assumption being that the lever is a lever of the 'first class' where the fulcrum separates the power and the weight. As a matter of fact, the oar is a lever of the *second* class: the fulcrum is where the blade dips into the water, and the weight (a portion of the weight of the ship) acts at the thole-pin. The water

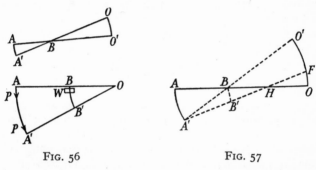

FIG. 56   FIG. 57

where the blade strikes it remains for practical purposes fixed and therefore acts as the fulcrum, and this is why the thole-pin, and with it the boat, moves forward in space when the rower pulls his end of the oar towards him. The author, in assuming that the lever is one of the first class, takes the view that the blade of the oar has to drive backwards the water with which it is in contact, i.e. that the blade *O* describes a circle *OO'* in the water corresponding to the arc *AA'* described by the handle of the oar about *B*, the thole-pin fulcrum. Hence the author deems it necessary to show (as he tries to do under the next problem) that the arc *OO'* will actually be much less than the arc *AA'*, so that, if *A* moves through the arc *AA'*, the oar will at the end of the stroke take the position *A'B'HF* in the annexed figure where *OF* is less than *OO'*. The line *A'F* will cut *ABO*, not in *B*, but in *H*, a point between *B* and *O*. The reason given for the arc *OF* being less than *AA'* is the rather absurd one that the same weight moved by the same force (strength, ἰσχύι) will go forward more in air than in water (851^{a}16–17) as if it were a question of the relative resistance of air and water.

The proof is given in 851^{a}19–28 :

'If A is transferred to A', it will not be where B' is; for OO' is equal to AA' [the assumption is evidently that B is equidistant from A and O], and, that being so, O will have moved the same distance (as A). But we saw that it moved a less distance. Let O then be at F. AO is now divided at H and not where B is, but below. For OF is less than AA'; and therefore HF is less than $A'H$, since the triangles $AA'H$, OFH are similar. Therefore the centre B will also have changed its position in a sense contrary to the motion of the extremity O of the oar which is in the water, that is, in the same way as the end of the oar in the ship, namely A, and A is transferred to the position A'. Hence the ship will have changed its position, and that in the same sense as that in which the handle of the oar moves.'

This difficulty does not arise if the proper assumption is made, namely, that the fulcrum is at O where the blade of the oar acts, not at B, the thole-pin.

(d) The rudder

Mech. 5. 850^{b}28–851^{a}37.

While regarding the rudder as a lever of the 'first' class, like the oar, the sea as the weight, and the steersman as the moving force (or 'power'), the author recognizes the difference between the cases of the rudder and the oar, namely that the rudder acts obliquely and not squarely on the water, for the rudder does not move the boat forwards as does the oar, but only bends its direction as it moves. What happens is that, as the boat moves along, the rudder, if moved right or left, is acted on by the resistance of the water, which tends to force it round in the opposite direction and so turns the boat round its centre of gravity until the rudder is put back in a position which is directly in a line with the boat's course. But what resists the moving of the rudder by the helmsman is only the resolved part of the water's resistance in a direction perpendicular to the rudder, which is small when it is moved through a small angle from a position in line with the boat's course.

In 851^{a}13 an angle subtended by a certain base (or subtending arc) is said to 'sit on' it (καθῆσθαι), whereas Euclid's word is βεβηκέναι, to 'stand on' (an arc).

Heron[1] considers the same question among others 'raised by the ancients'. He has a more correct idea than our author when he

[1] Mechanics ii. 34 (p).

says that 'the rudder rests or supports itself on the water and so is able to overpower the ship'. This clearly implies that, with the rudder as lever, the water is the fixed point or fulcrum.

Ib. 6. 851ᵃ38–ᵇ5. *The mast*

The idea of the mast acting as a lever about the socket as fulcrum, with the wind as 'power' and the ship as weight, is thoroughly misconceived. The explanation can only be that suggested by the Oxford translator.

(e) *Motion of a circle*

Ib. 8. 851ᵇ15–36

Of the three ways in which a circle can move, namely (1) rolling along like the wheel of a wagon, (2) rotative about the centre, (a) in a vertical plane, (b) in a horizontal plane, two are mentioned by Aristotle in *De caelo* II. 8. 290ᵃ9, where, speaking of the spherical shape of the stars, he observes that these are the only two motions proper to a sphere in itself, 'rolling' (κύλισις) and 'spinning' or 'whirling'.[1]

It is unnecessary to give a fresh translation of c. 8 or to add to the Oxford translator's notes more than a few mathematical details.

In 851ᵇ21–4 it is explained that the circle moves freely when rolling on a plane because it is in contact with the plane at one point only ('where the angle separates it from the ground'), thereby reducing friction to a minimum, ἀφέστηκε τῆς γῆς ἡ γωνία, literally 'stands away from the ground'. The angle is what used to be called the 'angle of contact', though Euclid proved[2] that the said 'angle' is less than any rectilineal angle and therefore is, in fact, no angle at all.

The statement in ᵇ30–1 that in this case of rolling the circle 'straightway moves more (when once started) on its path as if it had an inclination or bias (that way)' is a fallacy because, as the Oxford translator notes, the writer forgets that, though by moving the circle slightly you add to the half which is in the direction of the motion, you take away a part of it and add it to the opposite half.

The expression (ᵇ27) πρὸς ὄρθιον (with dat.) for 'at right angles' (to the plane) is a variation from the usual πρός ὀρθάς (γωνίας understood) with dative or ὀρθὴ πρός (with acc.).

Ib. 851ᵇ36–40

'For greater circles acted on by an equal force are moved, and move weights, more quickly because the angle of the greater circle has a certain bias in comparison with that of the lesser circle, being in the same ratio to it as the one diameter to the other.'

[1] On this I may refer to *Aristarchus of Samos*, pp. 234–5. [2] iii. 16.

'The angle of the greater circle': this expression has given much trouble to the commentators. Bernardino Baldi (1553–1617) took the things compared to be *sectors* bounded by equal angles; but these of course are in the ratio, not of the diameters, but of the *squares* on the diameters. On the analogy of the 'angle of a semicircle' (which is a survival in Eucl. III. 16), we might suppose that the 'angle of a *circle*' is here also the 'angle' formed by a diameter, at its extremity, with the circumference at that point. But these 'angles' in two unequal circles are not in the ratio of the diameters either. It is only the *arcs* of the circles subtended by the angles that are in the ratio of the radii or diameters; and it seems better on the whole to suppose that the subtended *arcs* are meant.

At 852ᵃ2 the writer passes to circles which are not rolling but are free to rotate about their centres in a vertical or horizontal plane (e.g. a pulley or a potter's wheel respectively). On this case the author has not anything better to say than to refer to his contention in c. 1, 848ᵇ9—849ᵃ1, that an object moving in a circle has *two* motions: which is irrelevant here. It is true that motion about an axis in these cases would go on for ever but for friction with the material axis: a fact which the writer seems to have been trying to express at 851ᵇ33–5, where he speaks of some who say that 'the circumference of a circle keeps up a continual motion, just as bodies which are at rest remain so owing to their resistance'.[1]

(f) *The balance*

Mech. 10. 852ᵃ23–8

When the writer tries to explain why the beam of a balance is easier to move when it has no weights on it than when it has, and a lighter wheel is easier to move than a heavier one, he is wrong in saying that the difference of weight is the reason. If they were suspended at the centre of gravity (a mathematical point), they would be moved about it by any force however small: but they are actually suspended on a material axis and, as Blancanus and Cappelle point out, the friction is likely to be greater when the weight of the balance or the wheel turned about the axis becomes greater, and this is the reason of the phenomenon.

(g) *Breaking a stick*

Ib. 14. 852ᵇ22–8

It is true that, when a stick is broken over the knee, the knee is

[1] Cf. the statement by Aristotle himself (*Phys.* iv. 8. 215ᵃ20–2), which is very like an attempt to express the truth stated in Newton's First Law of Motion (see pp. 115–16, above).

the fulcrum of the lever, but when the writer says that if it is broken
by putting the foot on it and lifting up the end which is not on the
ground, he is in error because he again takes the lever to be one of
the 'first' class (where the fulcrum is between the points of application
of the force and the weight), whereas it is one of the 'second' class, in
which the fulcrum is at one end (in this case the ground) and the
force and the weight act on the *same* side of the fulcrum, the weight
being nearer to it. Heron[1] also discusses the same problem of breaking a stick over the knee.

c. 16, 853ᵃ5–18, is about planks which bend when lifted up, according to their length. A flexible plank may be lifted up in one of three
ways: (1) by the hand supporting it in the middle, (2) by the hand
lifting up one end while the other rests on the ground, (3) by two
persons lifting it by the hand, one at each end. In the first case both
ends of the plank droop, in the second and third it droops in the
middle. The writer seems to be describing the first case, for he says
that when lifting 'the first portion' the hand becomes the fulcrum,
while the portion 'towards the end' (which must mean the portions
towards *both* ends) is the weight. The first portion must be the
middle part where the hand lifts the plank. Assuming that the
lifting force in the hand acts at a *point*, the power must be equal to
the weight of the sum of the two equal parts into which the point
divides the plank, and the weight acts downwards at the centre of
gravity of each part. The 'extremities of the lever' (ᵃ14) must be the
two centres of gravity, and these are said to be 'raised' (αἴρεσθαι).
Cappelle explains this by saying that the writer, accustomed to use
the term 'raised' in connexion with a weight lifted by a lever, uses
it here notwithstanding that the ends of the plank in fact bend
downwards. Perhaps the best translation in the circumstances
would be 'are suspended' or 'hang suspended', which expression says
nothing about drooping, though not inconsistent with the ends
drooping.

On the bending of planks cf. the similar discussion by Heron in
his *Mechanics*, ii. 34, h.

(h) The wedge

Mech. 17. 853ᵃ19–31

Cappelle observes that 'physici' differ as to whether the particular
'mechanical power' to which the wedge reduces is the lever or the
inclined plane. The writer of the *Mechanica* takes the former view,
making the wedge act as *two* levers which are represented by the
sides *AB* and *ΓB* of the wedge. As he seems to have regarded all
levers as being of the 'first' class he makes the weight to be 'that of

---

[1] *Mechanics*, ii. 34, g.

B below', and the fulcra to be Z and H respectively. The power must be the blow struck on the upper face $A\Gamma$ of the wedge. '$A\Gamma$ when struck uses each of the edges $(AB, \Gamma B)$ as a lever; for it forces B up', says the writer, but he does not explain at what point on each lever the power acts. Guido Ubaldo (1545–1607), according to Blancanus, made B the fulcrum and the weight the resistance of the wood at B, H respectively. No doubt we could regard the blow struck at the middle point of AB as resolved into two components, one along the perpendicular from the said middle point to the lever $(AB$ or $AC)$ and the other parallel to the lever, in which case the force perpendicular to the lever could be regarded as acting at the point on the lever where the perpendicular falls.

(i) Pulleys

Mech. 18. 853ᵃ32–ᵇ13

The accompanying figure shows how the system works with the

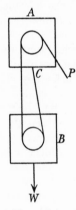

A

C   P

B

W

FIG. 58

two pulleys opposite to one another. The upper pulley is attached to the block A in a vertical position; the lower similarly to the block B. The block A is fixed, block B is free to move up and down with the pulley attached to it. The weight to be lifted (W) is suspended from block B. The rope is attached to the upper block say at C, then passes round the pulley in B, and then round the upper block. If the pulleys are equal, so that all the portions of the rope passing from one block to the other are vertical, the tension of the rope is the same thoughout. B is supported by two parallel ropes at tension P; therefore in the case taken $P = \frac{1}{2}W$.

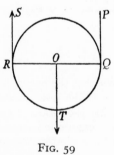

FIG. 59

Blancanus explains the remark that the pulley acts in the same way as a lever, in this way. Let $PQTRS$ be the portion of the rope passing round the pulley in B. Then ROQ may be regarded as a lever, of the 'second' class, with the weight hanging downwards from O and the force P acting upwards at S, so that Q acts (for the instant) as fulcrum. RQ being double of OQ, the moments of P $(= \frac{1}{2}W)$ and of W about Q are equal and there is equilibrium. In the somewhat similar case of the 'wheel and axle', as we call it, Heron[1] takes two concentric circles rigidly connected with dia-

[1] *Mechanics*, ii. 7.

meters *BC, DE,* both horizontal, and assumes a weight *H* so hung that it acts at *E* and a power *F* pulling downwards at *B*. Then if *AE* is small compared with *AB* the power will balance a much larger weight, for $F : H = AB : AE.$

In case the pulleys on the lower block carrying the weight are more than one there must be the same number, or one more, on the upper block. When the number is equal the rope is tied to the upper block, when one more, to the *lower block*. In Figure 61 (2) there are two pulleys on each block, in Figure 61 (1) three on the upper and two on the lower. Since the tension of the rope is *P*

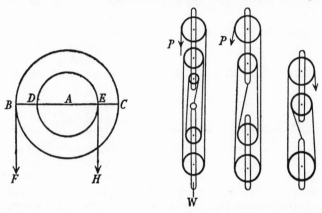

FIG. 60   FIG. 61 (1, 2, 3)

all through where *P* is the power, and there are four portions of the rope in one case and five in the other in which the tension *P* upwards acts on the block carrying the weight, we must have in the first case $4P = W$ and in the second $5P = W$, or $P = \frac{1}{4}W$, $P = \frac{1}{5}W$ in the two cases respectively. And generally if the number of portions of rope pulling *W* upwards is *n*, $nP = W$ or $P = \frac{1}{n}W$.

The theory of this system of pulleys is worked out, and the 'mechanical advantage' depending on the number of the portions of rope exerting lifting force on the weight is correctly stated, by Heron.[1]

The wording of the text is by no means clear, but the general drift of it can be understood in the light of the above. The remark ($853^{b}2$) that 'the two pulleys raise the weight with more than double the speed' is not literally accurate. As we have seen, three pulleys, two on the upper block and one on the lower block, are necessary to make *more* than two portions of the rope operate to lift the block.

---

[1] *Mechanics,* ii, c. 23 (ed. Nix and Schmidt); Pappus, ed. Hultsch, vol. iii, pp. 1118–22.

(j) The steelyard

Mech. 20. 853^{b}25–854^{a}15

The language of this problem is made unnecessarily complicated because the author uses several words to denote the same thing, namely the counterpoise, the weight at one end of the beam, which is made part of it instead of being hung in a pan like that which carries the object to be weighed. The counterpoise is called ἄρτημα, which means 'a thing (weight) hung on' (853^{b}25), σφαίρωμα 'a ball-like thing' (853^{b}32, 37; 854^{a}5, 14), σταθμός (853^{b}33, 38), σταθμόν (854^{a}5).[1]

The steelyard in question is of the type known as the Danish,

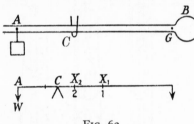

consisting of a bar AB, terminating in a heavy knob or ball B. At A is attached a hook or scale-pan to carry the body to be weighed. Let C be the fulcrum, the position of the σπαρτίον (string or loop on which the whole instrument is hung) when there

Fig. 62

is equilibrium. The way in which the instrument works can easily be seen from the description in any text-book of mechanics (e.g. S. L. Loney's).

Let P be the weight of the bar and scale-pan and let G be the centre of gravity of both together. Then we can suppose P to act at G, and W, the body to be measured, at A. If C be the fulcrum when the system is in equilibrium, we have by taking moments:

$$W \cdot CA = P \cdot CG$$
$$= (AG - AC)P$$
$$\therefore \quad (P+W)AC = P \cdot AG$$
$$\text{and} \quad AC = \frac{P}{P+W} \cdot AG$$

[1] In view of the use of σταθμός (-όν) in 853^{b}33, 38 and 854^{a}5 to mean the counterpoise, it is perhaps unfortunate that the Oxford translation in the second and third of the three places has 'weight' instead of counterpoise. This may mislead, because 'weight' would most naturally be understood as meaning the object weighed. It would be better, I think, in 853^{b}37–8, τὸ ἐπὶ τάδε ἐπὶ τὸ σφαίρωμα τὸ ἥμισυ τῆς φάλαγγός ἐστι καὶ ὁ σταθμός, to translate σφαίρωμα by 'ball' and σταθμός by 'counterpoise'. 'For each of which the part of the lever on one side, towards the ball, is the half of the lever, i.e. the counterpoise.'

To graduate the steelyard, proceed thus:

(1) When $W = P$, $AC = \frac{1}{2}AG$. Bisect AG at X_1, and mark the point by the figure 1.

(2) Let $W = 2P$ and we must have $AC = \frac{1}{3}AG$. Take AX_2 equal to $\frac{1}{3}AG$ and mark the point by the figure 2.

(3) Let W be successively $3P$, $4P$, etc., and the corresponding values of AC are $\frac{1}{4}AG$, $\frac{1}{5}AG$, and so on.

Since AX, AX_2... are inversely proportional to the numbers 2, 3, 4..., they are in harmonical progression.

For weights less than P, we may take $W = \frac{1}{2}P$ and AC must be $\frac{2}{3}AG = AG - \frac{1}{3}AG$, for $W = \frac{1}{3}P$, $AC = \frac{3}{4}AG = AG - \frac{1}{4}AG$

Therefore, we find the fulcra respectively by subtracting $\frac{1}{3}AG$, $\frac{1}{4}AG$, etc., from AG or measuring these lengths from G instead of from A.

I should be inclined to translate the last clause of the final sentence differently from the Oxford translation, which seems to take τὸ πρὸς τὸ σφαίρωμα βάρος as accusative after ἵστησι. I think it is nominative and the phrase from ἐνταῦθα δέ . . . would be better translated thus: 'while in this case it (the lever itself) produces equilibrium and it is the weight of the beam at (or in the direction of) the counterpoise which weighs (the object in the pan).'

(k) *Tooth-forceps and nutcrackers*

Ib. 21–2

There is no difficulty calling for notice in these chapters. In the case of the nut-crackers, the author naturally only mentions the variety in which the nut is placed beyond the hinge and in which, therefore, the two levers are of the 'first' class, though, of course, there is another variety in which we place the nut between the hand and the hinge but as near the hinge as possible.

Heron[1] considers this among other similar problems propounded 'by the ancients'.

(l) *The rhombus of velocities*

Ib. 23. 854[b]16–855[a]27

This long description applies the parallelogram of velocities to the particular case of a rhombus in which one diagonal is a great deal longer than the other. There is no difficulty in the interpretation of it, and the gist is to show that according to the inclination of the two velocities (whether it is an obtuse or an acute angle) the resultant velocity is greater or smaller.

[1] *Mechanics*, ii. 34.

On a first reading it seems odd (854^{b}22–4) to find (1) A moving towards B and (2) B moving towards A with the same velocity (apparently at the same time), and then to be told (3) that AB moves with the same velocity along AC parallel to CD (with its extremity A describing the line AC).

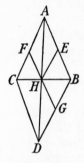

FIG. 63

What it is intended to contrast is the combination of (1) and (3), and the combination of (2) and (3). The first combination produces the resultant motion of A from A to D describing the longer diagonal, and the second produces the resultant motion of B from B to C describing the shorter diagonal BC. There is, of course, an intermediate stage when A has described half of the line AB, namely AE, while AB has moved half-way towards CD and is in the position FG; at this point A will be at H, half-way along the diagonal AD. Similarly when A has described BE, half the length of AB, and AB has moved half-way towards CD and is in the position FG, B will have described BH, half the length of BC.

The relative length of AD, BC depends only on the size of the angle CAB and the angle ABD respectively. When the angle ABD is obtuse, and as it approaches two right angles, the velocities represented by BA and BD tend to be more nearly 'opposite to one another' and therefore, as it were, to neutralize one another and to reduce the resultant speed (855^{a}16 f.); while the more acute the angle CAB is, the more the velocities represented by AB, AC tend to approach the same direction and therefore to increase the resultant speed AD.

(m) *The wheel of Aristotle*

Mech. 24. 855^{a}28–856^{a}38

This famous problem has little or nothing to do with mechanics, but its statement shows fine mathematical insight, and it continued to fascinate mathematicians down to the seventeenth century. Heron tried to throw light upon it, Cardano discussed it at length but without advancing its solution.[1] It was reserved for Galilei to give a real explanation in *Dialogues concerning two new Sciences*.[2] Another prominent mathematician who thoroughly understood the question was Jean Jacques d'Ortons de Mairan (1678–1771),

---

[1] *Opera*, Lyons, 1663, vol. iv, prop. 196, pp. 575–6.
[2] First published in 1638, but elaborated much earlier, during the period which he spent in Padua, 1599–1610.

generally known as Mairan, whose explanation is quoted at length by Cappelle.[1]

The difficulties and paradoxes involved are stated by the author with a point and piquancy which are worthy of admiration.

Given two concentric circles with centre A, suppose them fastened together so as to form one circle. Let AGF be a common radius and let the tangents at F on the larger and at G on the smaller circle be drawn as FI, GH. These tangents are, of course, parallel. Now suppose the larger circle, carrying the smaller circle with it, to be rolled along FI until a complete revolution has been completed, and the radius AF takes the position $A'I$ perpendicular to FI. Then G, being a point on AF, goes round with AF and when AF comes to the position $A'HI$, G must be at H on the line $A'I$, and GH is equal to FI. Now GH *appears* to have been described by the smaller circle EBG rolling along GH, just as FI has been described by the circle DCF rolling once round on FI. FI will be equal in length to the circumference of the larger circle. Since the smaller circle appears to roll along GH during the motion of the larger circle, we should expect GH to be equal to the circumference of the smaller circle, but it is not; for it is obviously equal to FI or the circumference of the larger circle. How can it be that the smaller circle, rolling as part of the larger, describes a straight line greater than the length of its own circumference and equal to that of the larger circle, whereas if they roll separately each describes its own circumference, which is proportional to its diameter? The following are the points taken by the writer of the *Mechanica*:

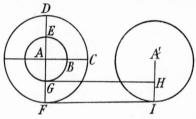

FIG. 64

1. Assuming that the circles have one centre and are fixed to one another, then

    (*a*) if the smaller rolls on its tangent, both circles describe a length equal to the circumference of the smaller circle;

    (*b*) if the *larger* rolls along a tangent, both describe a length equal to the larger circumference.

2. This is seen by simple observation. In a complete revolution each turns through four right angles about its centre, and the circumference corresponding to the four right angles is proportional to the diameter.

[1] pp. 263–7 of his edition.

3. (*a*) and (*b*) are illustrated respectively by the figure.

4. 'But it would seem absurd that, although [in the first case] the larger is never brought to rest for the lesser (for in both cases both circles move continuously), nor [in the second case] does the lesser circle skip over any point, the greater should nevertheless describe the same distance as the lesser, and the lesser the same distance as the greater' (855[b]23–8).

5. 'And besides it is surprising that, though the motion is always one, the centre which moves along should describe in the one case a larger, in the other a smaller distance. For the same thing moving at the same speed naturally traverses an equal distance; and to move a thing at the same speed is to move it an equal distance in both cases' (855[b]28–32).

Next comes the author's own explanation:

6. If a body that is naturally moved moves another body that is not naturally in motion along with it, its motion is slower than it would be if the former moved itself alone. And if a body that has no natural motion of its own is moved by something else, it cannot move faster than the mover (855[b]34—856[a]1).

7. Suppose the circles separate, *A* the greater, *B* the lesser. (*a*) Let *B push A* along, *A* being supposed to have no rolling motion (in this case presumably *B* would not roll either, but both circles would slip along the common tangent). Suppose, however, that *B* rolls, then *A* would roll too, unless the circumference of *B* were smooth and would slip freely on the circumference

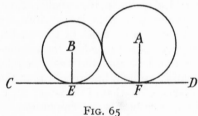

Fig. 65

of *A*; in that case *A* would *slip* along *CD*. If the contact between *A* and *B* were such that their circumferences did not slip over each other at all, the circumference of *A* would move in the opposite direction to *B*, and therefore at its contact with *CD* would have to slip all the more. In any case the two circles would move the same distance along *CD*, for the distance between the projections of their centres on the common tangent (*EF*) would remain the same. (*b*) The effect would be the same if it were *A* that moved *B* (856[a]1–16).

8. It is the fact of the circles being fastened together that makes all the difference. Neglecting the case where one is hung on the other anyhow, we consider only the case where they have the same centre. Then, whenever one circle moves, the other must be moved

first so far as the first is; the second has no motion of its own; it is as if it had no motion, or as if, having power to move, it did not exercise it. This applies equally whether the circle which moves the other is the greater or the lesser. When the person raising the question says that, while they have the same centre and it (the centre) moves them at the same speed, they nevertheless describe different distances, he is mistaken. It depends on which circle moves the other, the greater or the less; the centre acts only as the centre of the circle which moves the other—it is only incidentally the centre of the latter (856ᵃ25–35).

A note is required on the language of 855ᵃ32—835ᵇ1. 'When', the author says, 'the centre is one and the same, the length of line which they describe is at one time that described by the smaller circle [alone] and at another time that described by the larger circle [alone]. Now it is manifest that the greater circle describes the greater length. For simple observation shows that the circumference of each circle is the measure of the angle at the centre included by diameters of the particular circle, the circumference of the greater being greater and that of the lesser less, in such a way that, as observation shows, the circumferences have the same ratio as the lengths of line which they describe in rolling bear to one another.'

The last words (855ᵃ36–7) are difficult. Literally the writer says 'the circumference of each circle appears, as observation shows, to be the angle of the appropriate diameter'.

Cappelle (followed by the Oxford translator) takes the writer to be comparing the 'angles' made by the diameters with the respective circumferences at their extremities, that is to say, the angles ABE and ABD in the accompanying figure in which a larger and a smaller circle touch at B and, therefore, the diameters AB and CB are in one straight line. I cannot see how γωνία...

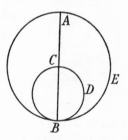

FIG. 66

ἡ περιφέρεια ἑκάστου τῆς οἰκείας διαμέτρου can mean 'an angle *between* the circumference and its appropriate diameter' in the absence of some words meaning 'formed by' or its equivalent.

A similar point arose in c. 8, 851ᵇ38–40 (see above), where I can only believe, in like manner, that the angles compared are the angles subtended at the centre in similar sectors, or by similar arcs.

A further difficulty in taking the angles to be the *mixed* 'angles' in this case is that they are not angles which can be taken to be in a certain ratio to each other, the ratio namely of the respective diameters, so that they are not really comparable, both of them being, as 'angles *of* semicircles', *greater than any acute rectilineal angle*.[1] Accordingly, I can only believe that the angles here compared are the angles of similar sectors, or angles subtended at the centre by similar arcs, of a greater and lesser circle having the same centre. I have translated accordingly. I am confirmed in my view by the fact that, after making the translation, I found that Blancanus' version is to the same effect: 'Quod autem maior solus in sua revolutione maiorem lineam describet, manifestum est hinc, quia sensu patet maiorem circumferentiam in maiori circulo subtendere angulum qui fit a diametris in centro; maiorem vero circumferentiam subtendere eundem angulum in minori orbe, ut etiam in 8. Quaest. dictum est: eandem igitur, ut proxime dixi, habebunt etiam proportionem illae lineae, quae a singulis seorsum orbibus revolutis designabuntur.'

That the framer of the problem possessed real mathematical insight is proved by two things in particular. One is his remark ($855^{b}28$–30): 'When the two circles have one motion, the *moving centre* describes in one case the greater, and in the other the lesser straight line.' The length the centre describes depends simply on which of the two circles is actually being rolled along its tangent; how the other circle actually rolls is irrelevant to this—the movement of the other circle is incidental ($856^{a}34$). This is the point taken by

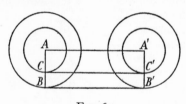

FIG. 67

Heron also.[2] If the circles have the common centre A and ACB is the common radius perpendicular to the common tangents BB' and CC', Heron takes the case in which the *greater* circle rolls along BB'. Then the *centre A* moves at the same time and describes the distance AA' which is necessarily equal to BB'; the radius AB at the end of the revolution takes the position $A'B'$. It does not matter, therefore, what has happened to the lesser circle. Even if it does not revolve with the greater, though having always the same centre, it is bound to reach the position in which A' is its centre. But if it is fastened to the greater circle, so as to revolve with it, the point C (on AB) cannot do otherwise than reach C' (on $A'B'$).

The other significant remark in the text is at $855^{b}26$–8, to the effect that it seems absurd that the circles should, when they both roll together, describe the same distance though the lesser does not seem to skip over any points or the greater to delay at any point. As a

---

[1] See Eucl. iii. 16.　　　　　　　　　　　[2] *Mechanics*, i.

matter of fact this supposed impossibility is what actually happens, as was shown by Galilei in his lucid explanation contained in the *Dialogues concerning two new Sciences*.[1]

To clear our ideas Galilei takes the case of similar and similarly situated regular polygons with the same centre and considers what would happen if we roll one of the polygons along a straight line so that each side successively comes to lie along the straight line and the polygon so describes a continuous length equal to its perimeter.

About G as centre, says Galilei, describe an equiangular and equilateral polygon of any number of sides, say the hexagon $ABCDEF$. Similar to this and concentric with it, describe another smaller one which we shall call $HIKLMN$. Produce AB a side of the larger hexagon indefinitely towards S; similarly produce HI indefinitely

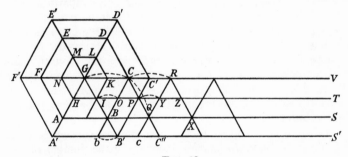

FIG. 68

towards T, and through the centre G draw GV parallel to AS or HT. Galilei now describes what happens to the sides of the inner polygon when the outer one is rolled along the continuation of AB. He draws another figure to show what happens to the sides of the outer polygon when the sides of the *inner* are made to roll along a straight line. (I have, after Cantor,[2] combined the two figures by drawing yet another similar and similarly situated hexagon $A'B'C'D'E'F'$ outside $ABCDEF$, and we shall see what happens to the sides of the former when the latter as in the first case rolls along $ABQX...$)

(1) suppose the polygon $ABCDEF$ rolls along AS; what happens to the sides of the inner hexagon?

First, the hexagon turns bodily about B as centre till BG takes the position BC, G having described an arc with centre B. In the same time C has described an arc CQ with the same centre, and the

[1] See the translation by Grew and De Salvio, New York, 1914, pp. 20–4 and 49–52.

[2] *Gesch. d. Math.* ii. 638.

side *BC* takes the position *BQ*. In the same time the point *I* on the smaller polygon has described the arc *IO*, and when *I* is at *O*, *IK* takes the position *OP*. That is, the side *IK* has passed over *IO* without touching it. Similarly, as the rotation goes on, the side *CD* will take the position *QX*, while *KL*, the side of the inner polygon, will reach the position *YZ*, having skipped *PY* altogether. Hence, when both polygons have made one complete rotation, the inner one will have moved the same distance along *HT* that the outer one has described along *AS*, but the sides of the outer will have described six lines *BQ*, *QX* . . . continuous with one another, while those of the inner will have described six lines *OP*, *YZ* but with gaps between each equal to *IO*. The centre *G* itself will only have touched *GV* at *six points C, R*, etc.

(2) Suppose that *ABCDEF* rolls along *ABS* but carries with it, not the inner polygon, but an *outer* similar and similarly situated polygon *A'B'C'D'E'F'*. Then when *BC* in the inner polygon comes into the position *BQ*, *B'C'* in the outer will have come into the position *bC''*, for *B'* will not have remained stationary but will have turned round *B* as centre *backwards* into the position *b*, and part of the new position of *B'C'*, namely *bC''*, will overlap part of *A'B'*. So with the next side that comes to lie on *A'S'*, and so on. The *net* advance of any side is equal to the side of the inner polygon, not of the outer.

To realize what happens in the case of two concentric *circles* rolling along, we have to increase indefinitely the number of sides in our polygons, until each side is indefinitely small. Then the same principles, in the one case of leaving gaps, and in the other of overlapping, apply; only the gaps and the overlaps are infinite in number and infinitely small so that they are not perceptible to sense.

We shall omit the next three chapters, 25–8, as they hardly require any commentary except indeed 25 about stringing the ropes under a bed; but the latter problem has little mathematical interest and the text towards the end is so bad that it defies emendation.

(*n*) *The weight on a pole*
Mech. 29. 857ᵇ9–20

In this case of a weight resting on a pole and carried by two men, one at each end, we are asked to say why, when the weight is not placed in the middle, greater strain falls on the man who is nearest to the weight than on the other. We should regard this as a case of finding the resultant of two parallel forces acting in the same sense. If *AB* be the pole, *P, Q* the weights which the men have to support respectively, and *W* the weight, placed at *C*, we have to find the ratio between P and Q when the resultant of P and Q acting upfind the ratio between P and Q when the resultant of P and Q acting

upwards through C is equal to W.
It is proved in any elementary text-book of mechanics that the resultant of any two forces acting at points A, B, the extremities of a weightless rod, is a force $P+Q$ acting at a point C of the rod de-

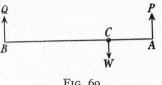

FIG. 69

termined by the relation $\dfrac{P}{Q} = \dfrac{BC}{AC}$. If, therefore, $P+Q = W$, the

two men at A, B respectively divide the strain in the proportion of BC to AC, so that the burden is greater on the man who is nearer to C, and in the proportion stated. It is characteristic of the author that he can only look upon the problem as one of the lever where C is the fulcrum, the burden borne by the nearest man the 'weight' raised and that borne by the other the 'power' supporting the weight.

(o) *Rising from a sitting position*

Ib. 30. 857^{b}21–858^{a}2,

At 857^{b}25 we observe the expression 'at *similar* angles to the circumference of the earth', where making *equal* angles with the circumference of the earth is meant. Aristotle, too, speaks of 'similar angles' where equal angles are meant.[1] According to Proclus on Eucl. i, p. 125 F., the expression 'similar angles' was used by those who brought an angle under the category of *quality* (i.e. as being a figure of a certain shape); cf. Aristotle, who specifies, as 'kinds' of 'figure', 'the angle, the straight, and the circular'.[2] Eudemus, who wrote a book on 'the Angle', agreed with those who put the angle ὑπὸ τὸ ποιόν. I should translate 857^{b}23–5 as follows: 'Is it because equality is everywhere a cause of rest, and the right angle comes under the equal and so causes stability?' (No doubt τοῦ ἴσου could be the genitive after αἴτιον understood with γωνία, making the right angle the 'cause' of the equal as the equal is of rest, but this would be too general a statement and I prefer to regard τοῦ ἴσου as a sort of partitive genitive.) The remark about the right angle is probably directly prompted by the definition of a right angle, which in Euclid took this form: 'When a straight line set up on a straight line makes the adjacent angles equal to one another, each of the equal angles is *right*, and the straight line standing on the other is called a perpendicular to that on which it stands.'[3]

[1] *De caelo B.* 14. 296^{b}20 and Δ. 4. 311^{b}34.
[2] *Phys. A.* 5. 188^{a}25. [3] Eucl. i, Def. 10.

The sentences διὸ καὶ φέρεται πρὸς ὁμοίας γωνίας τῇ περιφερείᾳ τῆς γῆς and οὐ γαρ ὅτι καὶ πρὸς ὀρθήν ἔσται τῷ ἐπιπέδῳ are very odd. Apparently the only possible subject for φέρεται must be the man who gets up from a sitting posture, but φέρεται is an odd word to use for this movement. On the other hand, the sentence so resembles as almost to echo a sentence in the De caelo :[1] ὅτι δὲ φέρεται καὶ πρὸς τὸ τῆς γῆς μέσον, σημεῖον ὅτι τὰ φερόμενα βάρη ἐπὶ ταύτην οὐ παρ' ἄλληλα φέρεται ἀλλὰ πρὸς ὁμοίας γωνίας, ὥστε πρὸς ἓν τὸ μέσον φέρεται, καὶ τὸ τῆς γῆς.

The remark would seem to have more point if one could understand with φέρεται something like τὰ φερόμενα βάρη and could treat the remark as a parenthesis. This (equality producing rest) explains also why (διό) falling bodies make similar angles with the circumference of the earth. The next sentence οὐ γὰρ ὅτι καὶ πρὸς ὀρθὴν ἔσται τῷ ἐπιπέδῳ constitutes a difficulty because it seems to contradict what has gone before, whereas it is obvious that something falling or standing at similar angles to the circumference of the earth *does* in fact fall or stand in a direction at right angles to the ground. Hence the Oxford translation, 'for it is not the case that he will actually be at right angles to the ground', can hardly be right. One remedy is to read with Monantheuil οὕτω γὰρ instead of οὐ γὰρ ὅτι; but it seems to me that it should be possible to translate οὐ γὰρ ὅτι, like οὐχ ὅτι, as 'although', 'not but what',[2] although, in fact, this means the same thing as being 'perpendicular to the ground'. But the subject of ἔσται must apparently be the same as the subject of φέρεται.

The interpretation of the rest of the problem presents no difficulty. It is curious that the writer states, as the object to be arrived at, that the feet should be directly 'under the head' (857b36), whereas they should, of course, be vertically under the centre of gravity of the whole body. It would seem (as Cappelle says), from this and other passages, that the writer had no conception of the centre of gravity.

(p) Inertia

Mech. 31. 858a3–12

The considerations in this chapter are just. Not only is it more easy to move a thing in a given direction if it is already moving in that direction than if it is at rest, but it is more difficult still to move it if it has a motion in the contrary direction than if it is at rest. The last is the most difficult case; that in which the thing is at rest is the next difficult: 'for even that which is at rest offers resistance'. This shows that the author had some conception of what we call *vis inertiae* (Cappelle).

[1] B. 14. 296b18–21.   [2] Cf. L. & S. (9th ed.) under ὅτι, v. 1 ad fin.

XII

TREATISE ON INDIVISIBLE LINES

WHETHER this treatise was written by Aristotle himself, or by Theophrastus, or by someone else, it was no doubt written in the School. Aristotle has an observation in the *Physics*:[1] 'For it is not a hard task to destroy the (theory of) indivisible lines'; and he may have suggested to some pupil that he should write up the subject. The arguments in the treatise are more in the nature of chopping logic than of a serious contribution to mathematics; and they tell us little that the historian of mathematics does not find in other sources. There is little to add in the way of commentary to the very full notes added by Joachim to his translation. There are a number of citations of definitions and propositions in a form differing little from that given to them by Euclid. The terminology is largely the same as that fixed by Euclid in his *Elements*: but we find (as in the *Mechanics* and *Problems*), alongside of Euclid's, survivals of somewhat antiquated and less consistent terminology from Aristotle's time or earlier.

In 968a23–b4 there is a supposed argument for Zeno's view of the Dichotomy and Achilles additional to what is stated in *Phys.* VI. 9, namely that 'If it be even admitted that the body moving along the line touches an infinite number of points in a finite time, then if we assume further that the quicker body traverses a greater distance in an equal time, and that the movement of thought is quickest of all, it will follow that thought will touch an infinite number of points one by one in a finite time, so that if thought touching points one by one is counting, it is possible to count an infinity of things in a finite time. If (as we must assume) this is impossible, there must be such a thing as an indivisible line.' That is (as Joachim says), if you are to avoid the absurdity of counting an infinite number in a finite time, *which recognizes the fact of motion*, the only remaining possibility is to postulate 'indivisible lines'.

The point is answered at 969a30–b3: 'Nor is thought's coming into contact with the members of an infinite series one by one *counting*. . . . Even if the possibility of thought's moving in this fashion be admitted, still this moving is not *counting*, for counting is movement combined with pausing.'

In 968b19 there is an allusion to two irrational straight lines called by Euclid 'binomial' (ἡ ἐκ δύο ὀνομάτων) and 'apotome' respectively. These are defined in Eucl. X. 36 and 73 respectively. The first corresponds to what we should write in algebra as $\sqrt{a} + \sqrt{b}$ where

[1] iii, c. 6. 206a17.

√a, √b are 'rational straight lines commensurable in *square only*';
that is a, b are commensurable but √a, √b are not. We may write
the binomial in the form $\rho + \sqrt{k} \cdot \rho$ where ρ is a rational straight line
and k is a non-square number so that √k is a surd. An apotome
can be expressed in like manner as √$a \sim$ √b or $\rho \sim \sqrt{k} \cdot \rho$ (where $\sim$
represents 'the difference between'). There is a difficulty in the
text here. The writer says: 'If any (unit-square) is cut in a prescribed and determinate line, it will not be either rational or irrational or any of the other (straight lines) ὧν νῦν δή (i.e. δή νῦν)
εἴρηται like the apotome or the binomial.' Apelt emended the text
by substituting for ὧν νῦν δή εἴρηται the words ὧν δυνάμεις ῥηταί
'whose squares are rational'. But this correction cannot be right,
because the square of √$a \pm$ √b or $\rho \pm \sqrt{k} \cdot \rho$ is *not* 'rational'. The
first is $a + b \pm 2\sqrt{ab}$ and the second $(1 + k)\rho^2 \pm 2\sqrt{k} \cdot \rho$. It occurs to
me to wonder whether we cannot get a good sense out of ὧν νῦν δή
εἴρηται by interpreting the phrase as 'none of the other irrationals
which have recently been discussed such as the apotome or binomial',
reading the words as referring to a recently propounded theory of
compound irrationals, viz. that of Theaetetus subsequently embodied in Euclid, Book X. The allusion might be not to Euclid but
to Theaetetus, because the discovery and discussion of the compound
irrationals including the binomial and apotome are definitely attributed by Pappus, on the authority of Eudemus, to Theaetetus.

969ª18: τοὔλαττον: Joachim translates: 'a premiss too narrow to
carry this conclusion', explaining the reason why in his note.
Heiberg suggests οὐκ ἔλαττον, the meaning of which would be that
the advocates of indivisible lines who base their theory on the Idea
of line make an assumption even more questionable than a direct
assumption of indivisible lines.

970ª4–8: ἔτι εἰ ἡ παρὰ τὴν μείζω τὸ πλάτος ποιεῖ παραβαλλομένη, τὸ
ἴσον τῷ [τῶν, τό, τῆς, codd.] ἀπὸ τῆς ἀτόμου καὶ τῆς ποδιαίας παραβαλλόμενον παρὰ τὴν διπλῆν [διποῦν codd.] ἔλαττον ποιήσει τὸ πλάτος
τῆς ἀμεροῦς· ἔσται ⟨γὰρ⟩ ἔλαττον τοῦ ἀπὸ [τὸ περὶ or τὸ παρὰ codd.]
τῆς ἀτόμου. What we require in this passage is simply this: 'From
a rectangle applied to a straight line, if an equal angle be applied to
a greater straight line, its breadth will be less than that of the
original rectangle; therefore the rectangle contained by the indivisible line and another a foot long, if applied to a line two feet long
will give a breadth less than the indivisible line [half of it, in fact];
therefore there will be (produced) a line less than the indivisible.'

Heiberg pointed out[1] that Apelt's reading παραβαλλομένη (in ª5)
will not do because in the technical language of Greek mathematics
what you '*apply* to a given straight line as base' is a rectangle (or

[1] *Math. z. Arist.*, p. 35.

area) not a line: therefore we must read παραβαλλόμενον here. Heiberg, therefore, reads as follows: ἔτι εἰ παρὰ (ΝΖᵃ omit ἡ) τὴν μείζω ⟨ἔλαττον⟩ τὸ πλάτος ποιεῖ παραβαλλόμενον τὸ ἴσον, τὸ ὑπὸ τῆς ἀτόμου καὶ τῆς ποδιαίας παραβαλλόμενον παρὰ τὴν δίπουν ἔλαττον ποιήσει τὸ πλάτος τῆς ἀμερούς· ἔσται ἄρα ἔλαττόν τι τῆς ἀτόμου. 'Further since an equal rectangle applied to a larger base makes the breadth smaller, the rectangle contained by the indivisible line and a foot-length applied to a [the base of a] two-foot length will make the breadth less than the indivisible line: thus we shall have something less than the indivisible.' This gives a quite satisfactory sense.

970ᵃ15–18. '⟨If this were not so,⟩ the square on the diameter would not be double of the square on the indivisible side. For if you subtract (from the diameter) a length equal to the side of the square the remainder is less than the indivisible ⟨side⟩. If it were equal [i.e. if the diameter contained twice the side], the square on the diameter would be four times ⟨the original square⟩.' Heiberg would read ἀνέγραφεν for ἔγραψεν literally 'the diagonal would have described on (itself) a square four times as large'. If d is the diagonal and s the side $d-s<s$; if not, i.e., if $d-s = s$ and $d = 2s$, d^2 would be equal to $4s^2$, not to $2s^2$.

970ᵃ11–15. ἔτι εἰ τὸ τετράγωνον ⟨ἐκ Joachim⟩ τῶν ἀμερῶν, δια-μέτρου ἐμπεσούσης καὶ καθέτου ἀχθείσης, ἡ τοῦ τετραγώνου πλευρά κτλ. 'If a square can be constructed from simples, then if a diagonal be drawn on it and a perpendicular drawn to it (from an angular point) the square of the side of the square will be equal to the square of the perpendicular together with the square on half the diagonal.[1] Hence the side of the square (by the hypothesis indivisible) will not be the smallest possible line'; in fact, the perpendicular and the half of the diagonal (which are equal to one another) are both smaller than the side. [Heiberg suggests ἔτι εἰς τὸ τετράγωνον for ἔτι εἰ τὸ τετράγωνον. This would make the genitive absolute διαμέτρου ἐμπεσούσης take the place of the conditional sentence εἰ κτλ.]

The arguments in 971ᵃ6—972ᵃ13 distinguished in the note on p. 971 a 17 in Joachim's translation run on very similar lines to the arguments in *Physics* VI. 1. 231ᵃ21—232ᵃ22 leading up to the conclusion that a line cannot be made up of points. As to these arguments see pp. 124–8.

Heiberg points out that in 970ᵃ9 it ought to be explained that the triangle in ᵃ10 is equilateral because the indivisible lines of which it is constructed must be supposed to be *equal* (which is indeed natural enough); otherwise the triangle would not be equilateral.

971ᵃ28: Heiberg would read instead of the MS. ὅλης, not ὅλως ⟨ἄν⟩ but ὅλη ⟨ἄν⟩.

[1] Eucl. i. 47.

S

XIII
PROBLEMS, BOOK XV
(a) Diameter

CC. 1, 2. 910^{b}11–22

'Why is it that, of all straight lines which divide rectilinear figures into two equal parts, that only is called a diameter which is drawn from an angle to an angle? Is it because a diameter divides the figure into two equal parts, as its name implies, without destroying the figure it measures? It will therefore be the line which divides it at its joints (I mean the angles) that will be the diameter; for that line does not destroy the figure but divides it, as those do who divide up implements of war ⟨between persons⟩. But a line which cuts up a composite figure through its sides destroys it; for a rectilineal figure is put together at its angles.'

c. 2. 'Why is it called a "diameter"? Is it because it alone divides (a rectilineal figure) into two equal parts, as though one should call it a "dichameter"? And why, of all lines which divide it into two equal parts, is this particular one alone called a "diameter"? Is it because it alone divides the figure at the places where its limbs are bent, while the others cut it in its sides?'

Both Aristotle and Euclid regularly use the word 'diameter' for the diagonal of a parallelogram as well as for the diameter of a circle. Euclid defines only the diameter of a *circle*: 'A diameter of a circle is any straight line drawn through the centre and terminated in both directions by the circumference of the circle, and such a straight line also bisects the circle.'[1] When Euclid comes to parallelograms[2] he says, without any explanation of the word, 'and the diameter bisects them' (i.e. 'parallelogrammic areas', by which he means areas contained by parallel straight lines, with the unexpressed restriction that only *four-sided* figures are meant; the shorter term parallelogram is used in the next proposition (I. 35) and thereafter). διαγώνιος for diameter does, however, occur in Eucl. XI. 28.

The idea in the above passage is that rectilineal figures are put together by joining certain straight lines at the ends, two and two, so as to form angles. Any straight line which bisects the area but cuts across the sides in any way is held to 'destroy' the figure.

(b) The number ten: decimal system

c. 3. 910^{b}23–911^{a}4

'Why do all men, whether barbarians or Greeks, count up to ten

---

[1] i, Def. 17.   [2] i. 34.

and not to some other number, such as 2, 3, 4, or 5, so that they do
not go on to repeat one of these and say, for example, "one-five",
"two-five", as they say "one-ten" [i.e. eleven], "two-ten" [twelve]?
Or why, again, do they not stop at some number beyond ten and
then repeat from that point? For every number consists of the
preceding number ⟨taken as base⟩ plus one or two, etc., which gives
some different number; nevertheless ten has been fixed as the base
and people count up to that. Chance cannot account for the fact
that, apparently, everyone does this always: what happens always
and in all cases is not the result of chance but is in the nature of
things. Is it because ten is a perfect number, seeing that it com-
prises all kinds of number, even and odd, square and cube, linear
and plane, prime and composite? Or is it because ten is the beginning
of number, since ten is produced by adding one, two, three, and
four? Or is it because the moving bodies (in the heaven) are nine
in number? Or because within ten (compounded) ratios four cubic
numbers are completed, of which numbers the Pythagoreans hold
that the universe is constructed? Or is it because all men had ten
fingers, so that having, as it were, counters for the appropriate
number, they employed this number for counting other things as
well? A certain race among the Thracians alone count up to four,
because like that of children, their memory is not able to take in
more, and they never use any large number.'

The suggestions of grounds for regarding ten as the 'perfect
number' are taken from Pythagorean doctrine. They are for the
most part found in Speusippus, who mainly followed Philolaus and
wrote a book *On Pythagorean Numbers*, the second half of which was
devoted to the number ten.[1] Speusippus declared the decad to be
the most natural and most creative basis for all things, being, as it
were, in itself a sort of model for the things which constituted the
universe as finally evolved. He also observed that ten has many
peculiar properties appropriate to a perfect number. The perfect
number must be even so as to contain an equal number of odd and
even numbers; it must also include the prime or
incomposite and the secondary or composite.
The addition of one, two, three, and four (making ten) formed the τετρακτύς, the Pythagoreans'
greatest oath and alternatively the 'principle of
health'. This also gave a triangular number with
4 as its side; on this Lucian has (*Vit. auct.* 4)
a story of Pythagoras. Pythagoras asked some-

FIG. 70

one to count. He said 1, 2, 3, 4, whereon Pythagoras interrupted: 'Do
you see? What you take for 4 is 10, a perfect triangle and our oath.'

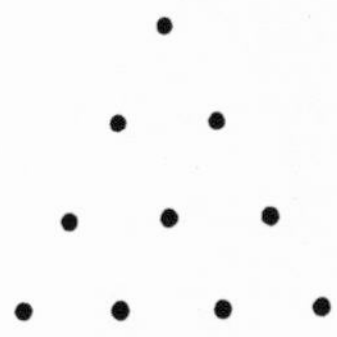

[1] See *Theol. Ar.*, ed. Ast, pp. 61–4.

Again, ten includes, according to Speusippus, linear, plane, and solid numbers: 1 is a point, 2 a line, 3 a triangle, and 4 a pyramid. It also includes certain ratios, that of equality (since it is twice 5), and the ratios 2 : 1, 3 : 2, 4 : 3 which represent the musical intervals, the octave, the fifth, and the fourth, as Pythagoras himself discovered.

The ten moving bodies in the heavens, according to the Pythagoreans (reckoning from the centre), were the earth, the counter-earth, the sun and moon, the five planets, and the sphere of the fixed stars: so we learn from Aristotle.[1] When the writer of the *Problems* speaks of *nine* revolutions in the heavens, he must be excluding one of the ten, perhaps the earth.

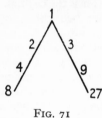

Fig. 71

'Ten (compounded) ratios' must mean a series in geometrical progression such as 1, r, r^2, r^3, r^4, r^5, r^6, r^7, r^8, r^9.

This includes four cubes, namely 1, r^3, r^6, r^9. The statement that it was from cubic numbers that the Pythagoreans constructed the universe reminds us of the construction of the world-soul in the *Timaeus*,[2] where we have the two geometrical progressions 1, 2, 4, 8 and 1, 3, 9, 27 traditionally represented as in diagram 71.

(c) *The sun's rays and length of shadows*

c. 5. 911ᵃ14–ᵇ2

'Why is it that, although the sun's motion is uniform, the increase and decrease in the length of the shadows is not the same in equal periods of time? Is it because the angles to the object seen, namely those contained by the rays and subtended by equal circumferences [arcs], are equal? And if these are equal so must those be which are

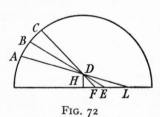

Fig. 72

contained by the rays produced within the triangle formed by the first [i.e. lowest] ray, the object seen and the shadow, and accordingly, these angles being equal, the line which is farther from the object seen is greater than that which is nearer; for this we know to be the case.

'Let the circumference be divided into any number of equal parts and let the object seen be *H*. When, then, the sun at *A* falling [reading προσβαλών] on *H* makes a shadow along *HL* (*DL*) the ray must fall on *L*. When the sun

---

[1] *Metaph.* A. 5. 986ᵃ8–12.   [2] 35, 36.

reaches B, the ray from B will fall within HL, and similarly when again the sun reaches C. Otherwise one straight line will meet another in two points. Since then AB is equal to BC, the angles under them (i.e. subtended by them) at D will be equal; for they are angles at the centre.[1] But if the angles are equal on this side [reading τῇδε] of D, so are the angles ⟨formed⟩ in the triangle, for they are vertically opposite the former.[2]

'Since, therefore, the angle [LDF] is divided into two equal parts, LE will be greater than EF [omit τῇ $\varDelta\varTheta$]. And similarly with all other (intercepts) made by the rays coming from the circumference.

'At the same time it is also clear that it is at midday that the shadow must be shortest and that the increments are then least. For it is at midday that the sun is most nearly above our heads.'

There is some confusion in the lettering of the text. The above translation follows the reading adopted (mostly after Bussemaker) by the Oxford translator; but I follow Heiberg in omitting τῇ $\varDelta\varTheta$ in 911ᵃ31.

The object is to explain why EL, the decrease in the shadow while the sun passes from A to B, is greater than EF, the decrease while the sun passes through an equal angle from B to C.

We should probably prove the proposition in this way. Since F is nearer to H than L is, $DF < DL$ (for $DF^2 = DH^2 + HF^2$, and $DL^2 = DH^2 + HL^2$, and while DH^2 is common $HF^2 < HL^2$, so that $DF^2 < DL^2$ and $DF < DL$).

And since the angle HDL is bisected by DE,

$$FD : DL = FE : EL.$$

But $FD < DL$

therefore $\qquad FE < EL$ or $EL > EF$.

The same question is raised in c. 9. 912ᵃ34–ᵇ3: 'Why does the sun when rising or setting make shadows long, when high in the heavens shorter, and at midday least of all? Surely because when it rises the shadow it makes will at first be parallel to the surface of the earth and stretch to an infinite distance, after which it will first be long and then become continually shorter because the straight line from the higher point continually falls within ⟨that from the lower⟩. Let AB be the ⟨needle of the⟩ sun-dial, let the sun be at the points C, D respectively. Then CF, the ray from C, will be outside DE. BE is the shadow when the sun is higher

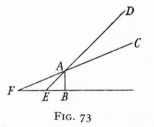

Fig. 73

[1] Cf. Eucl. iii. 27.   [2] Eucl. i. 15.

and *BF* where it is lower. The shadow is least when the sun is highest, when, that is, it is overhead.'

The remark (911ª26–7) 'otherwise a straight line will meet a straight line twice (i.e. in two points)' is based on an axiom which was interpolated in Eucl. I as Common Notion 9 in the form: 'Two straight lines do not enclose an area' (or space). 'Otherwise' of course means that if *BD* produced does not meet *HL* between *H* and *L*, it must either pass through *L* or meet *HL* produced, in which latter case it must cut *DL* in some point. In either case 'a straight line would meet another in two points'.

(d) Appearance of the half-moon

c. 7. 911ᵇ35–912ª4

'Why, although the moon is spherical, do we see it as a straight line when it is halved? Surely because our eye and the circle which the sun makes as it falls upon the moon are in the same plane. Whenever this takes place, the sun appears as a straight line; for, since anything which casts visual rays on to a sphere (and the moon is spherical) must see a circle, and the sun also sees it, the figure defined by the sun must be a circle.'

The circle 'made or defined by the sun' as it illuminates the moon is called by Aristarchus of Samos 'the great circle which divides the dark and the light portions of the moon',[1] and this circle, as he says, 'is in the direction of our eye when the moon appears to us halved'. This means that the plane of the great circle mentioned passes through our eye, or, our eye and the said great circle are in one plane—as the problem states. In his Proposition 5 Aristarchus is more exact; for in the enunciation he explains that 'the great circle *parallel to the dividing circle* and our eye are in one plane'. This is because, as he goes on to say, the dividing circle is in the direction

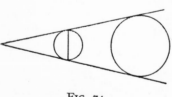

of our eye and the great circle parallel to the dividing circle is indistinguishable from it. For, in fact, since the sun is larger than the moon, its rays converge in a cone the apex of which is on the side of the moon away from the sun, and the sun lights up rather

FIG. 74

more than half of the moon, so that 'the circle dividing the dark and the light portions' is rather nearer to the apex of the cone, and therefore rather less than a great circle in the moon. But so far as

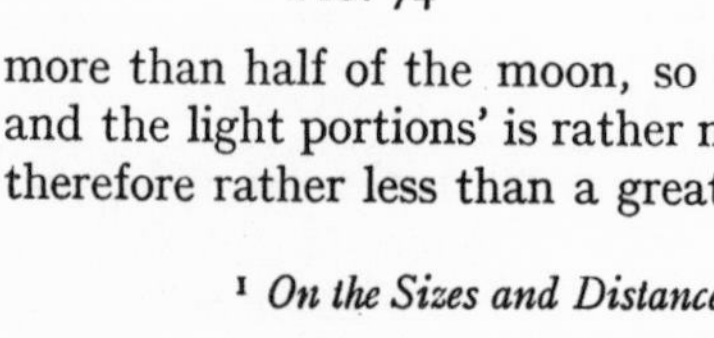

---

[1] *On the Sizes and Distances of Sun and Moon*, Hyp. 2.

our perception goes the dividing circle and the great circle in the moon parallel to it are so nearly equal as to be indistinguishable.

It is odd to say in 911ᵇ38 that when the moon is halved, 'the *sun* appears as a straight line'; what it does is to define what appears to us as a straight line.

The rest of the description in the problem relates to the phases and is quite intelligible. ὅταν ὁ ἥλιος ἐπιβάλλῃ (912ᵃ10) must apparently mean 'when the sun first strikes the moon on our side (or first begins to light it up)', i.e. at new moon.

912ᵃ10–13: 'And after the eighth day it (the moon) is filled up from the centre, because the sun goes farther past it [in our direction] and makes the circle incline more towards us; and when the circle is so situated relatively to our sight, it comes to resemble a section of a cone.'

This passage evidently refers to the time immediately after the moon appears halved, i.e. when the visible portion increases from half to full, and is 'gibbous'. During this time one side of the moon presents the appearance of an ellipse, while the other is, of course, a semicircle. This appears to be the only reference in the Aristotelian writings to a 'section of a cone'. Euclid, we know, wrote a treatise entitled *Conics*, but the sections of a cone were discovered and classified earlier by Menaechmus, who was a pupil of Eudoxus and flourished about the middle of the fourth century.

In 912ᵃ14 the author seems to revert to the new moon, for he says: 'The moon appears crescent-shaped when the sun has changed its position: for when the circle of the sun touches (literally 'gets at' or 'to') the extreme points at which the moon appears halved, the circumference of the circle comes into view, for the sun is no longer in a straight line with our eye [i.e. directly opposite to us behind the moon], but moves to one side. When this takes place, while the circle passes always through the same points, the appearance presented must be crescent-shaped. For part of the circle which before was opposite to us (i.e. at the back of the moon) now comes directly within our view so that a portion of the illuminated surface of the moon is cut off; and then, the extremities aforesaid remaining fixed as before, the moon must appear crescent-shaped. And it is more or less so according to the motion of the sun. For as the sun changes its position, the circle too which it sees turns round, while passing always through the same points; for the number of inclinations it may assume is infinite, seeing that the number of great circles (in a sphere) that you can draw through the same points is infinite.'

PROBLEMS, BOOK XVI

(a) Cylinder and cone rolling

c. 5. 913^{b}37–914^{a}24

'Why is it that a cylinder, when it is pushed along, is carried in a straight line and describes straight lines with the circles bounding it, whereas a cone is carried round in a circle, the vertex remaining fixed, and describes a circle with the circle bounding it? Both move with a circular motion, but the cylinder describes straight lines in the plane while the cone describes circles, because the circles in the cone [the circular sections parallel to the base] are unequal, and of things moving about one and the same centre the larger always travels the quicker. Now, when all the circles in the cone travel together but at unequal speeds, the effect is that the outermost circles move over the most ground, i.e. describe the longest line, in the same time; hence they all move in a circle. For they are all described by the same straight line, and as the straight line is carried round in a circle the different points on it do not all describe an equal line, whereas if carried straight they would. In the cylinders, since all the circles are equal and are about the same centre, the effect is that all the (corresponding) points in the circles touch the plane at the same time, and the circles roll along at equal speed because cylinders are uniform throughout, and each of the circles in one and the same cylinder arrives at (a new position on) the plane, after completing a revolution, at the same time, so that the straight lines described by them on the plane are equal, since the circles describe them by their contact and they are equal and move at equal speed. Now the lines described by the same line carried in a straight line are straight, and in consequence of their being straight the cylinder must move in a straight line: for it makes no difference whether you drag the cylinder along by the line in which it originally touched the plane or whether you roll it; for in fact it will always be an equal and similar line on the surface of the cylinder which will come into contact with the plane, whether the cylinder be dragged or rolled.'

When, in speaking of the infinity of the different circles described by the different circular sections of the cone as you roll it on a plane round its vertex (914^{a}5–11), the writer says that 'they are all described by one and the same straight line', i.e. by all the different points on that line, the phrase is not strictly accurate. It is true that the circles described on the plane are the same as those which would be described by (points on) one straight line equal to one of the 'generators' of the cone; the describing line, however, is not one all the time but is continually changing. As the cone rolls, *all* the generators *one after another* come into contact with the plane; but as they are all of the same length the effect is the same as if they were all one. This explanation is in essence quite clear. Only the wording is in some places strange.

At 914ᵃ11–12 the writer says that all the circles in the cylinder are about the same centre (περὶ ταὐτὸ κέντρον): this is of course inaccurate; the centres are all at different points on the axis of the cylinder. What the writer is trying to emphasize is that the speed of the circles is equal because their radii are equal, in order to contrast this case with that in 914ᵃ4–5, where it is explained that if you have a number of *unequal* circles about the same centre, the larger travels the faster when all are rotated about the centre by one movement.

The reading in 914ᵃ12–13 (συμβαίνει τὰ ἅμα τοῦ ἐπιπέδου ἐν αὐτοῖς πάνθ' ἁπτομένοις σημεῖα) is awkward because we must have a subject to go with φέρεσθαι in l. 13, and this must be, not 'all the points on the circles which are in contact with the plane as the circles touch it', but 'the *circles* which touch the plane at all corresponding points on them at the same time'. Taking the proper reading as συμβαίνει ἅμα τοῦ ἐπιπέδου τὰ ἐν αὐτοῖς πάνθ' ἁπτομένους σημεῖα φέρεσθαι, the Oxford translator gets the right subject for φέρεσθαι: 'it results that since they (the circles) touch the plane at all the points on them at the same time, as they roll they travel', etc., that is to say τὰ ἐν αὐτοῖς πάντα σημεῖα is the accusative of respect—'as to all the points on them', meaning thereby the *corresponding* points on all the circles, i.e. the points on all the circles which lie on one 'generator' of the cylinder.

(b) Oblique section of cylinder

c. 6. 914ᵃ25–39

The difference between the trace on a plane made by an oblique section when the cylinder rolls on the plane and that made by a right section is well brought out in lines 35 to 38. But the explanation in the last lines, 'for a straight line cannot be partly in one plane and partly in another', is not relevant, because the trace is anyhow in the plane on which the cylinder rolls and it might, for anything we know, be a straight line in the plane inclined at an angle to the straight lines traced by right sections of the cylinder. The words are an echo of the proposition in Euclid XI, that 'A part of a straight line cannot be in the plane of reference and a part in a plane more elevated.'

Let us try to get an idea of the curve traced out by the oblique section on the plane. Let $ABCD$ be the cylinder, BC the oblique

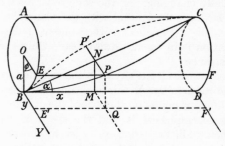

section, P any point on it. Let EF be the generator through P, ϕ the angle which the plane through the axis and the generator EF makes with the plane through the diameters AB and CD of the right circular sections, so that $\angle EOB = \phi$.

FIG. 75

Suppose the cylinder rolled towards us on the plane xBy till the generator EF takes the position $E'F'$ on the plane while Q is the position taken by P. If QM is $\perp BD$ and QM, MB are the coordinates (y, x) of Q, a the radius of the cylinder, then $y = a\phi$.

Now if PNP' be the principal ordinate of P in the section BC, PNP', Q, M are all in a plane through PQ parallel to the circle AB. If NR be perpendicular to BD, R is the same point as M, and BR or BM is equal to the coordinate x of the point Q.

Now the height of P or N above BD, viz. NM, $= a(1-\cos\phi)$ and $NM = MB \tan a$ where a is the inclination of CB to BD.

$$\therefore \quad x \tan a = a\,(1-\cos\phi).$$

From this equation and $y = a\phi$ we obtain the equation of the curve

$$x \tan a = a\left(1-\cos\frac{y}{a}\right),$$

from which we can get an idea of the form of the curve. Differentiating with reference to ϕ we have

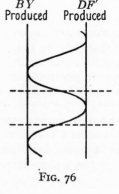

BY Produced   DF' Produced

FIG. 76

$$\frac{dy}{d\phi} = a$$

$$\frac{dx}{d\phi} = \frac{a \sin\phi}{\tan a}.$$

Thus

$$\frac{dy}{dx} = \frac{\tan a}{\sin\phi}.$$

When $\phi = 0$, this is ∞. Therefore the curve touches BY at B.

When $\phi = \dfrac{\pi}{6}$ this is $2 \tan a$

When $\phi = \dfrac{\pi}{4}$ this is $\sqrt{2} \tan \alpha$, or $\dfrac{7}{5} \tan \alpha$ nearly.

,, $\phi = \dfrac{\pi}{2}$,, $\dfrac{dy}{dx} = \tan \alpha$

,, $\phi = \dfrac{3\pi}{4}$,, $\dfrac{dy}{dx} = -\dfrac{7}{5} \tan \alpha$

,, $\phi = \pi$,, $\dfrac{dy}{dx} = \infty$

Thus the curve touches DF' produced when half a complete revolution has taken place: then it turns back until, when the complete revolution has taken place, it again touches BY.

(c) Objects impinging on a surface rebound at equal angles

cc. 4 and 13: 913^{b}6–36, 915^{b}18–35

These problems deal with the same question, though in the first the thing thrown impinges on the earth, while in the second the earth is not specifically mentioned.

In 913^{b}7 we have '*similar* angles' for 'equal angles' as elsewhere in Aristotle. ἅπτομαι in ^{b}8 has the regular sense of 'meeting', and not 'touching'. For πρὸς ὀρθήν 'at right angles' (^{b}9) the usual expression in Greek geometry is πρὸς ὀρθάς (γωνίας understood).

The nearest approach to the idea of a centre of gravity is that of the perpendicular (κάθετος) which divides the impinging object into two equal parts *in weight* (τῷ βάρει) (913^{b}27–8), and the extremity of which is supposed to impinge on the plane (^{b}10). The impact is supposed to make this perpendicular fall over, just as, if a thing is standing up and we cut a portion off suddenly at the bottom by a horizontal stroke, it falls backwards (i.e. in the direction contrary to that of the whole) (^{b}20–1). In the case of the object thrown, the impact has the effect of a blow in a sense contrary to that of the motion, and the perpendicular is thrown *forward*.

The proposition that there cannot be two perpendiculars to a plane at one point intersecting one another (at that point) does not appear in Euclid, but Euclid proves in XI. 6 that, if perpendiculars are drawn to a plane from two external points, they are parallel; hence, by the definition of parallels, they do not meet. The uniqueness of the straight line drawn in a given plane at right angles to a given straight line in that plane and from a point on it emerges from the construction for such a perpendicular in Eucl. I. 11, which directly satisfies Euclid's definition of a right angle (I, Def. 9).

c. 13 is interesting because it shows that the writer's thought seems to have been to resolve the motion into two, one of which is the motion, natural to the body, of falling perpendicularly to the ground, and the other is that due to the action of the thrower. If he throws the object in a direction obliquely inclined to the ground, the motion he imparts to it has two components, one parallel and one perpendicular to the ground. Now the component parallel to the horizontal surface of the earth is not affected by the impact but persists unchanged after the impact. The vertical components are, however, reversed in direction by the impact, in accordance with the unexpressed principle that action and reaction are equal and opposite. Taking the resultant of the two motions before and after the impact respectively, the parallelogram of velocities shows that the directions of the resultant motion just before and just after impact make equal angles with the surface.

The comparison with the theorem in optics that the angles of incidence and reflection in a mirror are equal and opposite is interesting. The proposition is assumed in Euclid's *Optics*, Prop. 19, with the remark: 'as is explained in the *Catoptrica* or theory of mirrors'. It was known to Archimedes. It is proved in Heron's *Catoptrica*.[1]

---

[1] See my *Greek Mathematics*, ii, pp. 353-4 as to this and to Archimedes' proof.

XV
PROBLEMS, BOOK XXIII

c. 3. 931^{b}9–18

The idea that a ship is lower in the water when it is in harbour than when it is in the open sea, and the reason given for this apparent difference, are odd, as Blancanus points out. Archimedes, of course, proves in his treatise *On Floating Bodies*[1] that 'Any solid lighter than a fluid will, if placed in the fluid, be so far immersed that the weight of the solid will be equal to the weight of the fluid displaced.' Hence *if the specific gravity of the water inside and outside the harbour is equal*, the ship will stand just as far out of the water in both cases. Blancanus quotes from Galilei's Italian treatise on floating bodies,[2] where Galilei states the same thing and points out that Aristotle is wrong in his statement here.

It occurs to me that it may have been observed that, in certain harbours where a freshwater river contributes to the water *inside* the harbour to a certain extent, but forms a less admixture in the water outside, the difference in specific gravity may have caused a certain difference in the extent to which the ship emerges from the water.

[1] i. 5.   [2] *Discorso circa le coso che stanno sù l'acqua*, p. 14.

XVI
NICOMACHEAN AND EUDEMIAN ETHICS
(a) General

N.E. I. 1. 1094^b25–7

'It seems just as wrong to accept merely plausible arguments from a mathematician as to require demonstrations from a rhetorician.'

Ib. II. 9. 1109^a24–6

'It is in every case difficult to find the mean; thus the finding of the middle or centre of a circle is not within the power of everyone, but only of the person with the necessary knowledge.'

This is, of course, the subject of Euclid III. 1.

Ib. III. 3. 1112^a18–26

'Do we deliberate about everything, is everything the subject of deliberation, or is there no deliberation about some things? . . . No one deliberates about things which are eternal, e.g. about the universe or the property of the diagonal and the side of a square, namely that they are incommensurable—nor again about things that are in motion but always remain in the same state, whether of necessity, by nature, or for any other reason, I mean such things as solstices and risings (of heavenly bodies).'

(b) Mathematical Analysis

Ib. 1112^b11–24 (cf. Metaph. Θ. 9. 1051^a21)

Aristotle is speaking of 'deliberation'. We do not, he says, deliberate about ends, but about the means to ends. A doctor does not deliberate whether he shall cure a man, or an orator whether he shall prove his point; 'but having determined on some end, they inquire how and by what means they can reach it, and, if there appear to be many ways, they consider by what means it may be reached most easily and best. If it is accomplished by one means, they consider how it can be realized by that means, and again by what means *that* can be attained ⟨and so on⟩, until they come to the *first* cause, which always comes last in the chain of discovery. The man who deliberates seems to seek a solution by an analysis of this sort just as if he were seeking a proof of a proposition in geometry. Now it would appear that it is not every search which is a case of deliberation—for instance mathematical inquiries—but every deliberation is a search, and the last step in the analysis is the first in the order of becoming.'

This is not a bad description of the working of the method of mathematical analysis. The *locus classicus* for a formal description of the method is Pappus, Book VII, on the 'Treasury of Analysis': 'The so-called Ἀναλυόμενος is, to put it shortly, a special body of doctrine provided for the use of those who, after finishing the ordinary Elements, are desirous of acquiring the power of solving problems which may be set them involving ⟨the construction of⟩ lines, and it is useful for this alone. It is the work of three men, Euclid the author of the *Elements*, Apollonius of Perga, and Aristaeus the elder, and proceeds by way of analysis and synthesis.'

Definition of Analysis and Synthesis

'*Analysis*, then, takes that which is sought as if it were admitted and passes from it through its successive consequences to something which is admitted as the result of synthesis; for in analysis we assume that which is sought as if it were already done (γεγονός), and we inquire what it is from which this results, and again what is the antecedent cause of the latter, and so on, until by so retracing our steps we come upon something already known or belonging to the class of first principles; and such a method we call analysis as being solution backwards (ἀνάπαλιν λύσιν).

'But in *synthesis*, reversing the process, we take as already done that which was last arrived at in the analysis and, by arranging in their natural order as consequences what before were antecedents, and successively connecting them one with another, we arrive finally at the construction of what was sought; and this we call synthesis.

'Now analysis is of two kinds, the one directed to searching for the truth and called *theoretical*, the other directed to finding what we are told to find and called *problematical*. (1) In the *theoretical* kind we assume what is sought as if it were existent and true, after which we pass through its successive consequences, as if they too were true and established by virtue of our hypothesis, to something admitted: then (a), if that something admitted is true, that which is sought will also be true and the proof will correspond in the reverse order to the analysis, but (b), if we come upon something admittedly false, that which is sought will also be false. (2) In the *problematical* kind we assume that which is propounded as if it were known, after which we pass through its successive consequences, taking them as true, up to something admitted: if then (a) what is admitted is possible and obtainable, that is, what mathematicians call *given*, what was originally proposed will also be possible, and the proof will again correspond in the reverse order to the analysis; but if

(b) we come upon something admittedly impossible, the problem will also be impossible.'[1]

The method is said by Proclus to have been invented by Plato and handed over to Leodamas. But it looks as though the statement were due to some confusion, some supposed connexion with Plato's method of division, which has, no doubt, some points in common with it. The method itself must have been in use before Plato: the Pythagoreans must certainly have used it.[2]

(c) Pythagoreans and mathematics: justice and reciprocity

N.E. V. 3–5. 1131ᵃ10–1134ᵃ16

It is, perhaps, scarcely correct to say that by ἀντιπεπονθός in their definition of justice the Pythagoreans meant pure retaliation or requital, 'an eye for an eye'; they probably also included in their definition cases where a fair equivalent was returned—fair all things considered, not necessarily the same. Aristotle objects to this definition because it does not fit either distributive justice (τὸ διανεμητικὸν δίκαιον) or 'corrective' justice (τὸ διορθωτικὸν δίκαιον).[3]

Aristotle has explained already that the benefits conferred by the State are properly distributed in proportion to some estimate of 'worth' (ἀξία) of the individual citizens.[4] 'Worth' may be differently accounted in different states according to the form of government; it may, for example, be wealth (in a plutocracy), wealth or birth (in an oligarchy), liberty (in a democracy), or 'excellence' (in an aristocracy).[5] But, whatever may be the standard, everyone agrees that distributive justice requires distribution in proportion to 'worth'. Aristotle is careful to define the particular kind of proportion here meant. Proportion is, he says, equality of ratios,[6] and must be between four terms at least.[7] The 'discrete' proportion has four terms, as when we say that as A is to B so is C to B. The 'continuous' proportion may appear to have three terms only, as when A is to B as B is to C, but it really has four even then because the middle term B occurs twice. The proportion in either case, says Aristotle, is what mathematicians call 'geometrical' (1131ᵇ12).

An example[8] is 'a distribution of moneys from the public treasury which follows the same ratio as the respective contributions (to the public revenues) bear to one another'. The shares of A and B being C and D respectively, $A : B = C : D$; and 'it follows *alternando*

---

[1] Pappus, Book vii, 'The Treasury of Analysis', translation quoted from *Greek Mathematics*, ii, pp. 400–1. See also Hultsch's edition (1876–8), ii. 634. 10–636. 14.

[2] Cf. my *Greek Maths*. i. 168.   [3] 1132ᵇ23.   [4] 1131ᵃ25–6.

[5] 1131ᵃ27–9.   [6] 1131ᵃ31–2.   [7] 1131ᵇ3.   [8] 1131ᵇ29–32.

that $A : C = B : D$ and hence the wholes are in the same ratio', i.e. $(A+C):(B+D) = A : B$ and the original ratio of A to B is preserved after the distribution.[1]

On the other hand, in the case of 'corrective' justice included in τὸ διορθωτικὸν δίκαιον, i.e. where, for example, one person has robbed another or has inflicted damage upon him, the proper readjustment 'is in accordance, not with the aforesaid kind of proportion [the geometrical] but with *arithmetical* proportion'.[2]

The use of the term 'arithmetical proportion' by Aristotle here and in 1132ª30 is rather remarkable, because it does not occur in Euclid, Archimedes, or Apollonius. The Pythagoreans apparently only spoke of arithmetic and geometric *means*, to which they added a third which at first was called 'subcontrary' and later the 'harmonic' mean (the change of name is attributed to Archytas and Hippasus). It was only the later mathematicians, after the beginning of the Christian era, with whom the terms arithmetical, geometrical, and harmonic *proportions* became common, though Nicomachus[3] says that the proportions which were recognized by the ancients, Pythagoras, Plato, and Aristotle, are the three first, ⟨known as⟩ the arithmetic, geometric, and harmonic.[4]

In 'corrective' justice, Aristotle says, the assumption is that A has obtained more and B less than he should have done, and the arbitrator produces equality by taking the arithmetic mean between the two shares, acting as a mathematician does 'with a straight line divided into (two) unequal parts, namely by taking away from the greater segment that (length) by which it exceeds the half and adding (the same length) to the lesser segment'. He adds[5] an unnecessarily elaborate explanation of the process. 'When', he says, 'given two equals, (a part) is subtracted from the one and added to the other, the latter exceeds the other by twice the amount [subtracted and added]; for if it had been subtracted from the one and not added to the other, the latter would have exceeded (the former) by *once* the amount only. Therefore it (the latter, i.e. the one added to) exceeds the mean by once the amount (subtracted) and the mean exceeds the one subtracted from by once the said amount. By means of this consideration we shall know how much we ought to take away from the person who has more and how much to add to the person who has less; for that by which the mean exceeds the share of him who has less should be added to his share, and that by which the mean is exceeded (by the share of the person who has most) should be taken away from that person. Let AA', BB', CC' be

[1] 1131ᵇ5–8.   [2] 1132ª1.   [3] ii, c. 22.
[4] Cf. my *Euclid*, ii, pp. 292–3; *Greek Mathematics*, i, pp. 85–6.
[5] 1132ª32—ᵇ9.

T

equal to one another. Let AE be subtracted from AA' and let CD be added to CC' so that the whole DCC' exceeds EA' by CD and CF, and therefore exceeds BB' by

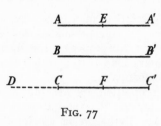

FIG. 77

CD.' The diagram and the argumentation about it are mathematically rather childish and the editors do not draw it in the same way. Jackson makes DC of the same length as AE, Burnet makes it equal to EA'; F on CC' in any case corresponds to E on AA'. The difference seems to me unimportant; the text admits of either assumption and the conclusion is the same.

There is more difficulty in dealing with Aristotle's expression in 1132^{b}31–3 where he says that 'in commercial bargains the bond of union is this sort of justice, that which is reciprocal in accordance with proportion and not in the sense of equality' ($\kappa\alpha\tau'$ ἀναλογίαν καὶ μὴ κατ' ἰσότητα). By κατ' ἰσότητα Aristotle denotes the supposed Pythagorean sense of ἀντιπεπονθός, which, he says, does not cover either corrective or distributive justice; in voluntary commercial bargains the just consists in the 'reciprocal' interpreted 'in accordance with proportion'. Does this mean the formal 'reciprocal proportion' in mathematics as defined in Euclid VI. 35, which would require that if A is a builder, B a shoemaker, C a house, D a pair of shoes, $A : B = D : C$? Jackson seems to have no doubt that it does;[1] but there are obvious difficulties. As in the earlier case A and B represented the 'worth' of two parties, so here we may suppose A and B to represent what the builder and the shoemaker are 'good for'. It might be measured, say, by the value of the work that they could respectively produce in the same time, say an hour, or a week. But in any case, before there can be barter between the builder and the shoemaker it is necessary, in the first place, to find a relation between the values of the things produced by the two respectively, namely, a house and a pair of shoes. As Aristotle says,[2] 'There is nothing to prevent the work of one from being superior to the work of the other; they must therefore be equalized' (cf. ἰσασθῆναι 1133^{a}18 and ^{b}10, ἰσασμένον ^{b}5); 1133^{a}22–4 'hence, as a builder is to a shoemaker, so must so many shoes be to a house (otherwise there will be no exchange and no κοινωνία)'.

Suppose, then, that a house C is equal in value to x pairs of shoes (D), or that B the shoemaker will give to A the builder x shoes in return for the house or xD for C, the supposed 'reciprocal proportion', strictly interpreted, would be $A : B = xD : C$. But the ground for

[1] pp. 90–1. [2] 1133^{a}12–14.

the two persons entering voluntarily into the transaction must be that according to their respective estimates of values (the estimate of the value of the house in terms of shoes or money by the shoe-maker, and the estimate of the value of the shoes in terms of the house or money by the builder), the said values are supposed to be equal. That is mathematically expressed by saying that $xD = C$ or $xD : C = 1$. Therefore the proportion $A : B = xD : C$ is not true unless the ratio $A : B$ (for the purpose in question at any rate) is equal to 1 or $A = B$. The fact is that the relative 'worth' of A and B has really nothing to do with the particular transaction. The key to the puzzle seems to be furnished by 1133ᵃ10–12 : 'if *first* we have proportional equality (τὸ κατὰ τὴν ἀναλογίαν ἴσον), and *then* reciprocity (τὸ ἀντιπεπονθός) is effected, the result of which we speak will be attained'.

The natural interpretation of this would be that the method of *proportion* only comes in for the purpose of deciding the relative values of C and D or of determining x in the equation $xD=C$; and when that is done, the 'reciprocal' in the sense of requital or a fair return is brought into operation. This would mean that by τὸ ἀντιπεπονθός κατ' ἀναλογίαν in 1132ᵇ32 Aristotle does *not* mean the technical 'reciprocal proportion', but that the reciprocal interchange is 'requital' in the Pythagorean sense, subject to the qualification that due proportion is observed between the things interchanged. This favours Burnet's view that we must first 'equate' the values of a pair of shoes and a house or determine x in the formula $xD = C$ (this would be done by 'proportion'—by considering, for example, the values in relation to the labour and skill required by A and B to produce their unit products respectively)—and then use the same method as that employed in 'corrective' justice, namely, that of 'arithmetical proportion' or the arithmetic mean. The 'reciprocal' comes in because we add to A a multiple of B's work D (and not C) and to B a quantity of A's work.

N.E. V. 3. 1131ᵃ29–ᵇ3

'The just is something proportional. For proportion is not a relation confined to numbers consisting of units [i.e. abstract numbers], but extends to numbers in general [i.e. numbers of anything, concrete numbers, numbers of horses, tables, or what you will]. For proportion is equality of ratios, and requires four terms at least. It is clear that a discrete proportion has four terms; but so also has a continuous proportion. For the latter uses one term as two and mentions it twice, as when, for example, as A is to B so is B to Γ; here B enters twice, and if we put down B twice, the terms which are proportional are four in number.'

Probably Aristotle's definition of proportion as equality of ratios is quoted from the Pythagoreans and he is speaking only of numbers abstract or concrete. Euclid, of course, has in Book V, Def. 5, the famous definition of proportion or rather of magnitudes that are 'in the same ratio', which is due to Eudoxus and applies not only to numbers but to magnitudes of any kind commensurable or incommensurable. But he adds as Def. 6: 'And let magnitudes which have the same ratio be called *proportional.*' He also has as Def. 8 the statement that 'a proportion in three terms is the least (possible)'.

Although Aristotle says that the term 'proportional' extends to concrete numbers of all kinds as well as the abstract numbers, it is obvious that the things the numbers of which are in a given ratio must be things of some one kind. We can have a ratio of 8 horses to 5 horses, or of 5 sheep to 3 sheep, but not a ratio of 8 horses to 5 sheep; although 4 horses and 8 sheep *componendo* have to 2 horses and 4 sheep the ratio of 2 : 1.

(d) Young people and mathematics

N.E. VI. 8. 1142ᵃ11–20

'Evidence for this is furnished by the fact that the young may be geometers and mathematicians and be wise in such subjects, but they are not thought to be prudent. The reason is that practical wisdom (prudence) is concerned with particular facts as well, which become known as the result of experience, while a young man cannot be experienced (some length of time is required to give experience). One might indeed inquire further why a boy may be a good mathematician, but cannot be a philosopher or physicist. May we not say it is because the subjects of mathematics are reached by means of abstraction, while the principles of philosophy and physics come from experience; and the young have no conviction of the latter, though they may speak of them, while in mathematics the "definitions" are plain (free from ambiguity)?'

On the 'abstraction' by means of which we arrive at the objects of mathematics see my pp. 64–5 (on *An. Post.* I. 27. 87ᵃ31 ff.).

(e) νοῦς and φρόνησις

Ib. ᵃ25–9

'The intellect is concerned with definitions, which are not matter for argument, whereas practical wisdom deals with ultimate [particular] facts of which there is no scientific knowledge but only perception, and that not the perception of the special senses but the sort of sense by which we perceive that the ultimate figure in mathematics is the triangle; for the process of analysis will stop in that direction too.'

On the subject of 'common sensibles' (κοινὰ αἰσθητά), which are the subject of the senses in common, not only of particular senses, reference should be made to the note of J. A. Stewart[1] and to the passages in the De anima specially referred to[2] with Hicks's notes.[3] Aristotle defines common sensibles first as motion, rest, numbers, figure, size, which are in iii. 1. 425ᵃ16 reduced to one, namely, κίνησις, 'motion' including change.

The arrival at the triangle which Aristotle has in mind is evidently the last step in the διαίρεσις or subdivision of figures which in Metaph. Θ. 9. 1051ᵃ22 the mathematician is said to use for the purpose of discovering or proving particular properties of figures. Every mathematician will recognize the sort of thing that is done. Given a certain figure you draw a number of lines, some joining pairs of points, others being perpendiculars, bisectors, and what not, on the chance that some property will leap to the eye that is useful as a step towards the desired conclusion. If angular points are joined to a sufficient extent in a rectilinear figure, there is nothing left but triangles, so that the ultimate figure is a triangle. When Aristotle says that the process stops 'on this side [or in this direction] too (κἀκεῖ)' he has in mind the contrast to the opposite process of ascending to the ἀρχαί or principles. In the latter case we proceed upwards to the more general, in the former we are descending to particulars. Aristotle goes on (1142ᵃ29): 'But this latter sense [the common αἴσθησις operating in mathematics] is sense rather than practical wisdom though specifically different from the other kind of sense [the particular senses].' A result or a property is seen by 'simple inspection'. The κοινὴ αἴσθησις, 'common sense', is a faculty which takes in the reports of the separate senses and, as it were, unifies them into what J. A. Stewart calls a consciousness of sensations. The mathematician takes in as the ἔσχατον, or particular, the particular shape of the figure before him (triangle, quadrilateral, or circle or whatever it is); shape is not the datum of a single sense but is realized as the result of the perceptions of more than one sense. But the realization is of the nature of sensation rather than of an intellectual process.

---

[1] Vol. ii, pp. 72–8.
[2] De an. ii. 6. 418ᵃ7 and iii. 1. 425ᵃ13.   [3] pp. 360, etc.

(f) The hypotheses of mathematics

N.E. VII. 8. 1151ᵃ16–18

'In actions the end (the final cause, the οὗ ἕνεκα) is the principle, as the hypotheses are the principles in mathematics; and neither in the one case nor in the other is it reason or argument that teaches us the principles.' As in actions we work backwards from the end to the means of obtaining it, so in mathematics we work forwards from the principles to their application in mathematical questions. The former process is, as Aristotle has said, like mathematical analysis; the latter is the method of synthetical proof.

I do not feel any doubt that the 'hypotheses' are the general unproved assumptions from which mathematics starts, e.g. the assumption of the existence of the subject-matter, points, lines, solids, etc. If the 'hypotheses' here include definitions the use of the word here would not be consistent with the explanation in *An. Post.*[1] 'Among immediate syllogistic principles' (or "basic truths") I call that a "thesis" which it is neither possible to prove, nor of which it is necessary for anyone to be persuaded who is to learn anything: but that which it is necessary for anyone to hold who is to learn anything whatever is an "axiom". . . . But of "theses", one kind is that which assumes one or other part of the statement, as for instance that something exists or does not exist, and this is an "hypothesis"; the other kind, which makes no such assumption, is a "definition".' I think that, in view of the non-mathematical character of the present discussion, the slight inconsistency could well be pardoned.

On the other hand, I doubt if Aristotle could mean 'the hypotheses in mathematics' here to be confined to the casual kind of hypothesis which one makes in beginning a process of mathematical analysis, namely, that a certain proposition required to be proved is true or that a certain problem has actually been solved. Our hypothesis may in the first case be false, i.e. where we assume it in order to prove the opposite by *reductio ad absurdum*, or the problem may be insoluble. But the 'end' of action, which is compared with the hypotheses of mathematics, is something quite fixed (though it may be good or bad) and there should be the same fixity about the 'hypotheses' of mathematics. I feel confirmed in my view by the language of the corresponding passage of the *Eudemian Ethics*:[2] 'As in the theoretical sciences the hypotheses are the principles, so in the practical the end is the principle. Given that a healthy condition must be produced in an individual (thing), it is necessary that such and such a thing should be present if that result is to follow:

[1] i. 2. 72ᵃ14–21.   [2] ii. 11. 1227ᵇ28–32.

so too in mathematics, if the triangle has (the sum of its three angles equal to) two right angles, a certain thing must hold good (ἀνάγκη τοδὶ εἶναι).'

What is the 'certain thing'? It is not the case that the 'hypothesis' is the truth of the proposition to be proved (that the angles of a triangle are together equal to two right angles) and that the 'certain thing' is, for example, the fact that, if from one point on an unlimited straight line and on one side of it there be drawn two straight lines, making angles with the given straight line and with one another, the three angles so formed about the point will together be equal to two right angles. The 'certain thing' must surely be the fundamental assumption as to the nature of a straight line; namely, that two straight lines meeting at an angle cannot meet at any other point, and that a straight line cannot be a 'closed series' (in fact a great circle on an infinitely large sphere) returning on itself, as it does on the theories of Riemann and Einstein.

If there were any doubt as to the above view, it should be removed by the general statement which follows and which, as Stewart saw, points in that direction. 'Neither in the one case nor the other is it reason (or argument, ὁ λόγος) which teaches us the principles.' The next words say that 'it is ἀρετὴ ἢ φυσικὴ ἢ ἐθιστή (excellence or virtue inborn or acquired by habit) that teaches us to judge aright about the end' (sc. in the sphere of action); while we know that in Aristotle's view the 'principles' of mathematics cannot be taught, but are intuitive and must be assumed without proof. It could not be 'reason' which 'teaches' us an hypothesis in the other sense of an *ad hoc* assumption made of a proposition being true or a problem being solved in order to lead to a proof or a solution.

(g) *The hypotheses and principles in mathematics*

Eudemian Ethics II. 6. 1222ᵇ23–41

'Immovable principles such as those of mathematics do not possess absolute authority (τὸ κύριον), although they are admitted as having similar force; for, even in mathematics, if the principle were changed, almost all the propositions proved (by it) would be altered, whereas, if one of these is destroyed by another, they will not all be changed mathematically unless by the destruction of the hypothesis and the proof by means of that. Now a man can initiate a motion of some kind; for action means motion. Since therefore, as in all other matters, it is the principle which is the cause of things which exist or come to be by reason of it, we must conceive of it as playing the same part as it does in the case of scientific demonstrations. If, because a triangle has its angles equal to two right angles, it necessarily follows that a square has its angles together equal to four right angles, it is manifest that the fact that the triangle has two right angles is the cause of the other proposition. Whereas, of course, if the triangle changes (in this respect) so must the square; if the sum of the angles is equal to three right angles for the triangle it will be six for the square; if four, eight. If, on the other hand, the triangle does not change but has the said property, so must the square have its corresponding property. That which we are trying to show, the necessity of the inference, is clear from the *Analytics*; at present it is not possible either to omit reference to it, or to treat it with precision, except to the extent indicated. If in fact there is nothing else that is the cause of the triangle's having the property in question, then the latter will be a sort of principle and the cause of what follows afterwards.'

It is clear that the word 'hypothesis' is here used in the sense of a general principle (one of the indemonstrable assumptions) in mathematics rather than as an *ad hoc* assumption in some proposition made as the starting-point of an 'analysis'.

XVIII

DE MOTU ANIMALIUM

THERE is not much that is strictly mathematical in this treatise, but one passage may be referred to which contains the equivalent of Newton's Third Law of Motion, namely that action and reaction are equal and opposite ('Reaction is always equal and opposite to action; that is to say, the actions of two bodies upon each other are always equal and opposite'). When, says Aristotle, in animals 'any part is moved, another must be at rest; this is why they have joints; animals use joints like a centre, and the complete part in which the joint is becomes both one and two, both straight and bent, changing potentially and actually by reason of the joint. And when it is being bent and moved, one of the points in the joint is moved and one is at rest, just as if the points A and D on the diameter of a circle were at rest and B were moved so as to give ⟨the radius⟩ AC. However, in the latter case the centre is thought to be every way indivisible (indeed in such cases the pro- cess of being moved is, we are told, a fiction, no mathematical object being really moved), but the centres in joints become, potentially and actually, at one time one and at another time divisible. Anyhow the origin, the point of attachment, as such, is always at rest while the part below is moved. Thus, for example, when the forearm is moved the elbow is at rest, and when the whole arm, the shoulder; when the tibia is moved the knee is at rest, and, when the whole leg, the hip. It is manifest, therefore, that each animal must have within itself some part which is at rest, from which the thing moved derives the origin (of its motion), and supporting itself on which it will be moved whether as a complete whole or in its several parts.'[1]

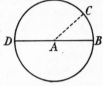

FIG. 78

Aristotle goes on to say (c. 2) that the point of rest in the animal is still ineffectual unless there is something outside it which is absolutely at rest and immovable. He illustrates by the case of a man in a boat who cannot move the boat by simply pushing at something in the boat itself; he must use leverage on something else—either the water (with an oar) or the bank (say with a pole). He passes to the case of the universe and asks the question 'whether, if something moves the whole heaven, this means that the movent must be unmoved, and that it must neither be a part of the heaven

---

[1] c. 1. 698ᵃ16–ᵇ7.

nor even in it. If what moves it is itself moved, it must move it by being in contact with something immovable, and this latter is no part of the movent. And, if the movent is itself immovable, it will, in like manner, be no part of that which is moved. In one point at least those argue correctly who maintain that when the sphere is moved circularly, no part of it whatever remains fixed; if any part remained fixed either the whole sphere would necessarily remain fixed, or its continuity would be torn asunder. But when they suppose that the poles have a certain force—though they have no magnitude, but are mere extremities and points—they are wrong. For, apart from the fact that no such things as points have any substance, it is also impossible for one motion to be caused by two things; yet they make the poles two in number.'[1]

It may be remarked that if the movement of the sphere 'circularly' is a rotation about an axis, e.g. that passing through the poles, it is not true to say that no part whatever of the sphere can be at rest, because all points on the axis would be at rest; if the sphere were moved as a whole in a circular orbit in space, no point of it would be at rest; neither would any point of it be at rest (except instantaneously) if it were rolled, say, on a plane, in which case the point of contact with the plane would be the instantaneous centre of revolution.

Aristotle passes to the myth that Atlas, standing on the earth, makes the heaven rotate, acting as a sort of diameter through the poles. This idea requires us to assume that the earth remains fixed and is no part of the universe. Also *'we must assume the strength or force of the movent to be equal to that of the thing which remains fixed.* For there is a certain amount of strength and power by virtue of which that which remains fixed does so, just as there is strength or power by virtue of which the movent moves anything; and, as there must of necessity be some proportion between opposite motions, so there must be between states of rest. Now equal forces are unaffected by one another; it is by reason of excess that one is overcome by another. Hence, whether the movent is Atlas or some other thing within the heaven acting in the same way, it must do no more than exactly balance the stability of the earth at rest— otherwise the earth will be moved away from the centre and its own place. *For as that which thrusts thrusts, so that which is thrust is thrust, and with the like force.'*[2]

[1] 699ª12–24.   [2] 699ª32–b5.

XIX

DE INCESSU ANIMALIUM

THERE are few passages here which require notice from a mathematical point of view. We may mention the following.

Dimensions

c. 2. 704^b18–22

'Further we must take for granted the dimensions of magnitude, (distinguishing) their number and their quality and to what sorts of things they respectively appertain. There are, namely, six dimensions forming three pairs, first, up and down, secondly, before and behind, and thirdly, right and left.'

c. 4. 705^a26–8

'The dimensions by which living things are naturally distinguished, up and down, before and behind, and again right and left.'

Aristotle goes on to explain (705^a28–^b8) that all living things have upper and lower parts, for up and down are found not only in animals but in plants as well; however, in plants the roots are the 'upper' parts, for it is from the roots that nourishment is distributed to the parts that grow; it is with the roots that plants take it in, as animals do with their mouths.

On Dimensions cf. *De caelo* 284^b6; *Metaph.* 1016^b25–31; *Topics* 142^b25; *Phys.* 206^a6, 208^b13.

On animals walking

c. 9. 708^a26–709^a4

'If there had been no flexion (in limbs), there could have been no walking or swimming or flying. For since footed creatures stand and support their weight on each of their pairs of opposite legs in turn, it is necessary when one leg steps forward that the other should bend. For their opposite legs are naturally equal in length, and that which supports the weight must be erect, that is, perpendicular to the ground. But when one leg goes forward it becomes the hypotenuse (of a right-angled triangle) and the square on it is equal to the square on the stationary magnitude [i.e. the leg which is perpendicular to the ground] together with the square on the (horizontal) straight line between. But since the legs are equal the stationary one must bend either at the knee—or if there were any kneeless animal which walked, at the joint (wherever it is).'

δυναμένη is used in the technical sense of δύνασθαι, 'being equal in square' to something else, i.e. having its square equal to the square on some other straight line or the square on more than one added together.

The same description is repeated in the later passage: c. 9. 709ᵃ16–24: 'Since one leg is at right angles (to the ground) it follows that ⟨if the leg that is being moved forward cannot bend⟩ the creature will either fall down when the right angle becomes less than a right angle, or will not be able to go forward. For if while the one leg is at right angles to the ground, the other has stepped forward, the latter will be greater than the other though it is equal to it, for the square on the forward leg will be equal to the square on the stationary leg together with the square on the distance (on the ground) subtended (by the two legs). Therefore the advancing leg must bend, and the creature after bending it must stretch out the other leg, thereby inclining forward and straddling, but so that (the body) remains on the perpendicular; for the two legs then form an isosceles triangle, and the head comes lower down, as it is perpendicularly above (the middle point of the) base of the triangle.'

FIG. 79

That is, when the two legs AB, AC form an isosceles triangle, H, the head, is on the perpendicular from A to BC produced.

The above translation is different at 709ᵃ19 from the Oxford translation because Farquharson, in dealing with the words δυνήσεται γὰρ τοῦτο τὸ τ' ἠρεμοῦν καὶ τὴν ὑποτείνουσαν, says that δυνήσεται is not here used in the mathematical sense as *supra* 709ᵃ1 but in the ordinary sense, and translates: 'For it will be equal to the stationary leg and also equivalent to the hypotenuse of a right-angled triangle.' Evidently this version is suggested in order, by hook or by crook, to make τὴν ὑποτείνουσαν mean the same 'hypotenuse' as at 709ᵃ1. I am, however, myself satisfied that δυνήσεται is used in the mathematical sense and that it is τὴν ὑποτείνουσαν which is used not in the sense of 'hypotenuse' but in its literal sense of the straight line *subtending* (the two other sides). This makes the sentence quite clear: 'the square on the forward leg will be equal to that on the stationary leg together with the square on the straight line subtending the two'. The statement is thus exactly the same as that in 709ᵃ1–2.[1]

---

[1] Mr. Platt agrees: *Journal of Philology*, xxxii. 297.

INDEX TO PASSAGES OF ARISTOTLE

GENERAL INDEX